The American Writer
and the Great Depression

THE AMERICAN HERITAGE SERIES

THE

American Heritage

Series

UNDER THE GENERAL EDITORSHIP OF
LEONARD W. LEVY AND ALFRED YOUNG

The American Writer
and the Great Depression

EDITED BY

HARVEY SWADOS

Sarah Lawrence College

THE BOBBS-MERRILL COMPANY, INC.

A Subsidiary of Howard W. Sams & Co., Inc.

PUBLISHERS • INDIANAPOLIS • NEW YORK • KANSAS CITY

Foreword

This anthology has two aims: to convey the impact of the depression of the 1930's on the life and thought of the American people and to present what Harvey Swados calls "a cross section of good writing of the period." The question with which Swados begins his introduction has been asked by many: "How is one to explain what life was like in America after the crash to those who did not live through the period?" For the American people who have never been subjected to the havoc of invasion or bombing, the depression was unquestionably the most searing experience of the twentieth century. Yet how does one convey the despair and the terror and the hope? This anthology suggests that the literature of the era—the novels, short stories, poetry, and reporting—as well as the unsurpassed photographs do this better than any other source available, be it government reports, newspaper accounts, or the analyses of social scientists.

Here are unforgettable images of the terror of the depression: desperate men scrounging through garbage dumps for food, hungry women on breadlines, youth on the road and on the bum. Here too are the signs of hope: millhands forming unions, farmers finding a way out through the TVA, writers discovering a half-forgotten historical heritage.

The writings of course are of interest as much for what they reveal about the writers as about their subjects and about an entire generation of ill-understood intellectuals. Swados belongs neither among those who denigrate the writers of the period as producers of propagandistic trash, nor among those who glamorize the era's "romantic" politics. He attempts to correct both views; and his selections should convince the skeptical that this period was truly "in many ways a triumphant one for American literary artists."

Harvey Swados was a happy choice to assemble a volume on the depression era. A novelist and essayist of the current generation with a grasp of American history, he was too young to have been part of that era, yet old enough to know what it was all about. His loyalty to his craft forbids him to accept the narrow political standards by which even some of the best critics of the thirties judged the literature of their day. Yet he shares "the radicalism, the humanity, the searching not for absurdity but for meaningfulness" which he believes animated the best writing of the period.

This book is one of a series of which the aim is to provide the essential primary sources of the American experience, especially of American thought. The series, when completed, will constitute a documentary library of American history, filling a need long felt among scholars, students, libraries, and general readers for authoritative collections of original materials. Some volumes will illuminate the thought of significant individuals, such as James Madison or Louis Brandeis; some will deal with movements, such as those of the Antifederalists or the Populists; others will be organized around special themes, such as Puritan political thought, or American Catholic thought on social questions. Many volumes will take up the large number of subjects traditionally studied in American history for which, surprisingly, there are no documentary anthologies; others will pioneer in introducing contemporary subjects of increasing importance to scholars. The series aspires to maintain the high standards demanded of contemporary editing, providing authentic texts, intelligently and unobtrusively edited. It will also have the distinction of presenting pieces of substantial length which give the full character and flavor of the original. The series will be the most comprehensive and authoritative of its kind.

Alfred Young
Leonard W. Levy

Contents

PART ONE

Miners, Millhands, Factory Workers:

MISSOURI, TENNESSEE, NORTH CAROLINA, PENNSYLVANIA, WASHINGTON

PART TWO

Farmers; Sharecroppers, Tenants, Migrants:

IOWA, NEW JERSEY, OKLAHOMA, ARKANSAS, ALABAMA, GEORGIA, MISSISSIPPI

PART THREE

Hungry Women and Faltering Homes:

MINNESOTA, COLORADO, NEW YORK

PART FOUR

Jobhunting:

EVERYWHERE

PART FIVE

Hitting Bottom:

ON THE ROAD, IN THE RING, ON THE BUM

PART SIX

Concern and Hope:

VETS, NEGROES, CIO, TVA, CCC

PART SEVEN

Organizers, Capitalists, Fascists, Communists:

"GUYS LIKE ME AND YOU"

PART EIGHT

America:

THE GRAND VIEW

Introduction

How is one to explain to those who did not live through the period what life was like in America after the Crash? Those who did live through it, like the survivors of a war, may vary in articulateness, but they can never be the same, even though to all outward appearances they seem no different from those carelessly living on loans, flying now and paying later, as though this is the way it always was and always will be. But even if they were not hungry and hopeless themselves, the depression generation had burned into them the dulled and shamed glances of men who were, and who could no longer feed their wives and children. It was my own experience as a schoolboy in Buffalo to open our kitchen door one morning after another to the knock of those grown and gaunt men whose predecessors had chalked our front sidewalk in token of the handouts I helped my mother provide for them. I grew up scrambling eggs for hungry strangers and watching my own father's face grow longer as if stretched by the hopeless tension of the seasons—and if I had no idea, really, of what life was like for the men at the door, how can those who have grown up hearing not even the knock but only that brassy klaxon, the horn of plenty?

"I think that my happiness, or talent for self-delusion or what you will," wrote Scott Fitzgerald in 1936 of his nervous collapse, "was an exception. It was not the natural thing but the unnatural—unnatural as the Boom; and my recent experience parallels the wave of despair that swept the nation when the Boom was over."[1] The key word in that terribly honest state-

---

[1] F. Scott Fitzgerald, *The Crack-Up* (New York: New Directions, 1945), p. 84.

ment is *despair*. It is the one aspect of those dread months that is echoed by survivors and historians alike. "The fog of despair hung over the land," says Arthur M. Schlesinger, Jr. at the beginning of *The Crisis of the Old Order*.[2] If his description that follows of ghostly factories, scavenging families, vagabond children, and looting farmers seems deliberately dramatized in order that subsequently we may share his unreserved admiration for the political genius of Franklin D. Roosevelt, nevertheless the basic characterization can hardly be disputed.

Beyond despair, however, what America was like as the thirties wore on is not easily determined. In a vast country, contradictory impressions were inevitable in the observations of journalists, novelists, and storytellers of vastly differing backgrounds and predilections; contradictory viewpoints were often expressed by the same writer. Thus the insouciant young William Saroyan, who had become an immediate literary success with his lightsome tales of a Fresno boyhood, gave way to bitterness at the end of "International Harvester," a story included in his collection *Inhale & Exhale*, in 1936:

These facts are encouraging: . . . Ten million unemployed continue law-abiding. No riots, no trouble, no multi-millionaires cooked and served with cranberry sauce, alas. . . . Less tangible, less concrete, less visible, but not less important, has been the change in sentiment which has developed during the recent years of misery. Hardly anybody is out to make a killing one way or another. Hardly anybody dreams of becoming the owner of an apartment building, a country home, and three expensive automobiles. Hardly anybody is interested in anything much. Hardly anybody *is* at all.[3]

Others, including more seasoned and more far-ranging observers, came to conclusions not dissimilar from Saroyan's.

[2] Arthur M. Schlesinger, Jr., *The Crisis of the Old Order* (Boston: Houghton Mifflin, 1937), p. 3.

[3] William Saroyan, *Inhale & Exhale* (New York: Random House, 1936), p. 81.

James Rorty could not keep the heartbreak from his voice when he noted, in the preface to his *Where Life Is Better: An Unsentimental American Journey,* that his fellow Americans remained resistant not just to radicalism but to any serious consideration of the problems facing them, long after the bubble had burst:

I encountered nothing in 15,000 miles of travel that disgusted and appalled me so much as this American addiction to make-believe. Apparently, not even empty bellies can cure it. Of all the facts I dug up, none seemed so significant or so dangerous as the overwhelming fact of our lazy, irresponsible, adolescent inability to face the truth or tell it. . . . If we, as a people, are to go down helplessly in a fatuous and seemingly unnecessary chaos, it will be this where-life-is-better daydream that ensnared and tripped us. . . .[4]

And occasionally the horror of what seemed to the sensitive to lie beyond despair—the apathy of dissolution—overwhelmed them so that they could only cry out in anguish. The novelist Nathan Asch was one of those who took to the road in an effort to discover a truth about what was happening to his country (as well as facts to reinforce pre-existing radical convictions). In *The Road: In Search of America,* Asch reported on a number of heartening situations, but when he hit bottom his reaction at what he encountered rose to a lyricism of terror:

The night I stayed in a flop house I couldn't bear to breathe through my nose, and I couldn't bear to look at the other men on the mattresses about me. I was there to see them, and see how they lived, but I didn't care if I missed this sight, because if I stayed out there another hour I didn't want to live. The lights were out, except in the hall, and I lay on my arms behind me, and I closed my eyes and I closed my mind. And then I began to hear that these men sleeping were beginning to breathe in and out together, as if they somehow had become one nameless unemployed, as if all this breathing in and out together had become one gigantic sigh. I rose, and put on

4 James Rorty, *Where Life Is Better* (New York: Reynal & Hitchcock, 1936), p. 13.

my shoes, and I walked out into the rain, and in doorways lay these men's future, lay what they would become: junk, with still beating arteries, huddled in doorways.[5]

And yet there were others, just as anxious to tell honestly what they had learned, who felt that America was not like this, but that—even in the darkest hours of the night before the New Deal and all the social ferment that accompanied it— beyond the admitted despair of those who had fallen completely out of society, was a genuine stirring, a readiness to break with the past, a receptivity to new ideas. Louis Adamic also traveled across the United States, perhaps more persistently and thoroughly than any other journalist of the period; he had certain advantages in his familiarity with the more rambunctious aspects of American history (his *Dynamite* was a history of social violence), and in his ability to converse freely with those laborers who, like himself, had been born in the Balkans; and he came to very different conclusions in *My America:*

Socially, America is a most sensitive country: and this is a fact whose importance cannot be exaggerated. During the last half of 1931, but especially since New Year's, I have been noticing everywhere a profound perturbation. Except on the very lowest levels, where a sort of paralysis continues to prevail, the country is alive again—painfully so, but alive; which to me, as I remember the deadly prosperity period, is wonderful. The middle and upper-middle classes are no longer stagnant, slothful, but acutely aware that the country is in the grip of a far-reaching wrong or incongruity, which, the more intelligent of them realize, is nothing new; the Depression is but the reverse side of the previous prosperity. . . . The country, unquestionably, is *alive* again: and that is something![6]

We can perhaps conclude that there was an element of truth

---

[5] Nathan Asch, *The Road* (New York: W. W. Norton, 1937), p. 185.

[6] Louis Adamic, *My America* (New York: Harper & Brothers, 1938), p. 303.

in each of these seemingly contradictory reactions—just as Adamic himself found, in his stint as a case-worker among New York families on relief, that some families were knit more closely together by their common suffering, while others were so devastated by economic catastrophe that they were torn apart and often destroyed by illness, desertion, and disappearance.

Despite the historic fact of recurring crises, the American people were as absolutely unprepared for the Great Depression as if it had been a volcanic eruption in Kansas or Nebraska, pouring red-hot lava from coast to coast and border to border. And they were even less prepared to meet it than to undertake war a dozen years earlier or a decade later. Reactions to the depression varied with family backgrounds, social status, individual character, and, to a much lesser extent, class loyalty. This may help to explain why certain spectators of the tragic drama were convinced that the United States was ripe for revolution, if only the right leadership would arise, while others insisted that the American people were not merely conservative but hopelessly hidebound even when they were half-starving.

Among all but the irretrievably foundered, however, there was an upsurge of national self-awareness—not a patriotic fervor like that triggered off by war or invasion, but rather a reawakening of the consciousness that America was a unified land, that its problems were national problems, that its misery was national, that solutions and resolutions would have to be national. Local officials continued to whistle in the dark, as had Herbert Hoover, and delegations of unemployed continued to demonstrate and picket before the offices of their mayors and councilmen; but increasingly there was acceptance of the fact that everyone was in the same boat and that steering orders would have to come from the nation's capital.

Inevitably, the writers, with rare exceptions like William Faulkner or Richard Wright (whose insistent focusing upon regional or racial drama was rarely recognized at the time as containing elements of universality), addressed themselves to the national scene and presumed—for the first time in a generation—to speak *of* the nation at large *to* the nation at large. Poets, novelists, journalists, critics, essayists, produced books throughout the 1930's with such titles as: *My America, Puzzled America, Tragic America, Some American People, America Was Promises, America Now, America: A Reappraisal, An American Exodus, The American Earthquake, The Road: In Search of America, Where Life Is Better: An Unsentimental American Journey, Five Cities (America's Coming of Age), Behold America! The People Talk, The Way Things Are, These Are Our Lives, Talk US! USA, US 1, Land of the Free, You Have Seen Their Faces.*

Perhaps writers had a special reason for nationalism: During the last half of the decade, the Federal Writers' Project of the WPA supported more than six thousand of those who had some claim to expertise in putting pen to paper. Between 1935 and 1939 the project completed 378 books and pamphlets published commercially. In this temporary but fruitful symbiosis of bureaucrat and creative spirit (with hacks and has-beens thrown in for good measure), serious writers, as well as playwrights and painters, were enabled to carry on their own individual work with a degree of basic security, and the government was enabled to complete such valuable collective projects as the archives programs, the folklore volumes, and the immensely ambitious state guidebooks.

In such an atmosphere, with the national government itself acting as both employer and instigator and feeling its way into hitherto unexplored situations, it is not surprising that despair was succeeded by experimentation. There was a willingness upon the part of great masses of Americans to be organized and often to organize themselves into industrial unions, and to improvise such revolutionary devices as the sit-down strike and the farmers' forced sales and milk blockades—just as there was a willingness to listen to any crank who bore an honorific: Senator Huey Long, Father Coughlin, Doctor Townsend, Reverend Gerald L. K. Smith. Much less should it have been wondered at that writers, with their sensitive antennae, reacted hypersensitively both to a depression which seemed endless (and which in hard fact ended only with the arrival of an even more awful and apparently interminable cataclysm), and to a world which seemed bent on resolving economic problems with the imposition of police terror, racial persecution, the garrison state, and the preparation of a new and hideously devastating war.

Thus, if the millions of ordinary Americans may not have been reading the *New York Times Book Review,* writers and intellectuals were, and there they could find the former United States Ambassador to Germany, James W. Gerard, writing coolly in the fall of 1933:

Hitler is doing much for Germany; his unification of the Germans, his destruction of communism, his training of the young, his creation of a Spartan State animated by patriotism, his curbing of parliamentary government so unsuited to the German character, his protection of the right of private property are all good; and, after all, what the Germans do in their own territory is their own business, except for one thing—the persecution and practical expulsion of the Jews.[7]

In numbers far out of proportion to the population at large, American writers turned away in revulsion from any such accommodation with fascism and toward various degrees of Marxism. It is one of the odder ironies of our history that in their eagerness to rejoin the America from which they had exiled themselves in the twenties, writers moved not simply from alienation to affirmation but to an identification with a political movement that was never to be accepted by the peo-

---

[7] James W. Gerard, "The Brown Book of the Hitler Terror," *New York Times Book Review* (October 15, 1933), 26.

ple at large. Despite its hard work in organizing the CIO, and although it captured the leadership of some unions, the Communist party never succeeded in sinking roots in the American working class; despite its turn to a popular-front politics in the midst of the depression, the party never succeeded in obtaining the ballots of more than a minute fraction of the voters, even though it achieved a modest middle-class respectability. But it did succeed—thanks to a shrewd mixture of what seemed like intransigent idealism and pragmatic rationalism—in gaining the acceptance ranging from passive to enthusiastic of a substantial proportion of the nation's most gifted novelists, playwrights, poets, and critics, all of whom expressed their conviction, through organizations established and controlled by the party, that radical changes based on Marxist analysis were imperative.

In extenuation of the American intellectuals' infatuation with Stalinism, it has been said that they loved only what they could not see; that America, in those years before World War II, was still an isolated country, with little knowledge or comprehension of the rest of the world; and that thousands of unemployed American workingmen, sick of being useless, queued up innocently on the chance of jobs in Soviet Russia, where depressions had been conquered. But of the crimes usually attributed by professional patriots to Communists there is one which neither has as yet truly comprehended: the perversion and betrayal of the idealistic dreams of a generation of writers and intellectuals who had confided their aspirations to the keeping of a clique of second-rate politicians.

There is reason to doubt, however, that the true believers would have been disabused of their illusions even if they had been able, all of them, to visit the Soviet Union personally. After all, some of them did—and the will to believe often triumphed over the evidence of the senses. That is why the *New Masses*, the party's journal of opinion, to which nearly every serious American writer contributed at some time during the thirties, was able to publish, unrebutted, the most preposterous claptrap about Russian communism—often to the accompaniment of applause from literary intellectuals.

The widow of Representative Victor Berger (first United States congressman elected as a Socialist) was taken aback at seeing Russian workers in rags in the streets of Moscow; but she was quite satisfied—as were her readers—with the explanation that the workers were simply wearing out their old clothes on the job during the day—for indeed everyone was well dressed in the cafes and theaters she visited at night! Some other of her reactions to Stalin's Russia, printed in the *New Masses* in the fall of 1935, may profitably be recalled:

We found that in their museums of revolutionary history, the work and contributions of Trotsky were omitted. We asked how they could honestly erase his name from that fierce history and they told us that he was a counter-revolutionary now, whose past usefulness must not be made into a present menace. We saw Lenin deified and we demurred that they were substituting one religion for another. One is the religion of science and activity, they said, the other is that of ignorance and death. We saw the picture of Stalin around every corner until, to our unindoctrinated eyes, it was almost comical. He has helped us to live, they said, and we saw people crowded still in inadequate rooms. There are only twenty-four hours a day for us to work, they said, and we knew that they used all the hours of day and night. We saw women doing heavy work and asked them why they did it, only to be told that they were quite free to enter any field and did this because they chose to.[8]

It need only be added that Mrs. Berger's paean to the happy lot of the ragged Russian workers was entitled "Seeing Is Believing."

Addressing the second congress of American writers in the summer of 1937, the playwright Albert Bein cried out, "When

---

[8] Meta Berger, "Seeing Is Believing," *New Masses*, XVII (November 5, 1935), 17–18.

I . . . see these people looking, with microscopes, for pimples on the shining face of the Soviet Union, I wonder, am I crazy or what?"[9] Mr. Bein was complaining about the handful of annoying dissidents, led by Dwight Macdonald, who had attempted to criticize Russian policies and assert their intellectual independence from Stalinist dogma. (The first writers' congress, held in the spring of 1935, had seen the establishment of the League of American Writers, dominated by Communist doctrine: "The interests of my own class," Malcolm Cowley had told the assemblage, "lie in a close alliance with the proletariat, and I believe that writers especially can profit by this alliance.")[10]

In addition to a passionate attachment to the mystique of the proletariat and a perfect Soviet state, there were also tremendous pressures—moral, psychological, even physical—to keep writers in line. The depression would not end, fascism would not go away, Hitler grew stronger. All your friends and associates were committed to the common struggle; Newton Arvin, Van Wyck Brooks, Erskine Caldwell, Marc Connolly, Malcolm Cowley, Waldo Frank, Langston Hughes, Archibald MacLeish, Lewis Mumford, Clifford Odets, Upton Sinclair, and Carl Van Doren were among those who issued the call to the second national congress of American writers, and thousands were turned away from the opening session at Carnegie Hall; where would you be, *who* would you be, if you were to question them and thus isolate yourself? (Even the most insignificant scribblers were petted or chivvied into line: I myself can still recall the types "assigned" to me, a mere apprentice writer on my college daily, to persuade me to forego my skeptical reservations about the Moscow Trials.)

But if, in the words of Malcolm Cowley, who should know,

---

[9] Quoted in proceedings, *The Writer in a Changing World,* ed. Henry Hart (New York: Equinox Cooperative Press, 1937), p. 241.

[10] *Ibid.,* p. 18.

those years were an "age of faith," we must hasten to add that in the midst of the thirties, well before the Nazi-Soviet pact revealed the true nature of Stalinism to almost all Americans, some of the best of the intellectuals and writers did turn away from the Stalinist faith. The literary journal *Partisan Review,* under the editorship of William Phillips and Philip Rahv, broke with the Communist party. In an article entitled "What Happened in the 30's," written a quarter of a century later, Phillips has explained: "Politically, this meant a stand for morality in politics. In literature, it meant a radicalism rooted in tradition and open to experiment, and an awareness that the imagination could not be contained within any orthodoxy. It meant that one could not rule out any literary beliefs or forms as incompatible with socialist aims."[11] The literary polemics of the anti-Stalinists in the thirties may make nearly as wearisome reading nowadays as those of their doctrinaire opponents, but they are nonetheless significant as reminders that the honor of American men of letters was not irremediably tarnished by those who, embracing intellectual servitude to a monolithic philosophy, claimed to speak for American writers as a class.

Furthermore, the writers who did stick with the Communists until the bitter end were, by the logic of circumstances, the very ones most adept at trimming their work to the demands of mass media commercialism. It was not the serious novelists but the young men on the make, willing to serve in the studios as Hollywood's hired hands (and one or two best-seller writers), who clung—long after it had been abandoned by others—to the myth of a stainless Soviet Union. They clung, not with winged words, but with dues . . . and dogged silence about their fellow-hacks who were doing likewise. In keeping with what their employers unctuously termed "the American Way," the blacklisted screenwriters were convicted and duly released

---

[11] William Phillips, "What Happened in the 30's," *Commentary,* XXXIV (September 1962), 207.

from prison—to find not ostracism, but Oscars, not contempt
but contracts assuring them of more money than non-com-
mercial writers could ever command.

How did their contemporaries evaluate the writers at work
during the depression years? The question is important because
present-day attitudes derive largely from judgments expressed
by the critics of the thirties and forties and reflect the two ex-
tremes of opinion—that depression writers were dramatically
bold and selfless, or that they were a poor lot, the ebb tide of
an earlier wave. Most of the so-called Marxist critics made a
predictable one-to-one correlation: those who were writing
about the depression were valuable (or redeemable, which was
sometimes even more significant, for this category permitted
the bestowal of approval upon those who had already won
recognition as bourgeois artists of substance). Writers who held
to previously established concerns, like Scott Fitzgerald or
Thornton Wilder, were regarded with contempt or worse—
unless they associated themselves politically with some of the
dozens of extra-literary campaigns of the official Left; those
who did write of the "little" people, like Albert Halper and
Daniel Fuchs, and of the anxieties of the depression, like Theodore Dreiser and Sherwood Anderson, were equally suspect, if
not more so, unless they exhibited the requisite qualities of disgust with dying capitalism, faith in the historical mission of
the proletariat, and confidence in its vanguard party.

"The discovery of the class struggle as the fundamental interpretation of American life" was the key to understanding
major trends in American literature, in the view of Granville
Hicks, who barely had any leeway to display his personal taste
until he had broken with the Communists.[12] "Obed Brooks"

---

[12] Granville Hicks, "American Fiction: The Major Trend," in *Proletarian Literature in the United States,* ed. Granville Hicks, *et al.* (New
York: International Publishers, 1935), p. 360.

(pen name of a Marxist critic who has since become a distinguished Ivy League academic) found in the poetry of Archibald MacLeish a foretaste of "the marching feet of the storm troops," but in a postscript noted that thanks to "certain public statements" and "with his changed attitude toward capitalism, MacLeish's will has been partially freed from the sensual and subrational evasiveness of his former social writing";[13] while Edwin Berry Burgum, already a certified academic and a stern Marxist, responded to Stephen Spender's account of the revolution:

> through torn-down portions of old fabric let their eyes
> Watch the admiring dawn explode like a shell
> around us, dazing us with its light like snow. . . .[14]

as follows: "The passive position of watching the dawn is hardly fitting to the revolutionary," opined Professor Burgum, "nor should the dawn daze like snow those who under self-discipline have known what to expect and are ready for the next move."[14] It is a sad truth that the advocates of proletarian literature in depression America are not often worth consulting (except by historians of the period) for their opinions about their contemporaries.

What is perhaps more unexpected is that those independent critics of the time who, by virtue of their reliance on intellect rather than dogma, should be more worthy of our attention, all too often reveal that most depressing failing of the professional critic: exaggerated reverence for those safely dead and incapable of upsetting judgments, coupled with a basic lack of respect and understanding for the original work of their own contemporaries. For example, John Chamberlain, who had not then developed into the conservative columnist that he is now,

[13] Obed Brooks, "Archibald MacLeish," *ibid.*, p. 329.

[14] Edwin Berry Burgum, "Three English Radical Poets," *ibid.*, p. 333.

was not merely sympathetic to radical viewpoints, but had been hospitable to new writing in his influential capacity as daily book reviewer for *The New York Times*. And yet, looking back over the decade in 1938, he could only find it in himself to say: "The 'great writers' whose absence Van Wyck Brooks had deplored seemed more absent than ever. Why? What had happened to the promise of the '20's? . . . Beyond Hemingway, Lewis and Dos Passos, beyond Farrell and Wolfe, the fiction of the '30's that one remembers is sparse indeed. . . . Erskine Caldwell and William Faulkner have their points, but they have not developed into major artists."[15]

The reader who finds such a statement more patronizing than illuminating may be assured that the attitude was not unique with Mr. Chamberlain. Alfred Kazin, who was in his early twenties when he wrote *On Native Grounds* (1942), undertook in that remarkably precocious critical survey an examination of "The Literature of Crisis (1930–1940)," which is still unsurpassed in sweep and comprehensiveness. Yet he too was moved to speak of "the decline of the novel all through the period, a moral and physical decline. . . ."[16] The novelists, it seemed, were too harsh: "One saw it in Caldwell's necrophilism and Farrell's inexhaustible interest in brutality . . . in the diseased impressionism, really a prose of hysteria, of Edward Dahlberg's novels. . . ."[17] And Faulkner's "mountainous rhetoric, with its fantastic pseudoclassical epithets and invertebrate grandeur, its merely verbal intensity and inherent motor violence, is the effort of a writer to impose upon himself that which he cannot create simply and evocatingly. It is the articulation of confusion rather than an evasion of it; force pass-

---

[15] John Chamberlain, "Literature," in *America Now*, ed. Harold E. Stearns (New York: Charles Scribner's Sons, 1938), pp. 37, 47.

[16] Alfred Kazin, *On Native Grounds* (New York: Reynal & Hitchcock, 1942), p. 491.

[17] *Ibid.*, p. 379.

ing for directed energy. With all its occasional felicity and
stabbing appropriateness of phrase, Faulkner's style is a dis-
cursive fog. . . ."[18] Mr. Kazin has, of course, since written more
admiringly, indeed admirably, of William Faulkner. The fact
remains, however, that those of us in the sixties who would
understand Sheriff Clark and Sheriff Rainey—or Fannie Lou
Hamer and Rosa Parks—will gain more insight from the novels
of William Faulkner than from his contemporary critics.

On Native Grounds is surely still the outstanding literary
study of the period. Yet, like Mr. Chamberlain's essay, and like
the writings of lesser literary journalists, it is charged with
negative assertions. "For what emerges so unmistakably from
the enormous descriptive and historical literature of our day is
how unready so many writers have been to seek its imaginative
truth, how lacking they have been in the requisite confidence
or detachment. . . ."[19] Taken aback by such a sweeping condemnation, one searches the book in vain for even an index
listing, much less an appraisal, of such writers as Nathanael
West or Daniel Fuchs or Henry Roth (although, again, in
recent years Mr. Kazin has been one of the more eloquent
exponents of the literary virtues of Roth's singularly powerful
novel, *Call It Sleep*). Surely we may legitimately wonder
about the effect upon a novelist when his own name, and any
possible literary virtues he may possess, go quite unmentioned
in a study which does not hesitate to castigate *en masse* the
writers of his own day—including, presumably, himself—for
their unreadiness to seek its imaginative truth.

In short, even the best of the serious critics of the depression
years were as quick to condemn contemporary writers for one
set of supposed shortcomings as the Stalinist critics were for
another—or to praise them for extra-literary virtues. They even
condemned them for falling silent—seemingly without realiz-

---

[18] *Ibid.*, p. 463.

[19] *Ibid.*, p. 490.

ing the adverse effect that such a condemnation might have upon those struggling to express some valid notions about the world in which they all lived. Thus, Alfred Kazin wrote off an even dozen novelists and short-story writers by name, only to have Edward Dahlberg and Tillie Lerner turn up many years later, not only stubbornly alive but stubbornly writing. "Dahlberg," Kazin asserted definitively in 1942, "was exhausted by his own sensibility";[20] but in 1964 the novelist rose from the ashes with his autobiography, *Because I Was Flesh*, the third and perhaps the most remarkable reworking of material he had already twice told in the thirties—and Alfred Kazin was moved to describe it, justly, as "one of the most important American books published in our day."

It is particularly odd that critics of all people should reproach novelists for falling silent, when the occupational hazard is one afflicting not just novelists, but men of letters in general. We need only think of Van Wyck Brooks, stricken dumb in mid-career after a great expense of spirit, and able to resume an incredibly industrious life only at the cost of turning his back on the literary mood of the thirties and the ensuing decades, and casting an undiscriminating, benevolent eye over the works of dead American authors.

Unquestionably, most of the writers whom Alfred Kazin listed, aside from being (as he was keen enough to recognize) bad novelists and worse politicians from the outset, did fall silent after one or two books, but not necessarily as a direct result of addiction to the naturalist method, or because of a slavish readiness to subordinate slender literary gifts to the dictates of Communist orthodoxy. A similar paralysis did not afflict European naturalistic or Communist writers in comparable numbers; and in fact some of the American novelists and poets whom we should value most are precisely those who have liberated themselves from the esthetic and political precepts of the thirties—

---

[20] *Ibid.*, p. 382.

but not necessarily from that era's social concerns—and have gone on to create work of enduring quality. Others who fell silent were the victims of physical or mental breakdowns attributable to their suffering during the depression. What is more, one could call the roll of American writers of the twenties or of earlier periods who have lapsed into silence, and it is at least possible if not probable—no one knows, for such a comparative study has never been made—that more American writers have persisted in their careers in the past thirty years than ever did before.

What we can say (although here again it must be a matter of supposition) is that over the generations far more American literary men than Europeans seem to have dropped out of sight after an ambitious early effort. Surely it would seem most probable that lack of self-confidence or profound fear of failure is a function of the difficulty of being a writer in the United States. It is, quite simply, not *natural*, even now, to be a poet or a novelist in this country, in the sense that it is say in England or in France. We need only cite Tom Kromer's harrowing cry from the lower depths, *Waiting for Nothing* (1935), which was followed by nothing.

The situation for the serious American writer in the bottom of the depression was in its own way as "unnatural" as that of the novelist during the fifties or sixties, after the dropping of the bomb and the burgeoning of the so-called mass society. It was unnatural not because the government repressed the writer, for in fact it gave him an unprecedented stipend; not because society spurned him, for in fact it opened its halls and its heart to his poems and plays, his complaints and prescriptions; but because the financial and moral collapse had called all values into question, and beyond despair lay only a faith that was itself to be called into question before the decade was out.

If we are told now, unfairly, that contemporary novelists cannot compete with sociologists in evoking the insane, robotized quality of American life, we were told then, unfairly, that novelists could not compete with journalists or reporters or photographers in evoking the desperate, confused, floundering quality of American life in the thirties. If we are told now, unfairly, that contemporary novelists have become the spoiled campus pets of a soft society, capable only of forking over their own night soil, we were told then, unfairly, that writers had become the kept men of the Communist agitators, capable only of sloganizing their verse and banalizing their stories into acceptable variations on the party line.

Among the new generation, on the other hand, now that the work of the Roaring Twenties has been thoroughly exploited, there is already discernible a tendency to glamorize the thirties. As if in direct reaction to those who have denigrated the depression writers, we are now beginning to hear that the bards whose excruciating verse heralded the dawn of a Soviet America were something like "freedom fighters" in their day, and that the scribes of windy epics about the Folk finding their way from the back country to the front lines of the revolution, complete with hillbilly dialects and country folksongs, were the forerunners of the antipoverty campaign. This is simply foolishness, overvaluing minor writers who were at best clumsy and tedious and at worst smug and venomous, at a time when it seemed that almost any trash could get published as long as it had an air of purposiveness and serviceability. ("Serious literature is a precision instrument that labor cannot do without," said the editorial at the end of a pamphlet of Communist-line stories and poems about trade-union people.[21])

But what remains? What do the writers of the thirties have to say to us now? If the writers of more recent years have sought in their various ways to answer the question: Who am I? then it can be said that during the depression, American

---

[21] *Get Organized,* ed. Alan Calmer (New York: International Publishers, 1939), p. 47.

writers struggled to answer the question: Who are we? And if no more than a fraction of the attempted answers seemed to make sense, then any more than now, surely the earlier question itself should serve to remind us that the history of the novel has encompassed both the quest for social identity and the more current quest for individual identity (which is now defined existentially so patly and so often that we tend to forget other alternatives). In parallel fashion, the history of art may remind us that even painters obsessed with their own changing and dissolving image—Rembrandt, Munch, Beckmann—did not thereby shrink from the effort to capture an image of their world as well.

To answer the question of who we are, the novelist of the thirties often tried to find out where we had come from, to retrace the footsteps of the preceding generation and determine the direction in which they pointed. As the decade opened, Michael Gold published an autobiography that has gained its place in American literary history, if only as a footnote, because it reviews the terrific struggles of his immigrant parents to achieve a decent life for themselves and their children in an indecent, squalid slum on the Lower East Side; in consequence, Gold's *Jews Without Money* entered the language almost as *Babbitt* had. His book, however, is a sentimental caricature, not only because his version of American Jewish history leads in a straight line to the revolution, but because he invokes his mother as the guardian of his revolutionary morality:

Mother! Momma! I am still bound to you by the cords of birth. I cannot forget you. I must remain faithful to the poor because I cannot be faithless to you! I believe in the poor because I have known you. The world must be made gracious for the poor! Momma, you taught me that![22]

This incantatory prose can be read as the forerunner of the

[22] Michael Gold, *Jews Without Money* (New York: Liveright, 1930), p. 158.

plays of younger "rebels," who were also taken seriously in
their day—Clifford Odets, for example ("See this ankle, this
delicate sensitive hand? Four hundred years to breed that. Out
of a revolutionary background! Spirit of '76! Ancestors froze at
Valley Forge! What's it all mean! Slops! The honest workers
were sold out then, in '76. The Constitution's for rich men
then and now. Slops!")[23] and Arthur Miller ("Attention must
be paid.").[24] Compared to the best fiction and poetry of the
period, the social theater of the depression possessed few virtues beyond those of sympathy for strikers, Negroes, and anti-
fascists, and the mere thought of reviving the plays of Albert
Maltz, George Sklar, or John Wexley is an embarrassment.

Within a few years after *Jews Without Money*, other writers
did succeed in relating their mothers and fathers to the American immigrant experience, and also to the hard but challenging
world of young people coming to maturity in the depression.
Among the most remarkable of these writers were Henry Roth,
who in 1934 published *Call It Sleep*, a portrait of a beautiful
woman struggling to give her little boy a sense of the wonder
of the world on the hard pavements of New York; Jack Conroy,
whose *The Disinherited*, in addition to being a *bildungsroman*
of a young revolutionary, was an ode to the hero's miner father
and to his widowed mother, who took in washing in a Missouri
coal town so that he might go to school; and Edward Dahlberg,
who told the tough, epic story of his mother, the immigrant and
itinerant lady barber, in two novels, *Bottom Dogs* and *From
Flushing to Calvary*, which heralded her son's entrance into the
literary world as a revolutionary leftist. Indeed, all these writers
who apotheosized their mothers were deeply involved during
the depression with at least the literary aspects of the Com-

---

[23] Clifford Odets, *Waiting for Lefty*, in *Three Plays* (New York:
Covici Friede, 1935), p. 47.

[24] Arthur Miller, *Death of a Salesman* (New York: Viking Press,
1949), p. 56.

that which obsessed such vastly different writers as James Agee and Nelson Algren and Kenneth Fearing and Sherwood Anderson, was composing short stories both gothic and baroque, and as true to his understanding of his country as Gorky's had been to Russia.

What united writers of such diverse origins and temperaments was the passion of their response and their determination to bring to imaginative life the terror and the glory of their countrymen as they struggled to cope with the economic and social darkness that had descended upon them. Whether they were, like Anderson, Steinbeck, and MacLeish, hopeful by nature and convinced that their writing could in some way contribute to a general amelioration, or whether they were as despairing about their fellow men as Nelson Algren, Tom Kromer, or Weldon Kees, they conceived the very act of creation as one of affirmation of the value of human life; and the relentlessness with which they pursued—wherever it was to take them—the truth not just about themselves but about the American experience can very well serve as a model for the apprentice artists and the questing students of another day.

A word is in order about the selection of the material in this volume. A number of those whom we regard as the greatest writers of the pre-depression generation—Fitzgerald, Faulkner, Hemingway—as well as lesser but distinguished figures—Daniel Fuchs, Henry Roth—have been omitted because their works do not deal with the depression as such, even though the three novels of Mr. Fuchs, for example, are instinct with the clamor and terror of the Brooklyn streets throughout the thirties and deserve to be read in their entirety.

On the other hand, a number of those whose names are primarily associated with the depression generation, or with the cult of proletarian literature—Michael Gold, Clifford

munist movement; and two of them stopped publishing fiction at the time that their radical faith was declining; but one must hesitate before making an exact correlation between these two data. In their various ways, these authors elevated their parents' experiences to the level of art and linked them to the terrible trials of the depression decade.

When it came to looking directly at that decade, many of the writers did so, as we have already observed, through glasses that were either red-tinted or frankly red, white, and blue—and often, in the oddest way, through a combination of the two (sometimes spurred on by the line that communism was "twentieth-century Americanism"). More important, however, than the temporary attractiveness of either Marxism as a philosophical world-view pointing the way out for an obviously lost society, or a Whitmanesque pose of nationalist brotherhood, was the peculiarly American marriage of journalism and fiction. European expressionists of the period, like Alfred Döblin with his *Alexanderplatz, Berlin,* had attempted an integration of the headline and the news story into the novel. But none, not even the French chroniclers with their multivolume historical sagas, had precedent for the brilliant juxtapositions—pop tunes, mass media clichés, gutter-press horror stories, anti-capitalist interpretations of the national history, rebel heroes charging blindly to their doom—that John Dos Passos brought off in *USA.*

It was natural for American novelists, who were usually semi-educated newspapermen rather than men of letters, to support themselves at a trade that was both honorable and understandable to the public at large. Besides, it seemed a logical respite from novel-writing to turn, not to the literary essay or the lecture tour, but to the journalistic job of work as a means of making some money and getting away from one's solitary desk. And when disaster struck, it was inevitable that American novelists, curious and wondering about their neighbors, should leave their studies and wander through the land in search of news about their fellow Americans. *Puzzled America, Tragic America, Some American People, The Road: In Search of America,* all were the work of journalist-novelists.

Those who, like Alfred Kazin, have cited the journalistic outpouring of the depression years as an indication of its superiority to the wornout factualism of the naturalistic novel as a medium of communication, would seem to have missed this point. Just as Truman Capote has devoted most of the first half of this decade to a book of reportage, a study in depth of a midwest murder case, not because he had lost faith in the novel but rather from a desire to do something different from and larger than his earlier work, so many of the best writers of the thirties, from Erskine Caldwell in Georgia to Ernest Hemingway in Spain, turned to reportage as an alternate means of communication.

Indeed, if there is one book of the thirties that should speak directly, above all others, to readers and writers of the sixties, it is the poet-novelist James Agee's triumphant work of reportage, *Let Us Now Praise Famous Men.* Although it did not appear until 1941, this book, which is located, so to speak, in the summer of 1936, expresses in quintessential form everything most ardent and unafraid about the creative men of those years. A collaboration of two poets, one with a camera (Walker Evans) and the other with a pen, it came about as the result of a request that they "pry intimately into the lives of an undefended and appallingly damaged group of human beings, an ignorant and helpless rural family, for the purpose of parading the nakedness, disadvantage and humiliation of these lives before another group of human beings. . . ." It opened ringingly with the epigraph:

Workers of the world, unite and fight. You have nothing to lose but your chains, and a world to win.

"These words," Agee explained in a footnote, "are quoted here to mislead those who will be misled by them. They mean, not

what the reader may care to think they mean, but wha say."[25]

Therewith the true radicalism of the depression, the goi the root of our common troubles, emerged on page after of this lovely and horrifying book. It embodied a humane unselfishly impersonal examination of American life the of which we have hardly experienced on the American liter scene since its appearance. This radicalism, this humanity, searching not for absurdity but for meaningfulness, not for dividual dissolution but for the profoundest kind of comrad ship—this is what animated the best writing of the depressic years, and this is what the record of those years by the best its chroniclers has to offer us.

Although political conviction or philosophical commitmen may have influenced the depression writers' choice of subjec matter and stylistic manner, at their best they transcended poli tics. The intensity of their concern sprang from a richer and deeper source, a desire to wed their craft to an interpretation of the bewildering complexity of American life. This union produced, we need to be reminded in the sixties, not simply the tedious naturalism of the ungifted, but a continuation of what had been seen a hundred years earlier in both Europe and America as the fundamental task of the literary artist: laying bare the corpus of modern society with every tool at the artist's disposal. In the case of James T. Farrell this meant, to be sure, a naturalism that, if it owed more to Norris and Dreiser than to Joyce or Proust, produced in *Studs Lonigan* a book that will not die. During the same period John Dos Passos, experimenting with every innovation devised by the postwar generation and adding some of his own, completed ir *USA* another trilogy that continues to resist oblivion. And Erskine Caldwell, fired by a rage at the spoilage of life lik

[25] James Agee and Walker Evans, *Let Us Now Praise Famous Me* (Boston: Houghton Mifflin, 1940), p. xiii.

Odets, Grace Lumpkin, Fielding Burke—will not be found in the pages that follow, simply because it was felt that the areas of social concern with which they deal are more memorably described by others who are included.

In short, the selective principle has been twofold: first, to ensure that as wide a social spectrum as possible would be represented, so that the reader might have a historically balanced account of the effects of the depression on all segments of the American people; and second, to present a cross-section of good writing originating during the depression decade without regard to the writer's sociopolitical convictions (or lack of them). This is not to argue that a Louis Adamic ought to be regarded as having the intensity, brilliance, or wit of a Sherwood Anderson, a Horace Gregory, a Nathanael West; but simply that there were good journalists and reporters observing the dark corners of America then, just as were the good novelists and poets. Nothing dated or meretricious has been included on the assumption that it would be edifying or in some way historically significant. Bad writing can be instructive only to the reader who is already thoroughly aware of the good.

Finally, it is the editor's keen desire that a new generation of Americans will go on to explore with discoverer's delight the complete works of some of the authors excerpted here, and thus come to share his feeling that the depression was in truth not just a tragic era but in many ways a triumphant one for American literary artists, one which, as certain earlier periods in our history, may be an inspiration to those who are yet to create, with their hands and their spirits, a greater society.

Gratitude is due to the librarians without whom the anthologist is helpless; in this instance, most particularly: Ermine Stone, Librarian Emeritus of Sarah Lawrence College; Louise Heinze, Librarian of the Tamiment Institute; Romana Javits,

Curator of the Picture Collection of the New York Public Library; and to Bette Swados, Comrade and Collaborator.

Harvey Swados

Valley Cottage, N.Y.
September 1965

Selected Bibliography

Bibliographies of the fiction and poetry of the period dealing with the depression are to be found in the works of Donald Drew Egbert and Stow Persons, Walter B. Rideout, Leo Gurko, and Robert Spiller, *et al.*, listed below in *Secondary Works*. In the first part, *Contemporary Writing*, I have listed the principal writings of the decade concerned either with the depression itself or with the writers. I have not listed volumes excerpted in the anthology.

CONTEMPORARY WRITING

Reporting, Commentary, Short Stories

American Stuff. New York: The Viking Press, 1937.

ASCH, NATHAN. *The Road*. New York: The Macmillan Company, 1937.

CALDWELL, ERSKINE, and MARGARET BOURKE-WHITE. *You Have Seen Their Faces*. New York: The Macmillan Company, 1937.

CHASE, STUART. *Rich Land, Poor Land*. New York: Whittlesey House, 1936.

COWLEY, MALCOLM. *Exile's Return*. New York: W. W. Norton and Company, 1934.

DREISER, THEODORE. *Tragic America*. New York: Simon and Schuster, 1935.

FILLER, LOUIS, ed. *The Anxious Years. America in the Nineteen Thirties. A Collection of Contemporary Writing*. New York: G. P. Putnam's Sons, 1963.

HART, HENRY, ed. *The Writer in a Changing World*. New York: Equinox Cooperative Press, 1937.

HICKS, GRANVILLE, *et al.*, eds. *Proletarian Literature in the United States*. New York: International Publishers, 1935.

LANGE, DOROTHEA, and PAUL J. TAYLOR. *An American Exodus.* New York: Reynal and Hitchcock, 1940.

LEIGHTON, GEORGE. *Five Cities: The Story of Their Youth and Old Age.* New York: Harper & Brothers, 1939.

LYND, ROBERT S., and HELEN M. *Middletown in Transition.* New York: Harcourt, Brace and Company, 1937.

McWILLIAMS, CAREY. *Factories in the Field.* Boston: Little, Brown and Company, 1939.

NIXON, HERMON CLARENCE. *Forty Acres and Steel Mules.* Chapel Hill: University of North Carolina Press, 1938.

RAPER, ARTHUR F., and IRA DE A. REID. *Sharecroppers All.* Chapel Hill: University of North Carolina Press, 1941.

RORTY, JAMES. *Where Life is Better.* New York: Reynal and Hitchcock, 1936.

SCHMALHAUSEN, SAMUEL D., ed. *Behold America.* New York: Farrar, 1931.

SELDES, GILBERT. *Years of the Locust.* Boston: Little, Brown and Company, 1933.

SHANNON, DAVID, ed. *The Great Depression.* Englewood Cliffs, N.J.: Prentice-Hall, Inc., 1960.

STEARNS, HAROLD E. *America: A Reappraisal.* New York: Hillman-Curl, 1937.

ZIMMERMAN, CARLE C., and NATHAN L. WHETTEN. *Rural Families on Relief.* Washington: U. S. Government Printing Office, 1938.

Theater

BLAKE, BEN. *The Awakening of the American Theatre.* New York: Tomorrow, 1935.

Federal Theatre Plays. 2 vols. New York: The Macmillan Company, 1938.

FLANAGAN, HALLIE. *Arena.* New York: Duell, Sloan & Pearce, 1940.

FLEXNER, ELEANOR. *American Playwrights, 1918–1938.* New York: Simon and Schuster, 1938.

KOZLENKO, WILLIAM, ed. *The Best Short Plays of the Social Theatre.* New York: The Macmillan Company, 1939.

WHITMAN, WILLSON. *Bread and Circuses.* New York: Oxford University Press, 1937.

WITTLER, CLARENCE J. *Some Social Trends in WPA Drama.* Washington: Catholic University Press, 1939.

Criticism

CALVERTON, V. F. *The Liberation of American Literature.* New York: Charles Scribner's Sons, 1932.

FARRELL, JAMES T. *A Note on Literary Criticism.* New York: Vanguard Press, 1936.

HICKS, GRANVILLE. *The Great Tradition.* New York: The Macmillan Company, 1933.

RAHV, PHILIP. "Proleterian Literature: A Political Autopsy," *Southern Review* (Winter 1939), 615–628.

SMITH, BERNARD. *Forces in American Criticism.* New York: Harcourt, Brace and Company, 1937.

WILSON, EDMUND. *The Triple Thinkers.* New York: Harcourt, Brace and Company, 1938.

SECONDARY WORKS

General History

EGBERT, DONALD DREW, and STOW PERSONS, eds. *Socialism and American Life.* Vol. II, *Bibliography, Descriptive and Critical.* T. D. S. Bassett, bibliographer. Princeton: Princeton University Press, 1952.

MITCHELL, BROADUS. *Depression Decade. From New Era through New Deal, 1929–1941.* New York: Rinehart and Company, 1947.

SCHLESINGER, ARTHUR M., JR. *The Age of Roosevelt.* 3 vols. Boston: Houghton Mifflin Company, 1957–1960.

WECTER, DIXON. *The Age of the Great Depression, 1929–1941.* New York: The Macmillan Company, 1948.

Literary History

AARON, DANIEL. *Writers on the Left. Episodes in American Literary Communism.* New York: Harcourt, Brace and Company, 1961.

BEACH, JOSEPH WARREN. *American Fiction, 1920–1940.* New York: The Macmillan Company, 1941.

BONE, ROBERT A. *The Negro Novel in America.* New Haven: Yale University Press, 1958.

CARGILL, OSCAR. *Intellectual America: Ideas on the March.* New York: The Macmillan Company, 1941.

GEISMAR, MAXWELL. *Writers in Crisis: The American Novel, 1925–1940.* Boston: Houghton Mifflin Company, 1942.

GELFANT, BLANCHE HOUSMAN. *The American City Novel.* Norman: University of Oklahoma Press, 1945.

GLOSTER, HUGH M. *Negro Voices in American Fiction.* Chapel Hill: University of North Carolina Press, 1948.

GOLDWATER, WALTER. *Radical Periodicals in America, 1890–1950.* New Haven: University Place Book Shop, 1964.

GURKO, LEO. *The Angry Decade.* New York: Dodd, Mead & Company, 1947.

KAZIN, ALFRED. *On Native Grounds. An Interpretation of Modern American Prose Literature.* New York: Reynal and Hitchcock, 1942.

MILLGATE, MICHAEL. *American Social Fiction.* New York: Barnes and Noble, 1964.

RIDEOUT, WALTER B. *The Radical Novel in the United States, 1900–1954.* Cambridge: Harvard University Press, 1956.

SPILLER, ROBERT, *et al.*, eds. *Literary History of the United States.* Vol. III, Bibliography edited by Thomas H. Johnson, Supplement edited by Richard M. Ludwig. 2nd ed. New York: The Macmillan Company, 1962.

Memoirs and Reflections

CLURMAN, HAROLD. *The Fervent Years. The Story of the Group Theatre and the Thirties.* New York: Alfred A. Knopf, 1945.

COWLEY, MALCOLM. "A Remembrance of the Red Romance," *Esquire,* LXI (March 1964), 124–130.

————. "The 1930's Were an Age of Faith," *New York Times Book Review* (December 13, 1964), 4–5, 14–17.

————. "While They Waited for Lefty," *Saturday Review,* XLVII (June 6, 1964), 16–19, 61.

FARRELL, JAMES T. *The League of Frightened Philistines.* New York: Vanguard Press, 1945.

————. *The Fate of Writing in America.* New York: Falcon Press, 1946.

————. *Literature and Morality.* New York: Vanguard Press, 1947.

KEMPTON, MURRAY. *Part of Our Time. Some Ruins and Monuments of the Thirties.* New York: Simon and Schuster, 1955.

PHILLIPS, WILLIAM. "What Happened in the 30's," *Commentary,* XXXIV (September 1962), 204–212.

The American Writer
and the Great Depression

PART ONE

Miners, Millhands, Factory Workers:

MISSOURI, TENNESSEE, NORTH CAROLINA, PENNSYLVANIA, WASHINGTON

---

1. The Disinherited

JACK CONROY

In the 1930's the American working class came into its own. Along with the foolish debates about proletarian literature— whether it had to be written about workers, or for workers, or against capitalism, or for the Soviet Union—there was a re- affirmation of belief in the worth of those who had been the producers of American prosperity and the victims of its disap- pearance. Even though it is unlikely that the novels of Jack Conroy (1899–) were ever read widely by workers (except for such special groups as seamen, and the radical fringe at- tracted to ideas, American workers have never been particu- larly interested in books), he was nevertheless a proletarian writer par excellence. A son of the working class who had neither scorned nor forgotten his origins, he reached back, in

---

From *The Disinherited* (New York: Covici-Friede, 1933), Chap. VII, pp. 44–83. Copyright 1933 by Jack Conroy. Used by the permission of Crown Publishers.

The Disinherited, *far before the depression to his miner fa-*
ther's life and death, his mother's devoted drudgery, his own
early labor and slow education, with tenderness and honesty.
In Moberly, Missouri, where he was born, he formed a group
of "Rebel Poets," then edited Anvil, *a proletarian short-story*
magazine, and wrote a propagandist novel, A World to Win.
The thirties ended and Conroy went on to other things, among
them free-lance reviewing; but he left behind something essen-
tial not only to a chaotic era, but to all Americans, no matter
what their persuasion: the sense of the continuity of radical
convictions that we can feel in the following pages, arising
from the workers' tradition of mutual aid in the struggle against
the degrading and dangerous conditions of labor imposed
upon them.

One morning my Aunt Jessie came to take me to the home
of a miner who had been crushed by a fall of rock in the
Monkey Nest. It was thought that the sight of a dead man
might serve to counteract my excess of youthful spirits, for in
those days joy was invariably associated with the Devil, and a
lugubrious manner and countenance were esteemed as hall-
marks of sanctity. Though I had no desire to see the dead man,
I was not a bit averse to the trip thither, for the day promised
to be glorious. The wild plum thickets along the lane were
carpeting the ground beneath with their petals. As we cut
through a clover field, bees trafficked busily in the blossoms
underfoot, and I trod warily with my bare feet, for I had once
been stung on the ankle by a bumblebee.

Aunt Jessie was a pretty girl with full red lips and a rope of
wavy chestnut hair, but she kept it twisted in a tight knot. She
was a good Christian girl and never went to dances. Sometimes she asked me questions about whether boys talked dirty
about the girls around me.

"Did you ever hear Rollie Weems say anything about me?"
she asked as we struck across the fields.

"Well, yes, I did," I admitted, "but I don't dare tell you, or you'd tell Mother and have her whip me."

"Oh, no, I wouldn't!" she assured me eagerly. "No matter what it was, I want to know. Go on and tell me and I'll do you a favor some time."

"Well," I said boldly. "He was talking to a bunch of fellows down by the saloon. He said you was the dandiest baby doll this side of the Mississippi, and that he'd give forty acres and a team of mules to get in your britches."

"Ooh!" she squeaked indignantly, but her eyes sparkled. "Would you allow anybody to talk about your aunt that way? You ought to have slapped him square in the mouth!"

"I didn't know he meant any harm," I countered hypocritically. "I didn't know what he meant by that, anyway."

I was lying, and I suspected that Aunt Jessie knew it.

The collie scared up a quail and it ran limping and fluttering away with the dog barking excitedly after it. Then I knew that the bird's nest was near; and that as soon as the dog had been decoyed far enough away, the quail would rise up and fly back. I found the nest burrowed in the ground, and it was full of eggs. For a moment Aunt Jessie was smiling as she knelt to look, but the realization of her grim mission brought her back to her feet, and she pressed resolutely on, telling me to hurry.

We waded knee deep in lush grass on which the dew had dried only at the top; we passed through a meadow infested with tickle grass and it worked up my pants leg and set my aunt to scratching, too. She pinned her skirt beneath her arms, but her petticoat was soon drenched and stained green. When we came to a fence, she looked cautiously in all directions to see if anybody were about, then she knelt and crawled under as I held up the bottom strand. Her stays were laced so tight that her face reddened every time she stooped over.

The dead man's hovel was jammed with sorrowful relatives and curious neighbors. Rollie Weems was standing in the yard among some men who were talking solemnly in undertones. Rollie's face brightened when he saw us.

"How do, Jessie!" he cried, doffing his hat.

"How do, *Mister Weems!*" she returned icily, sweeping past him into the house. But she turned to the window and looked back.

As we entered the front room, the dazzling sunlight was instantly blotted out and with it my exuberance. For a moment I could see nothing but a dim, shrouded figure reclining upon one of the folding biers that undertakers used. One of the relatives who seemed to be a sort of master of ceremonies came forward and with a dramatic gesture ripped the sheet off the corpse. There he lay like a trussed blue fowl, his feet protruding from beneath a cheap cotton shroud. His scarred hands were folded across his chest; coal dust still blackening his nails and showing between his toes. His lips were glued in a hideous grin. I wailed in fright and attempted to retreat to the outdoors, but my aunt was not to be diverted from her purpose and what she considered her Christian duty.

"Touch his face!" she cried sternly.

She seized my hand and planted it on the dead man's forehead. Revulsion overwhelmed me—I snatched my hand away as though the dead flesh were burning instead of icy. I grew faint and felt as though I must retch.

For days the dead man's face appeared before me every time I closed my eyes. I awoke in the night a-sweat with terror, fancying my hand was still on his brow and that the curious paralysis which often affects one in dreams would not allow me to withdraw it. There was a mouse between the walls in the room where I slept and I could hear his sharp teeth nibbling, nibbling, and bits of plaster and lath falling. My imagination transformed the mouse into a dead man scratching with long finger nails at the lid of his coffin. I recalled grewsome anecdotes of people buried alive and how, when they were unearthed later, it was found that they had turned over on their faces in the casket, fighting for breath, and had wrenched handsful of hair from their heads.

"If you ever hear that ornery Rollie Weems say anything more about me, you let me know," Aunt Jessie told me as we trudged home from the dead man's house.

That night I heard Mother and Father talking in the kitchen.

"It's all I can do, and I must do it," Father said. "I could tend the garden in the morning, go to work at noon and dig till four, then fire the shots. Four dollars extra on the day will soon pay up our debts and leave enough over to send Larry to school in town. The way it is now, we're like the frog in the well. Every time he jumped up one foot, he slipped back two. We might figure ourselves to Hell, but never to the top of the ground."

Mother protested that shot firing was a single man's job, and that nobody ever lasted long at it. Shot firers were paid a premium rate for an hour or two of work after the other men had finished. When a man accepted the job it was considered that his days were numbered—that the Angel of Death had already checked his name on the waiting list.

But Father was obdurate. After a great deal of indecision, he had found what appeared to be a way out. He said he would be very careful; moreover, Mike Riordan would be his partner, and Mike was an old hand who had fired shots unscathed in the days when miners still used sulphur squibs. The squibs were like Fourth of July nigger-chasers. When a match was touched to one end, the squib began to fizz and back up. They were placed in small copper tubes tamped in drill holes containing a charge of powder. One end of the tube extended into a paper cartridge filled with powder; the other projected from the drill hole, and into this end of the tube the squib was placed and lighted. Then the shot firer had to heel it pretty lively to dodge the flying chunks of coal, for it didn't take the squib long to reach the powder.

Presently the slower safety fuse was invented. Miners were

compelled by law to leave four feet of this fuse protruding from the drill hole, and it burned slowly, allowing the firer ample time to leave the room. This did not eliminate accidents, however. Shots frequently blew through into adjoining rooms; rocks were loosened and fell; there were dust explosions.

The miners fashioned their powder cartridges from newspapers by rolling a sheet tightly about a section of smooth pipe. Then the edges were glued with laundry soap and the cigarette-like cylinder crimped at one end and filled with coarse grained blasting powder. Sometimes when a heavy charge was required, several of these cartridges were pushed with the tamping rod to the back end of the drill hole, the last cartridge having a fuse end tucked into it. Several cartridges filled with drill dust were then tamped in around the fuse, the end of the fuse was split so the shot firers could light it readily, and the shot was ready.

Mike lived alone in one of the camp-houses clustering at the foot of the hill upon which our slightly more pretentious house stood. None of the girls thereabout would have anything to do with him, for it was said that he had the evil eye and had been talking to the Devil in his shanty at night. Also, the girls didn't like the idea of a one-legged beau, and Mike was past middle age. The girls jeered at him and called him "Peggy." If a child fell suddenly and unaccountably ill or a man was hurt in the mine, Mike's evil eye was blamed.

We frequently went to visit him in the evening after he came home from work. If there were any rats in his cellar, they must have had webbed feet, for the place was always full of foul smelling water. We crept down the rotting steps at the side of the house and watched the mosquito larvae wriggling about in the water, and there was a frog that perched on a floating shingle and became so tame that he would not dive off with a splash, but sit and watch us solemnly, his whitish underthroat throbbing like a beating heart. Mosquitoes in dense clouds swarmed about Mike's shack; he burned rags to keep them away. The company doctor was always wondering why Mike did not die of malaria, living, as he did, over a pool of stagnant water. Mike always replied that one born to be hanged would never perish otherwise.

He never mentioned his rats or tried to scare us when we went to see him. He would descend the cellar steps, roll up his sleeves, grope about in the black water, and fish out a bottle of beer. Before the Fourth of July or a Miners' Union picnic, he would have a keg of beer floating in the cellar. I didn't like the beer at first, but after a while I begged Mike for more than he would give me. After he had drunk three or four bottles, he would begin to curse the English and to extol the military and cultural glories of Erin. Presently, in a more jocular mood, he'd dance a hornpipe as best he could, his peg sinking in the earth when he stamped too vigorously. He stumbled and fell, but scrambled up merrily, laughing and jigging away fit to kill. He explained that age was stiffening his joints, and that he'd have to catch some fishing worms and put them in a bottle to melt in the sun. He said that all the circus acrobats used fishing worm oil to lubricate their joints.

At first, Mike sang a merry ditty such as:

> "In Ireland they have buttermilk ninety days old.
> The maggots and wiggletails get very bold.
> It would put any man in the greatest surprise
> To see them turn up their great goggle eyes."

But as dusk thickened and lamps began to twinkle in window panes, he grew mellow and shifted to reminiscences of his old Irish mother and the peat bogs of Erin and the River Shannon. His tongue thickened and his words blurred. He mumbled a sentimental ballad which all the miners knew, and we joined in the chorus:

> "Down in the coal mines underneath the ground,
> Where a gleam of sunshine never can be found;
> Digging dusky diamonds all the seasons round,
> Down in the coal mines underneath the ground."

For us Mike held the irresistible attraction of the devilish and verboten. How he could spin glamorous tales of far horizons! He told us how to induce a monkey to throw down cocoanuts by thumbing one's nose at him, of savages whose lips had been artifically distended to form ducklike bills, of deserted jewel-studded temples reclaimed by the jungle and forgotten by man.

Willy Stafford came up and rubbed against Mike like an affectionate dog. Mike was Willy's best friend, and protected him against abuse from adults and children alike by threatening to exercise his occult powers against anybody who molested him.

"Ye'd best scoot home, Willy, me boy," Mike advised him. "You come back tomorry night and Mike'll cut yer hair. You're gettin' shaggy as a wolf."

Willy moved off in the twilight, gurgling thoughtfully.

We sat entranced, listening to Mike's tales till the stars began blossoming, and his voice became more incoherent and drowsy, fading as thin as a worn-out phonograph record. His head dropped forward and the rising moon silvered his hair. It became so still that we could hear a cricket chirping beneath the house. A snore told us that the story telling was ended for that night.

Father made so much firing shots that he soon had all the bills paid up, and he talked about sending me to school in town. Getting a large sum for back rent pleased Fred Dodson, and he put up some screens to the doors. Screens were almost unheard of on miners' houses at that time; they were considered luxuries for the rich only. Flies usually buzzed around the table as though they owned the place, and one of the family had to stand guard at mealtime, slowly waving a leafy wand of alder or buck brush over the victuals. But the flies soon got used to this and settled tenaciously on everything that tempted their appetites.

Father was paying Koch every Saturday night, and he

brought home a striped bag full of hard stick candy as a treat. It was a gala event and we always waited up far past our habitual bedtime. The candy was vile, unpalatable stuff, no doubt, but we relished it keenly, licking a stick with the air of a connoisseur sampling a rare vintage, and then laying it aside for future consideration. Sugar was a precious item in our diet, and in lean times sorghum might be used for sweetening coffee. At other times both the coffee and the sorghum were lacking.

Father arose at six and labored diligently in the garden till noon. He was proud of the garden. He fought potato bugs and cut worms and slashed weeds. When the ground was dry, he scanned every floating cloud before he descended into the mine at noon and hoped that it might be raining pitchforks when he came up again. Weather never intruded in the mine—the miners left the upper world behind for the period they were below.

The shot firers calculated their route so as to avoid the powder fumes and smoke which the powerful fans drove along the entries. They left the mine by climbing up an airshaft ascending from the end of the main entry leading from the shaft bottom. Father and Mike ran from room to room, touching their lamps to the fuses and pausing a moment until the end hissed and sparkled to be sure that it was really lighted. They shouted "Fire in the hole!" to one another as they lighted each shot. The steel cap on Mike's peg knocked fire from the rails and sometimes he struck a soft place and sank to the stub of his leg, where he had the vacant pants leg folded as a pad. The stub was tender on the end, and when Mike struck it on a rock he'd swear luridly. Some of the men were afraid to curse while in the mine, but Mike never was.

The airshaft had a shed above it with a door which was always sucked tightly shut by the inrush of air. We laid our ears to the cracks between the rough planks and listened to the dull booming of the exploding shots. They vibrated the earth.

Then we could hear the sharp click of Mike's peg as he and Father neared the top of the spiral stairs, though the incessant roaring of the air current inside drowned most sounds. Sometimes we contrived, by exerting our combined strength, to pry open the door. We peered fearfully within, clinging to the jamb. The boarded walls sweated icy globules of sulphurous water, and flabby white toadstools reared from crevices. When we sighted the glare of the lard-oil lamps or heard Mike's peg hitting the steps, we withdrew and shut the door, for we had been ordered never to venture inside the shed.

One night we waited at the airshaft a long time but nobody came up. We heard a few shots going off, and then nothing. We pried open the door and I descended cautiously a step or two, but the steps were treacherous with slime and the roaring darkness of the nether regions terrified me. As I retreated, the whistle at the tipple began blowing. It never paused—its level piercing blast echoing among the hills. We knew something was amiss and set out for the shaft. Before we arrived the whistle had ceased blowing.

At the pit-head a group of men and women had gathered. Mike was lying near the engine-house on a folded stretcher, his face covered with blood and his peg leg shattered. Mother was standing silently near. She was afraid to ask any questions, but she was hoping that somebody would tell her something. Six or seven miners' wives surrounded her and led her back home, for the rescue party below had signalled to the engineer to hoist. They had arranged beforehand to blow three blasts if it were better for Mother not to see. Mother walked along quietly. She had inherited the stoicism of a long line of miners; fainting and hysterics are practically unknown among the Spartan women of the mining camps.

Father was found crumpled under a huge lump of coal with another chunk imbedded in his side, but he was still alive. His right eye was gone. The rescuers could tell that a shot had blown from the adjoining room. The intervening wall had been too thin. But it was after Mike was able to talk coherently that the full story was learned.

Mike had come to a wet hole in his rounds—a hole drilled but not loaded with powder or tamped. Whenever a miner drilled a hole into which he thought might seep enough dampness to prevent the powder from igniting, he prepared the cartridges and fuse and laid them near the hole, leaving a sign indicating that the shot firer was expected to load and tamp the shot and fire it instantly while the powder was still dry. It took five minutes or more to prepare the shot, and Father came in to help Mike. As Mike lit the shot and turned to go, he stepped in a soggy spot and his peg plunged down in it. Father helped him to his feet, but he had sprained his ankle and could not walk. Behind them, the ignited fuse was hissing and burning toward the powder. However, only the loose end outside the hole was as yet burning, and Father cut it off close to the coal. But as he prepared to help Mike outside, the wall of the room leaped toward them with a terrific detonation. Ordinarily, the shot in the next room would not have harmed them, but the shot must have had too much powder in it or it might have been drilled at the wrong angle. The wall between was too thin to withstand the blast.

The lamps were blown out. Mike said he felt flying chips of coal stinging his face like needles, but, luckily, the only large lump that struck him was the one which knocked his peg leg off. He heard Father calling for help, but he could not see him. When he tried to stand, he remembered his sprained ankle. He found that half of his peg was blown away. So he groped on all fours to where Father lay beneath the coal and tried to lift it off him, but he couldn't budge it. He felt around and found a stout mine prop, but even with it he could not move the lump.

Father by this time was silent, and Mike thought he must surely be dead. He followed a rail to the main entry, and his keen sense of direction enabled him to crawl toward the shaft.

He could not find his lamp, and a match would not burn in the strong draft. Mike was bleeding badly, and he knew that he must hurry, for the powder fumes were making him dizzy. He held his head close to the ground and pressed doggedly on, rocks and lumps of coal lacerating his palms and knee and the stub of his leg. Red and blue spots were blooming before his eyes when he saw a faint beam of descending light. He knew that he had reached the shaft. He was able to pull the signal cord before he collapsed, and the rescuers who came swarming at the whistle's screeching found him unconscious with the cord clasped tightly in his hand.

An incessant procession of visitors invaded our house, and relatives we had not seen for years appeared to take charge of everything. "What's the use of havin' kinfolks if they can't he'p you in a time like this?" they'd say. Meals were served continuously, and the pallets of self-invited guests littered the floors. Madge and I roamed about disconsolately, for Mother had taken to her bed and nobody seemed to pay any attention to us—we seemed aliens in the house.

"You all has certainly got my sympathy, Jessie," said Rollie Weems soberly to Aunt Jessie, who flew about the house constantly.

"Thank you, Rollie, thank you!" said Aunt Jessie, forgetting to call him Mister Weems. "I certainly need every bit of it; and if it wasn't for just *havin'* to hold up, I ought to be in bed right now."

I walked up and down the rows of potatoes in the garden, and noticed that weeds were pushing up here and there and the bugs were coming back. I picked a few off and mashed them between a thumb and finger, but I remembered that that would raise a blister. The bugs were called blister beetles. Some of the farmers who came on horses turned them loose in the yard and before long they were ranging in the garden and cropping the potato tops and pea vines. The ground was pock-marked with hoof prints and tender tomato plants were being trampled.

Father had been proud of the garden, and I wanted to go into the room where he lay and tell him about it. I wanted to tell him, too, that I knew he had taken the shot firer job in order to send me to school, though I had never said anything about it before. But the nurse wouldn't let me in. Through the door of his room, I could hear him puffing louder than he ever had with the miners' asthma. I grew discouraged about the garden, for nobody seemed to take any interest in it any more. Cutworms were clipping off the cabbage plants. I went along the rows, and where a plant had wilted down, I probed in the earth and pulled up the roots with the slaty slug curled about them. I squashed the marauder with savage satisfaction.

The third day after the accident, I became obsessed with the notion that my own sin had been responsible for what had happened. So I built a tabernacle of gunny sacks and poles behind the shed and fashioned an altar from a wooden box. On it I sprinkled "holy water" from the rain barrel under the eaves and burned candles left over from a Christmas tree. I slashed my wrist with broken glass and daubed a bloody cross on the altar. I had an inchoate idea of appeasing an angry God with prayer and sacrifice. But nothing did any good. On the fourth day, Father tried to raise himself in bed, but stiffened out. His hands clenched on the counterpane and could scarcely be pried loose.

He lay on a bier in the front parlor for two days, and during this time hundreds filed past, paused, looked at his face, and passed out the front door. Lionel Stafford and Paul hurried past, averting their eyes, as though they were rushing through a disagreeable duty. Their faces were pale as that of the corpse. Even Ben Haskin and Bonny Fern came. Mike Riordan had come every day on crutches asking to see Father, and each time he was refused he swore horribly and went away, vowing never to return. All the women thought that he should not be allowed to come even after Father was dead.

Mike's face was speckled with blue lumps of coal under the skin; he would carry them till he died. The miners had taken up a collection to buy him a cork leg. He told us that the leg looked good, all right, and bent at the knee just like a genuine one, but he didn't like it—it didn't feel natural. Besides, he had to wear two shoes. He said that before that he had just waited in the shoe-store till a man with the other leg off came in and they got their heads together and bought only one pair of shoes, each paying half the price and each taking one shoe. We didn't know whether to believe this or not. Mike's new leg creaked like a leather wallet or new harness as he walked.

Inside the parlor, relatives and neighbors were gathered— most of them women. They greeted Mike with frigid silence, remembering his indecent language of the last few days. He might be tolerated as a painful act of humanitarianism, but never welcomed. He appeared to sniff the hostility in the atmosphere and halted in the middle of the room, balancing himself with difficulty on his sore ankle and unfamiliar cork leg. He braced himself as though facing a gale at sea or the roll of a shifting deck. Then he hobbled awkwardly to the casket.

"Goodbye, Tom! Goodbye, you poor old son of a bitch!" he said steadily. Then he turned to his horrified audience. "Goodbye, you sluts! I hope you all miscarry!"

On the day of the funeral somebody was electrified to hear a rapid gasping noise apparently issuing from the coffin. In those days death was considered as assured if a mirror remained unclouded when placed before the lips, and it was said that a pin hole in the flesh of a dead person would not close up again. By these tests, Father was dead. Everybody was rooted to the spot by amazement, when our collie emerged from the curtains hung around the bier. The day was warm, and he had been lying beneath the coffin, panting.

I stood directly in front of the coffin while the funeral was being preached, and I could see Father's nose above the edge. The undertaker had a folding organ and the organist from the Methodist Church knew how to make it quaver in a way to make everybody cry. The Methodist choir sang "Jesus, Lover of My Soul." The preacher was thought to be very eloquent, but many were disappointed because he did not choose the verse about "greater love hath no man, than this; that he lay down his life for a friend." Of course, Father had not really laid down his life for Mike, at least not intentionally—I felt that he had laid it down for me—but that was a dramatic, soul-stirring text and the disgruntled auditors recalled many strong sermons that had been preached from it. The preacher could have caused a lot more tears to be shed if he had used it.

The stifling scent of hothouse flowers filled the room. The wreaths were banked about the casket; waxy, unearthly petals floated down. Each wreath had a card bearing the name of the donor inscribed with flourishing letters, and tied with ribbon. I heard two or three people say that they would rather have the flowers while they were alive and could enjoy them. They said it with the air of one voicing a trenchant apothegm for the first time.

The yard was full of carriages hired from the livery stable. The only time the miners used a livery rig was for a funeral or maybe when one of the young bucks got drunk and wanted to cut a dash. The hearse was shiny black with folded curtains carved on the sides. Somebody said that the undertaker didn't know his business, for the hearse should have been grey for a man as old as Father. White for a child, black for the young and middle aged, grey for the old.

But the carriages soon filled and the hearse pulled out of the yard with the horses stepping high and easy. Mike was leaning on the fence across the way, his crutches propped against a post. We were in the coach reserved for relatives, just behind the hearse. As we passed, Mike's hand was raised as though in salute. His sleeves were rolled up, and the naked woman tattooed on his arm was plainly visible. I thought everybody must be noticing him, but the other occupants of the coach were sitting and sobbing or burying red noses in handkerchiefs. Mother's nose showed red through her heavy black veil.

At first I thought that Mike was making the woman dance, but I decided it was the heat waves shimmering between, for Mike looked solemn and as I turned to watch him a little longer, I saw that tears were running down his face, or he might have been sweating. The driver of the hearse slapped the horses' backs with the lines and clucked loudly. As we went around a bend in the road I looked back through the diamond-shaped pane in the back of the coach and saw the carriages stretching out of sight. I thought that the funeral procession must be a mile long, or maybe even longer.

Ben Haskin was plowing corn in a field adjoining the graveyard. Bonny Fern was with him, and as we dismounted from the coach, she eyed us with pert curiosity but with no sympathy. Tears started to my eyes as I envisioned myself lying in the casket, and Bonny Fern's heart wrung with belated penitence.

After Father's funeral, our house slowly quieted. For days, I had fallen asleep with the chatter of sympathetic friends and relatives still going on, but after a few nights I began to awaken when the house was so silent I could hear the clock ticking at the foot of the stairs, unless the rats in the garret were making too much racket. I had never minded the rats before, for they had been there since I could remember, but now the fear of them harried me night and day. I dreamed that my bed was an island lashed by waves of blue noses and cold, naked tails. When the wind was high, the house swayed drunkenly and its timbers groaned like a human in pain. The darkness teemed with fearsome shapes—miners moaning beneath cave-ins, graves yawning at midnight to disgorge the undead, and vampires ranging abroad to slake their grisly thirsts.

"There's nothing to be afraid of in the dark," Mother reassured me. She threw wide the door and revealed the black curtain of outdoors. But I was unconvinced. The kerosene lamp flickered in a draft, and Mother shut the door quickly and bolted it. Cane had been planted in the field across the road and it had grown until the blades rustled incessantly, even when the wind was not stirring. It sounded like somebody whispering stealthily. My sister slept placidly, and it irked me that she should be so unconcerned.

The nearest houses were the camp houses at the foot of the hill, and before Father had died Mother had often said that anybody could eat us up hide and hair before help arrived from the camp. The miners came home dog-tired, gulped down their suppers, and almost immediately fell into a death-like sleep. It was said that on the Judgment Day Gabriel would not be able to arouse them with his trumpet; he'd have to go around shaking shoulders. But Mother never mentioned anythink like that any more. She kept telling us that the camp houses were too close for anybody to molest us.

We heard a hesitant rapping one night, and when Mother opened the door a huge Negro staggered in and plopped heavily on a chair. He had evidently been badly beaten. One eye was closed. The other glistened chalky white. His lips were battered. Mother stood stock still, but I could see her trembling.

" 'Scuse me! 'Scuse me! 'Scuse me, Missus, fo' my bad manners!" he burst out. "Some white folks like to 've killed me and th'owed me in a coal car. I tumbled out at the crossin' up heah. I been askin' all the farmers fo' a drink, but they set their dogs on me. I'm so hongry an' thirsty, I cain't hardly stan' it.

But doan be a-skeered o' me, Missus, I wouldn' hurt you none. I ain't no bad nigger, jes' a po' boy long ways from home. From Alabama. Tha's wheah I come from, Alabam."

"Why did the men beat you?" Mother inquired, trying to appear calm.

"Dogged ef *I* know, Missus! I never *did* fin' out. They jes' beat me up an' called me a scab, and tol' me not to come back no mo'."

"Oh, you were scabbing!" Mother said accusingly. "You were taking another man's job. You should expect to get beaten up for that."

I was afraid this would incense our guest, but he appeared to be astonished. The eye which was still open widened.

"Shoot me fo' a black buzzard ef I knew I was doin' any hahm," he exclaimed earnestly. "White boss man come up to me in Mobile an' ast me how I'd lak t' wuk on a job in Missoury. I ain't never wukked in this country befo' an' I thought I'd try it. They shipped me to a little town up the line heah named Sevier, and the fust night I left the bunk house t' look aroun' a little, them white folks jumped on me an' beat me up. They tho'wed me in that air coal car, and heah I am. But I certainly didn't aim t' do nobody no dirt."

The Negro ate and drank gratefully, and departed with fervent vows never to be inveigled into such a situation again. I had always regarded a scab as a sub-human beast endowed with an inherent vileness. I had never before regarded a scab as a puppet manipulated by those who stood to gain the most, but who never braved the wrath of the strikers. I could not hate the Negro with his doggy, pleading eyes, his humble, ingratiating smile.

Mother bolted the door a little more carefully, and let down all the windows, though the heat was stifling. The house was like a furnace. We all slept in the same room now, Mother and Madge on one bed, and I on another. I was afraid of the empty rooms upstairs. In the night I awakened sweating and heard a swish-swish as Mother plied a palm leaf fan over my sister's face. Then she turned to me, and I felt the stale air circulating and cooling—though almost imperceptibly. In the morning Mother looked worn out, blue shadows underscoring her eyes.

Though we had never lived luxuriously, we found that we could live on a great deal less than we had before. The miners and their wives brought small gifts for a time, but after a few weeks these ceased. Aunt Jessie brought a batch of home-baked light bread.

"Where's Rollie Weems?" she asked me. "I haven't seen him around the camp for a long time."

"Why!" I answered, surprised. "Haven't you heard? He's pulled out for the Indian Nation. He left two weeks ago."

"What for?" Her voice was low and troubled.

"Mike Riordan said he had knocked up Mattie Perkins, but I believe that's a lie. I saw her the other day, and she didn't look like anybody had hurt her. I don't believe that Rollie would hit a woman. I don't believe he would knock Mattie on the head." I maliciously feigned innocence, but when I saw Aunt Jessie's face screwing up, I was sorry. She turned her head to hide her face.

One day a group of church workers came to see us. They sat decorously in the front room, their inquisitive eyes ferreting into every crevice.

"We have come," announced a lady with a heroic bust, "to make some arrangement for the adoption of the children and for your own support and welfare. We know you are having a hard time, and we wouldn't be Christians if we didn't help you. We have been told that the children haven't enough to eat and wear, and we have talked the whole thing over. Mr. Ryerson" (indicating an angular old fellow with mutton-chop whiskers) "will take the boy, and I'll take the girl. It'll be several years before she's big enough to earn her salt, but the boy is big enough right now to work in the fields. Jethro

Haines' wife has been bedfast for several years, and we have found a place for you there, doing the housework and taking care of her."

Mother's face clouded. She nervously laced and unlaced her fingers.

"You folks are mighty kind," she said, "but I don't like to break up my home. I'm going to try to raise the children the best I can. If I can't do it, then I'll have to make other plans."

The committee members made it plain that they considered themselves bitten by that keenest tooth—ingratitude. They arose collectively and stiffly, and visibly washed their hands of us, saying they were sorry that we would not allow them to help us.

Mother took my face between her hands and looked at me so earnestly I felt uncomfortable. I turned my head away.

"You've got to be a man now," she said solemnly. "You're the only man I've got left. These people will never offer to help us again."

Though I wasn't sure what being a man involved, I readily promised to be one henceforth. I was eager to run outdoors, for I heard some of the camp children on the hillside playground chanting:

> "Bushel o' wheat,
> Bushel o' rye;
> All not ready
> Holler 'I'."

I knew that a game of hide and seek was in progress, and I ran to join in. Before I reached the base where the boy who was "it" was hiding his eyes against a tree trunk, he gave his final warning before he began the search:

> "Bushel o' oats,
> Bushel o' clover;
> All ain't hid
> Can't hide over."

The next morning Mother said we must go to the communal spring to wash clothes. The spring was within the semicircle of camp-houses. Even when drought parched all the fields thereabout, the cold, clear water gurgled from a fissure in the rocks and trickled down a ravine, around which lush grass and vegetation flourished. Here the miners' wives did their washing. It saved carrying the water home, moreover there were always people coming and going so that the spot was a social center. All of the miners' wives did their own washing, but some of the men were bachelors or widowers and had to hire their washing done.

Mother went to the spring every day. She was taking in washings not only from miners but from Koch, the butcher.

My sister and I considered the excursions to the spring quite a lark. Mother humped all day over the steaming tub, but we had only to gather firewood, help carry water, and dump suds into the creek. Crawfishes had bored their shafts in the damp earth, erecting at the mouth of them a mound of the slatish clay that lay below the stratum of gumbo. Mason wasps came for mud with which to fashion their multi-celled homes. So many came that we thought this must be the only muddy spot within miles. The wasps alighted at the rivulet's brim and buzzed earnestly, as though they were gossiping with one another.

Mother's hands were always puckered and grey while she was washing, but when they dried for a while at night, her palms were red and shiny. The wrinkles never smoothed out. Her ordinarily pale face became flushed as with a perpetual fever. Her head was enveloped in a cloud of steam all day. The washboard kept her waist frayed, and the front of her dress was always moist with soapy spray. She bobbed up and down, up and down, as tirelessly and as mechanically as an automaton on a peanut roaster, pausing only long enough to hang out a batch of clothes or to stir those in the boiler with a stick.

The iron boiler was propped up on flat stones, and my sister and I carried firewood to keep up the blaze under it. The ground was covered with brittle branches the wind had torn off the oak trees. Mother always cautioned us not to burn wood with ants in it. She said anything which lives also feels. If we thrust a stick in the fire and saw ants swarming out of it, we quickly withdrew it and rubbed it in the dirt to extinguish it.

Mother had to be most careful with Mrs. Koch's clothes. She had garments the like of which we had never seen before. Mr. Koch's shirt bosoms were resplendently pleated, and each pleat had to be ironed separately. If the starch was a little lumpy or the clothes not immaculately white, Mrs. Koch complained volubly.

Mother had to iron at night, heating the heavy sad irons on a coal stove which sent a withering, sirroco-like blast coursing through the house. Long after Madge and I were abed I could hear the monotonous rhythm of the irons sliding back and forth across the scorched and padded board. Sometimes, in desperation, Mother threw open the door, but the cheep of a night bird or a roving gust rustling the cane sent her scurrying to lock everything tight. I stole to the middle door and watched her standing with arm moving as inexorably as a piston. She pushed her greying hair back from her eyes with her suds-wrinkled hand. Sometimes her eyes were closed as she ironed. Blinding sweat dripped from the tip of her nose and from her chin.

Years afterward I was working with an extra gang on a track job. It was so hot that the rails were said to stretch a foot a day. The ballast heated like live coals; the rails ahead warped and writhed in the heat rays. One of the bullies holding a spike with a pair of tongs while another started it in the tie with a maul toppled forward sunstruck and the long point of the maul crashed through his skull as though it were an eggshell. In morose silence we propelled the hand car back to the bunk cars. We all felt woozy and sick as we sat down to supper. The cook brought in a stew and when we whiffed the steam off it, we all felt our stomachs rolling. It stank like something dead a long time. One fellow found two flies in his dish. He sprang to his feet and flung the mess full in the cook's face, howling like a wolf. Instantly we were electrified with unreasoning rage. The cook leaped from the car and bounded down the track with all of us after him in full cry. We hurled rocks after him and hunted him clear to the city limits of a small town.

As we ran past a house surrounded by a baize-green lawn a fine looking lady came hurrying out. There was a small boy in a bathing suit lolling under one of those revolving sprinklers that are used to water well-kept plots. The lady hugged the wet boy to her and told him she wouldn't let the bad men hurt him. We were a hard-looking lot, unshaven and ferocious. Still, we wanted to tell the mother that the sun had made us a little dippy, but we wouldn't hurt the kid for the world. Her haughty manner struck us dumb, and we didn't say a word. The anger which had buoyed us like the momentary exultation of whisky died out, and we felt only sick and shaken and ashamed. The cook disappeared around a corner, and we all trudged back to the cars to get our clothes.

So when they spread the goo on Mother's Day, I don't get any lump in my throat. It seems that it was all designed for mothers like that boy's mother. What could you say to a coal camp mother ironing away at midnight on someone else's clothes? I never found one of those Western Union canned greetings that fitted my mother—I never saw one that I could send her in remembrance of the nights she sweated over the irons or the days she spent bent over the steaming wash tub.

The rural mail carrier left a bulky package one morning. This was such an unusual event that we were afire with curiosity as Mother clipped the strings. The package contained three books: "Robin Hood and his Merry Men," "Lays of Ancient Rome," and "Curlyhead and his Neighbours." They were from our father's sister in Montreal. Her husband sent a formal letter inquiring if we were in need of anything, and hoping we would like the books. Mother had Madge and me to write a polite note of thanks and she assured our aunt that we were doing very well. We never heard from them again.

Robin Hood entranced me for a while, I prowled through the buck brush and white oaks searching for a stout yew tree for a bow, or a sturdy ash for a quarterstaff. The greenwood resounded with blasts from a cowhorn as I summoned my merry rogues, the rachitic spawn of Monkey Nest miners.

Then Macaulay's orotund passages captured me. They rolled so melodiously out of one's mouth. The "great Lord of Luna," in the guise of a one-gallused urchin, "fell at my deadly stroke, As falls on Mount Alvernus A thundersmitten oak." We neglected even our small part of the work connected with the washing, and often wandered far away through the underbrush to the mound we had christened "The rock Tarpeian Where the wan burghers spy A line of blazing villages Red in the midnight sky." Imagination magnified the thin spiral of smoke from the fire under the wash boiler into a mighty conflagration. Mother never called us, but conscience frequently spurred us back to the spring, just as the murderer is said to return to the scene of his crime. We would find Mother heaping sticks on the greying embers or breaking fagots under her feet. The smoke stung our eyes, but we were soon away again. Mother stood all day with the muggy vapors of the tub curling about her.

In the character of Horatius, I valiantly defended the log foot bridge across the creek against the combined assault of all the Monkey Nest boys. I modeled a "molten image" of Horatius out of an agglutinous lump of gumbo and baked it to a turn in the fire beneath the boiler. I raked it out with a stick and let it cool for a moment. When I picked it up to admire my handiwork, I realized that I had not allowed it to cool long enough. It scorched my fingers and I let it plop into the boiler full of clothes. It sank to the bottom and the water quickly assumed an amber tint. Stricken with dismay, I retreated into the brush, but remorse dragged me back. Mother was fishing the clothes out of the boiler with a stick. All of the garments were stained a hideous saffron; Horatius was a semi-dissolved gob. Mother must have been sure of my guilt, for she had seen me molding the image.

"These are Mrs. Koch's clothes," she said more dejectedly than angrily. "I'm afraid that stain will *never* come out, and she's *so* particular."

I quaked inwardly at the prospect of facing Mrs. Koch's fishy blue eyes, steeling with resentment, her double chin congealing into lines of disapproval. Mother divined my thoughts.

"I'll take them back myself. You're only a lad, and I don't want to see your spirit crushed too soon. There's little enough fun for a lad in a coal camp."

She scrubbed vigorously, but the saffron cast would not entirely fade out. She ironed till midnight and the next morning set out with the bundle. When she came back, her eyes were red and swollen. I was afraid to ask her what Mrs. Koch had said, and she did not tell me. I delivered several more washings before Koch deducted anything from the bill. Koch was allowing Mother to wash clothes to help pay our bill. It kept getting bigger. Koch assumed a reproachful air as he handed me the slip showing "total amount due." It seemed that we ate faster than the Koch family dirtied clothes.

Mike Riordan had not been seen since Father's funeral, but that evening I saw a light in his shack. It was thought that he had been in Kansas City on one of his periodic sprees. I went down the hill to talk to him. He said that some leprecauns had carried him away, tying him in a hollow tree. He had a peg leg again in place of the cork leg the miners had bought him. We found out later that he had pawned the cork leg in Kansas City when his money began to run short. He said he liked the peg better, anyhow, as he could use it for a potato masher or to punch holes in doughnuts.

When I told Mike about the ruined clothes and the grocery bill at Koch's, he sat sucking his pipe throughtfully. He rattled the stem against his teeth. I told him about the Negro scab who had been ignorant of any wrongdoing.

"I thought all the scabs were just born that way," I said. "Why don't the union men talk to the scabs and make them see that they are just being used for tools by the operators?"

Mike was not so sure about that. He grunted dubiously. He said he had seen many a scab in his day, and he had found that the most efficacious way of getting them to see the error of their ways was to massage their craniums with a pick handle. But he supposed somebody as guileless as Willy Stafford might be innocently misled into strikebreaking.

A few nights after Mike came back we heard somebody walking around the house. Mother whispered for us to be still, and we listened for a long time without moving. Then Mother grasped the stove poker and tiptoed to the door, opening it cautiously an inch at a time. A large wooden box was resting on the sill, and we found it was full of groceries.

One of the boys in the camp had been lending me his paper-backed novels, and I was well acquainted with the theory and practice of such eminent criminologists as Nick Carter, Old Sleuth, and King Brady. If I could have found some cigar ashes, I'd have considered the mysterious visitor as good as caught, but all I could find were some circular imprints in the hard earth of the pathway. Then I thought of Mike's peg leg.

"Somebody left a big box of groceries at our house last night," I told Mike. "Who do you suppose it could be?"

"Leprecauns, like as not," he answered gravely. "The little buggers like to do a good turn now and then to make up for some of their divilment."

"I believe it was you," I charged boldly. "I found some holes that looked like your peg had made them."

I was surprised when he flew off the handle and told me if I mentioned anything of the kind to Mother he'd skin me alive. So I kept mum, and the groceries appeared on the door-step regularly.

I realized now that the grandiose plans for making me an educated man had gone on the rocks, and I did not care much. Yet I knew that Father had wished it more than anything else and Mother was mad enough to dream about it over the wash tub. She wanted me to find a job in town to work for my board while I went to school, but this was hard to do. Meanwhile, the miners struck again.

This time Mr. Stacpoole declared that he was tired of their foolishness and would run his business to suit himself.

"I'll make them bullies draw in their horns; I'll have 'em crawlin' back to eat out of my hand," he boasted.

He imported a gang of strikebreakers and some city plug-uglies for guards. Eviction notices were served on all the strikers living in camp-houses, and tents were stretched near the pit-head. Here the strikebreakers and guards ate and slept, but they soon fell to grumbling at their rough fare. The super-intendent came to see Mother about cooking for them, and letting them eat in our house.

"I could get plenty others to do it," he said, with the manner of one determined to do a good deed, let it cost him what it might, "but I got to studyin' about you bein' a widder woman and I made up my mind to he'p you. They're all decent, well-behaved boys from Christian homes and I won't stand fer no bla'guardin' around the kids. No use of you breakin' your back over the wash tub no more."

"You'd better get somebody else to feed the scabs," Mother said quietly, but with such finality that he knew it was no use to argue further. He seemed very much disappointed, for our house was the only one of any size within easy reach of the mine.

A day or so later Fred Dodson came down to the spring where Mother was washing. He stood clipping clover blos-soms with his buggy whip, and after a bit he blurted out:

"Mr. Lorton told me he'd made you a proposition about feedin' some of the miners. . . ."

"Yes, he did. I refused it."

"Well, I reckon you know your own business, but a person's gotta do lotsa things in this life they don't wanta. You gotta look out fer number one. He says the house is the only one around here big enough t' feed the miners in. He offered me double rent for it, but if you was t' change your mind and decide t' feed 'em, the rent wouldn't cost you a penny more'n it does now. He'd make up the balance hisself. So's your rent wouldn't be no more, but I'd get twicet as much as—ahem!— I'm supposed to. I think he made a purty fair proposition. I sh'd think cookin' would be easier and better payin' than takin' in washin'."

"I can move," Mother said resolutely.

"Pshaw, no!" Dodson deprecated. "I wouldn't have you do nothin' like that fer a forty-acre farm. But I'm a poor man; my crops burned up this year and I don't see how I'll feed my stock through the Winter. I jist thought if you wanted to take up the proposition, we'd jist wipe off that four months back rent you owe me off the slate. But I don't want t' face the Judgment Bar knowin' I was the cause o' bringin' sorrow to a poor widder woman. You jist think it over in a cool way; nobody wants t' be a bullyraggin' you."

After Dodson left, Mother said we must look for another house. I was almost thirteen then and getting rather large. Mother could no longer find washings, but I had determined to earn my own money. I had been reading some of the Alger stories of boys making their way in the world, and I was eager to make a start.

Rollie Weems had not gone to the Indian Nation after all. He came back to the camp with a new suit on and said he had a good job in the railroad shops in town. He told me I could get a job as an apprentice, and after I had served my time, I'd have a trade at good wages. I'd never have to work in the

mines then. Rollie said that had been a false alarm about
Mattie Perkins, and it was a load off his chest.

After I had delivered Koch's wash the next day I meandered
into the railroad yards. It was a fearsome region, with engines
snorting and darting here and there, cars banging and moving
about on every hand. I had been expressly admonished against
such ventures, but this time I excused myself on the grounds
that I was on business. The tracks spread out like an immense
spider-web, and I was kept looking in all directions for engines. Trainmen ordered me out of the yards, some in fatherly,
others in vitriolic tones, but I kept on doggedly, stepping high
and gingerly over the switch frogs. I had heard of a man who
had been caught in such a trap and lost both his legs when a
locomotive bore down on him. After dodging about for some
time and becoming more and more confused, I came to a section of the yards where men were tearing down and repairing
box cars. The ground was littered with nail studded planks,
and a sharp stab in my foot reminded me that I was bare-
footed.

An impish, freckled boy of about fifteen came along with a
greasy stool, a long iron hook, and a pail. He planted the stool
before a box car truck, sat down, and began pulling the lubri-
cating waste known to railroaders as "dope" out of a journal
box. I stood behind him and coughed sharply. He turned
about, and I was scandalized to see that he was chewing
tobacco.

"Hello, kid," he grinned.

"Hello, goat!" I retorted insolently. This was considered a
crushing reply to the salutation frowned upon by the well-bred.

"What 're you lookin' for?" he pursued genially.

"For the general foreman," I announced importantly. "I want
a job."

He doubled with exaggerated mirth.

"You go to the tool room and ast 'em fer a left hand monkey

wrench. I gotta take the nut offen one o' these box bolts. Then I'll show you the foreman."

"G'wan!" I jeered. "I ain't as green as I look. Don't try to feed me that."

"I see you ain't to be fooled," he said with feigned astonishment. "That's the foreman comin' down the line there."

"That man with greasy overalls? He looks just like a common working man to me."

"Jist dresses that way t' be comfortable. Besides, he c'n slip up on loafers easier when he dresses same 's anybody else. G'wan and ast 'im. He hired about a hundred this morning."

The man appeared bewildered when I accosted him, but he grinned when he saw the frolicsome dope puller howling with glee. He explained to me that my informant was joshing me. When I turned to reproach the dope puller, he had vanished behind the box car. The laborer told me where to find the general foreman. I caught him rushing out of his cubby hole of an office with a handful of papers. He almost fell over me.

"Are you hiring anybody today?" I inquired, manfully, drawing myself to my full height.

He paused long enough to eye me scornfully.

"Hell, no! We ain't hirin' no *men,* let alone kids! You ain't got all your teeth yet, have you? Better go home and get some titty. Get outa here 'fore I spit in yer eye and drown you! *Skiddo, 23!*"

Fear buoyed my feet till I reached the yard limits, then humiliation overwhelmed me. Gusty sobs shook me. I dreaded more and more being a man, but I also knew that retreat I could not. As I turned into the Monkey Nest lane, I saw Rollie Weems and Aunt Jessie strolling along close together. When I told Rollie what had happened he said you had to pull some strings first to get the job. He said he would fix it up for me with the master mechanic.

I came through the woods adjoining Ben Haskin's clearing,

and sat down for a while near the edge of the field to see if I could catch a glimpse of Bonny Fern. While I was sitting there a tough looking fellow appeared, walking from the direction in which the Monkey Nest lay. Though the scabs still lived in their quarters near the pit, I felt that this was one of them, and I resolved to awaken his conscience and set him on the right path, as Mother had done with the Negro.

"Hello, buster," he greeted me, speaking out of the corner of his mouth. "Do you live far about here?"

"Yes. Do you?"

"That's for me to know and you to find out. But turn about is fair play. Sure! I'm cooped up at the Monkey Nest and if I have to stay there much longer, I'll be daffy for true. We're all getting pretty horny, for one thing. Old Man Stacpoole promised to bring some women out from town, but he claims he can't get any to risk it with such a bunch. Show me one that even has got to walk with a cane, just so she's got one tooth left in her head. . . ."

"Don't you know that you oughn't to work at the Monkey Nest?" I broke out reprovingly. "You're taking other men's jobs. Maybe you didn't know that. You ought to go back and tell the scabs to go back where they came from. They're working men just the same as. . . ."

"What's it to you?" he cut in savagely. "Don't try to preach to me. I've had my job taken when I came out on strike, and now it's my turn."

He strode over to me and grasped me by the throat. I tried to tear away.

"Don't go babbling you saw me here, either," he commanded. "You fan your butt away from here and don't let any grass grow under your feet."

He slapped me smartly across the face to speed me on my way. I ran a short distance, but crept back to the edge of the clearing. Then I saw Bonny Fern moving among the trees at the farther edge. I was electrified to see the scab peeping from behind a tree bole. Bonny Fern was a big girl now, and she was beginning to look like a woman. Her breasts were as big as oranges and stretched proudly against her tight sweater. She was wailing in a lugubrious tone:

"There's just three things in this world I wish for,
'Tis my coffin, grave and shroud.
But when I'm dead please come and see me;
Kiss the girl whose heart you broke."

I tried to tell myself that she had me in mind. The scab edged from behind the tree. I selected a stout hickory cudgel from the fallen limbs near my feet. My knees were trembling and my heart thumping so against my ribs that I was sure it could be heard both by the scab and Bonny Fern. A kaleidoscopic sequence of events flashed in my mind: The scab lying with bloody, bashed-in skull. Bonny Fern in a semi-faint, her arms flung about my neck. Ben shaking hands with me and thanking me again and again. "You saved her from a fate worse than death, my boy."

The scab emerged from the trees and Bonny Fern halted in her tracks with a sharp cry. "Now! Now!" I thought, but stir I could not. A terrible weight anchored my feet as effectively as if they had rooted and thrust radicles deep in the earth.

"Hello, honey!" The scab's face was lighted with a desperate hunger that I was just beginning to comprehend. "Hello, honey! I won't hurt you. Come and sit down with me."

Bonny Fern began to scream.

"Don't do that, honey! Please don't! Look!" He pulled a roll of bills from his pocket. "I'll give you five dollars! Ten dollars! Hush! Hush! Oh, for the love of God, hush!" He was slobbering at the mouth; his eyes rolled pleadingly.

"You'd better get away from here! You'd better hurry, too, or my papa'll kill you!" yelled Bonny Fern, turning to run.

The scab's face twisted up as though he had bitten in a green persimmon. He wheeled about and made off through the brush, sobbing like a cow bawling. Bonny Fern stood watching his flight with amazement. I had ventured out into the clearing, and she saw me for the first time.

"Oh," she said suspiciously, "what do you want here?"

"Nothing," I answered, regretting that I had shown myself. I was eager to hide.

"Come here," she called imperiously. "I want to talk to you."

At any other time I would have felt encouraged, but I was overwhelmed with shame. Confronted by a crisis, I had failed miserably. I was half way home before I realized that Bonny Fern's voice had sounded rather friendly.

The next evening Rollie told me everything was fixed up with the master mechanic, but he couldn't be expected to buy a pig in a poke. He wanted to look me over first to see that I was sound in body and reasonably sound in mind.

Mother and I walked through the echoing halls of the division office building till we came to the master mechanic's door. Mother slicked down my hair and straightened my necktie.

"Don't be afraid to speak right up to him," she whispered sepulchrally.

There were several girls sitting at tables inside the outer office. We stood within the railing and waited. Mother's hands gripped the rail. She looked tired, and I wished that somebody would ask her to sit down. I had thought until a moment ago that her Sunday dress was rather stylish, but when I saw the natty garb of the clerks, I realized that she was dressed pretty shabbily and old-fashioned. I could tell that she knew it, too. One of the girls was tapping away at a typewriter. Writing machines were no longer a novelty, but I had never heard of one in Monkey Nest camp.

The girls chattered and frisked about as spry as chipmunks. Though they undoubtedly saw us, they ignored us completely, as though to impress us with the fact that the ponderous wheels of the railroad must revolve inexorably, and our petty concerns could wait. Mother shifted from one foot to the other. I knew that her feet must be blistered from the long walk. At last one of the girls looked me directly in the eye and asked me what she could do for me. I thought I would have a hemorrhage. My hair seemed to bush up like a Hottentot's, and my feet loomed monstrously in their unfamiliar shoes. My heart hammered furiously, a lump arose in my throat, and I was struck with consternation to find that I could not utter a sound.

Mother answered for me, and we were soon ushered into the private lair of the great man himself. I sat by a window watching some garrulous English sparrows quarrelling on the ground below. Mother had to nudge me frequently when the master mechanic directed a question at me. I answered in a subdued tone, and wished I were almost anywhere else.

"You want to watch that boy," the master mechanic advised Mother. "Looks to me like he's coming down with a fever. His color ain't natural."

"Don't you feel well, son?" he asked me. "Do you feel strong enough to work?"

I told him that I did, and Mother explained that I was just bashful and always got red when I talked to strangers. I did not particularly relish the prospect of spending my days in the shops. The clanging of locomotive bells, the couplers crashing as cars banged together, the hoarse shouts of the workers drifted in the window like a bad dream.

My heart sank when the master mechanic announced with the air of a sovereign bestowing a knighthood that he would put me to work as an apprentice in the car department. Then he launched into a story of his own courageous ascension from nadir to zenith. He had once been a water boy for an extra gang working on the section. He did not need to tell us what he was now, for the aura of consequence hovered about him. He had had no Aladdin's lamp to rub, he said, no genii to do his bidding. He had fought every step of the way. He intimated that I might ascend to the same dizzy heights ultimately if I attended to business and made a good and faithful hand.

"Do you smoke or drink, lad?" he asked, rolling a fat black cigar in the corner of his mouth.

"No, sir, I don't," I replied virtuously.

"That's the boy!" he applauded. "You'll find a bunch of rough boys here—bad eggs—but you want to stay clear of them. You want to go to Sunday School every Sunday and mind your mother. I always did."

My wages would be eighty cents a day, and we made arrangements for my lodging with a relative until Mother could find a house in town. Dodson was looking more reproachful every day; he palpably considered himself a martyr for allowing us stay in the house for which he had been offered double rent. Moreover, all of our friends were clearing out of the camp, and strikebreakers moving in. Mike Riordan was one of the last to go, and when he left, the baskets of groceries appeared no more upon our doorstep. Though Lionel Stafford had never worked in the mine, he considered himself among the dispossessed, and moved into town. It was no use trying to teach Willy anything, but Paul was bright enough.

When we reached home after the interview with the master mechanic, Mother set to patching my clothes. After they were all collected, the bundle wasn't very large. I dallied about all day, somewhat reluctant to start out. I ran to the clearing and gazed earnestly toward Haskin's. But nobody was stirring around the place. I wondered if Bonny Fern would even know we had moved; I wondered what it was she had wanted to tell me. I was conscious of breaking loose from moorings—I knew that something epochal was happening to me, and I shrank from the dark ahead. It was past dusk when I kissed Mother and my sister goodbye. The kerosene lamp had already been lighted, and through the unshaded window I saw that Mother had gathered Madge on her lap. I thought this was ridiculous, for she was nine years old and her legs dangled on the floor. Mother was singing to her a lullaby that had put all of us to sleep time and again:

> "Bobby Shafto's gone to sea,
> Silver buckles on his knee;
> He'll come back and marry me,
> Bonny Bobby Shafto.

> "Bobby Shafto's fat and fair,
> Combing down his yellow hair;
> He's my love forevermore,
> Bonny Bobby Shafto."

It struck me that Mother might still be afraid to stay in the old house with its creaking timbers, the rats stamping in the garret, and the memories of her dead. When I stepped into the lane, the ripening cane blades rustled harshly. The night became peopled with eyes and tongues—became vocal and spying. I began to whistle, but the sound startled me. I kept clear of the cane field, fearing something unnamed that might be hiding in the mysterious depths between the rows. I could have saved a mile by cutting through, but I preferred to walk down the middle of the lane. I was glad that my feet made no sound in the velvety dust. The lights from the town stained the sky. Monkey Nest camp retreated into the dark. There were few lights in the windows now. Some of the strikers had been stealing back at night to stone them out.

My life had been dominated by the Monkey Nest. We had set our clock by its whistle. When it was silent, we were hungry and anxious to know when it would open again. When it hummed with activity, there was the fear of the rocks, the faces tired as death beneath the grime. Miners' wives clutch at their hearts when there's an unexpected knocking at the door. So when I left the camp, I felt that Father would have been glad, had he known. He wanted passionately to keep me out of the mines, and I was going away.

Though the Monkey Nest was getting old as mines go, it

lived a few years after it retreated in my mind to the status of a memory. Years crowded in on the Monkey Nest. A mine dies young in the sparse croppings of Missouri; twenty years is a hoary old age. But the Monkey Nest left monuments to its memory in many cemeteries, particularly Sugar Creek grave-yard, where the pine headboards bristle among wild black-berry vines and rampant tiger lilies that long ago burst the borders of prim beds and sent their progeny adventuring across the mounds. Frenchy Barbour's grave caved in before he had been buried many years, for his coffin was cheap and not made to withstand much weight. Sand and gumbo must fill his skull and stain his squirrel-teeth browner than tobacco did. Father and my three brothers are side by side.

Worked-out mines marked only by a hummock of vegetation-defying soapstone or a rusty boiler tilted on one end, its flue holes resembling a great Swiss cheese, hedged the Monkey Nest in. Tunnels that radiated in all directions from the shaft were always breaking into abandoned works. Deadly black damp and water seeped in. Incombustible sulphur gleamed in the coal like gold, and the dwindling veins faded until a man was forced to crawl on his belly like a snake to pick out the sparse coal.

Then the tipple fell in a whirlwind, and the stiff legs stuck ludicrously in the air like those of an overturned wooden horse. Time has had its way with the Monkey Nest. In its quiet grottos crumbling rails and phosphorescent ties are sinking in pallid slime, while flabby fungi cling to the rotting timbers. Bats scream and fight. A venturesome boy climbed down the shaft, but fled in terror when he was covered from head to foot with pulsing, furry bodies before he could travel twenty feet into the main entry. It was lucky for him at that, because the black damp knocks you out without warning. A lamp flame will not live in it.

To keep cows from falling in the open shaft, it was decided to fill it. The assorted urchins of a superannuated miner volun-teered to perform this incredible feat, more stupendous than any storied Herculean labor. In casting about for a comparative peg on which to hang their undertaking, I must mention the persistent Mr. Beers of the poem, who, amidst his neighbor's jeers, has been resolutely digging in his garden, with China as a goal, for forty-seven years. Think also of that prodigious rock in Svithjod land, a hundred miles high and a hundred miles wide. To it every thousand years comes a canary bird to whet its dainty beak. When that Gargantuan boulder shall have been worn to the level of the plain, preachers are fond of saying, it will be only breakfast time in Hell.

But the boys rigged up a coaster wagon that had been discarded by some more fortunate child, and began wheeling soapstone and slag to fill the gaping void. At first a faint splash was the only evidence of their toil, but within six months they could see bottom by throwing down a kerosene-soaked and ignited cattail. It took them a year to complete the job, but they were paid twenty-five dollars in cash, not in trade out of a company store.

So the Monkey Nest's mouth is stopped with dust, but in its time it had its pound of flesh. Yes, I figure it had its tons of flesh, all told, if laid side by side in Sugar Creek graveyard.

2. Puzzled America

SHERWOOD ANDERSON

By the time the Great Depression struck, Sherwood Anderson (1876–1941), like such others of his generation as Sinclair Lewis and Theodore Dreiser, was already a writer of inter-

From *Puzzled America* (New York: Charles Scribner's Sons, 1935), pp. 145–153. Copyright 1935 Charles Scribner's Sons; renewal copyright © 1963 Eleanor C. Anderson. Reprinted with the permission of Charles Scribner's Sons and Harold Ober Associates Inc.

national repute. More than a decade had passed since Winesburg, Ohio *made its extraordinary appearance, and during the twenties the self-educated boy from Camden, Ohio, had added to his stature with* The Triumph of the Egg, Dark Laughter, Poor White, *and other books in which he probed, haltingly but sensitively, the psyche of small-town America. Anderson had grown up during the horse-and-buggy days, had gone on to become a sophisticated literary man, and was at home with all kinds of people. During the depression he took to the road to rediscover America, and in the course of his countrywide wanderings he rediscovered himself, if only temporarily. "I am accepted by working people everywhere as one of themselves and am proud of that fact," he wrote, and surely this was one of the reasons why* Puzzled America, *collected from his travel pieces about the country that he loved, remains one of Anderson's most characteristic books. For in addition to insisting upon himself as one of the working people, he shared in the confusion into which they had been thrown and in their groping toward a better life than that offered in depression America. In the selection that follows, on the unionization of rayon workers in a Southern mill town, he is able to transmit to his readers a marvelously rendered sense of that confused groping toward brotherhood.*

Elizabethton, Tennessee

To Elizabethton, Tennessee, where there had been a recent flareup of labor trouble among the employees of a huge rayon plant. This is the town so often written up as "the wonder city," "Elizabethton the beautiful," etc. To me it seemed neither very beautiful nor very ugly.

But surely the town is in a lovely place. I had with me a woman engaged with an organization that works for the betterment of the condition of mill women and as we drove down through the beautiful valley toward the town she told me many interesting and sometimes terrible things about the condition of working girls in Southern mill towns.

To me the town, when we got into it, seemed not unlike hundreds of Iowa, Illinois, and Ohio county-seat towns. Earlier there was a period of better building in America. New England felt its influence as did parts of Pennsylvania and all of the South. For some reason these earlier buildings, of stone, brick, and heavy timbers, had more beautiful outlines than the buildings of a later period.

Then followed a period of box construction. Some one discovered the scroll-saw. Cheap buildings with cheap do-dads on them.

Here is a town that, when I was there, was not more than five years old. Already the buildings had that half-decrepit, worn-out look that makes so many American towns such disheartening places. There is a sense of cheapness, hurry, no care for the buildings in which men and women are to live and work. "The premature aging of buildings in America," said my friend Van Wyck Brooks, "is the saddest thing in America."

We went to the hotel to dine and I went into the washroom. Such places—intimate, personal places—mark a town. The hotel, but a few years old, already had that shoddy, weary air characteristic of cheap, careless construction.

There were a few tiny fragments of cheap soap. The washbowls were dirty. Such things are important. They tell a story. "We are not in this place to live. We are here to make money."

We drove out to the two great rayon plants in the evening, just as the employees were leaving. This was mountain white labor. About three-fourths of all the laborers employed were girls.

They were shockingly young. I saw many girls that could not have been beyond twelve or thirteen. In these towns, I am told, children have two ages, the real age and the "mill age." It is easy to escape responsibility. "If she lies about her age," etc.

Of course she lies. These are the poorest of poor people, from
the hills, the mountain gullies. They went with weary steps
along the road. Many of the young girls were already developing goiters, that sure sign of overwork and nervous debility.
They had thin legs and stooped shoulders.

The mills themselves had that combination of the terrible
with the magnificent that is so disconcerting. Any one working
in these places must feel the power of the mills and there is a
sense in which all power is beautiful—and also, to be sure,
ugly. Oh, the beauty and wonder of the modern intricate machine! It is said that many of the girls and women in these
places are half in love with the machines at which they work.

There is always the old question—to make men rise in
nobility to the nobility of the machines.

It is obvious there had not been much nobility in Elizabethton. The girls there were underpaid, they were not organized,
they had no power.

A strike flared up, starting I was told, as a kind of spontaneous movement among the girls. It might have been met
easily at first. The employers were brutally casual about it.

The girls began to organize and the American Federation of
Labor sent an organizer. His name was Hoffman, a fat man, of
the characteristic sledge-hammer, labor-organizer type. A
group of men of the town—they had not all been identified yet
—went to his hotel at night and escorted him out of town at
the point of a gun.

Another bit of characteristic stupidity. He came right back.
Such a man would know well the publicity value of such a
crude performance on the part of the local business men. It was
all nuts for him. Obviously it is true that labor as well as industry and capital has the right to organize. If you own a factory you do not have to employ organized labor if you can get
out of doing so. But you cannot stop labor organizing. You
cannot throw a man out of town because he comes there to
help labor organize. Modern, more intelligent and shrewd
industrialists have learned there is a better way to handle such

matters. They give labor what it wants. Tack the price on for the buyers at the other end. They throw the burden on over to the consuming public. The middle-class do not know how to organize and apparently the farmers will not organize. And the industrialists are slowly finding out that cheap, underpaid labor is in the end no good.

So here were these girls organizing and the movement grew like wildfire. The men came in. All Elizabethton was apparently being organized. Later, as almost always happens, it all fell to pieces.

There is one thing about being a writer. You can go anywhere. Had I not written a book called *Poor White*? It was the industrial history of a town very like Elizabethton. And I had written *Winesburg, Ohio,* stories of the private lives of poor people in small towns.

I myself came from the working class. When I was a young man I worked in factories. These working people were close to me, although I was no longer a working-class man. I had my own class. I kept looking and wondering. Occasionally I tried to put down in words what I saw and felt.

And here is a peculiar thing. I am thinking now of working women. I take it that all women want beauty of person. Why not? How often I go to dine, for example, at one of the hotels in my own town. There are the guests coming in. We, in my town, are on the Lee Highway. Many women come here. They are rich women, going South to Florida, or returning to the North from Florida. They are dining at the hotel.

How few of them have any grace of person, any grace of body. I look from these women to the working women, the waitresses. How much nicer they seem.

It is true everywhere I have been. In the great fashionable hotels a man does sometimes see beautiful young girls but the older people among them are usually quite miserable looking. I mean they are usually smug, self-satisfied about nothing, without character. Hard work, trouble in life does, it seems, after all beautify, to one with an eye at all trained to see beauty.

A moment ago I spoke of my own position in life. I am accepted by working people everywhere as one of themselves and am proud of that fact. The other evening in Elizabethton there was a secret union meeting being held. I went up into a rather dirty hallway, crowded with girls. "Perhaps this Mr. Hoffman has read some of my books," I thought, "he may let me in here." There was no doubt about the woman I had driven to Elizabethton. They would let her in. And so I sat in a window-sill and along came this man Hoffman, the labor organizer. "Hello, Sherwood Anderson," he said. "Do you want in here?"

"Yes, of course. I want in everywhere. To go in is my aim in life. I want into fashionable hotels and clubs, I want into banks, into people's houses, into labor meetings, into court-houses. I want to see all I can of how people live their lives. That is my business in life—to find out what I can—to go in."

I did not say all this. "Sure," I said.

And so I was escorted into a room packed with girls, with women, boys, and men.

It was a business meeting of this new trades organization, a certain local of the Textile Workers of America.

There were girls everywhere. What a different looking crowd from the one I saw, but two hours ago, coming from the factories.

There was life in this crowd. On the evening I was there some fifty new members were sworn into the organization. They came forward in groups, awkward young girls, awkward boys, men, and women with prematurely old faces, not tired now, full of life. As each member was sworn in, applause shook the room. A woman was outside who had no money to join. "I'll pay for her," cried a working man, coming forward out of the crowd. He put his hand into his overall pocket and slapped the money down on a table.

More and more men and women were crowding up the narrow hallway outside. They wanted to join. The crowd laughed, jokes were shouted about the room. "Why, there's Red. Hello, Red. Are you in?"

"You bet I am in."

There is a report that the company is going to fire all those who join. "Well, then we will go back to the hills. I lived on birdeye beans before there was any rayon plant and I can live on birdeye beans again."

At least there was joy in this room. Men and women, for the time at least, walked with new joy in their bodies. The men became more dignified, more manly in their bearing, the women more beautiful.

And many of these mountain girls are lovely little creatures. They have, at least when excited, straight hard little bodies, delicately featured faces. I sat beside a child that couldn't have been over thirteen—no matter what her "mill age"—and as I looked at her I thought how proud I would be to have been her father.

I felt that way about all of the people in the room. Those working men I could accept as brothers, those girls as sisters. They were and are closer to me, as are men everywhere who work in fields, in factories, and shops, than any other class of men or women will ever be.

And who loves luxury more than myself.

It is very puzzling. I came away from Elizabethton puzzled. How will it all come out?

"At least," I thought, "these working men and women have got, out of this business of organizing, of standing thus, even for the moment, shoulder to shoulder, a new dignity. They have got a realization of each other. They have got for the moment a kind of religion of brotherhood and that is something."

It is a great deal more than any wage increase they may win from their struggle.

They had built a monument in Elizabethton. It was at the head of the main street. I fancy they felt that the town should have a monument. Almost all towns have. Perhaps also there was nothing in particular to build a monument about. Apparently they just built one anyway. I walked around it several times but could find no inscription on it. It was built of brick with a thin outer coating of cement. Already it was falling to pieces. How I would have liked to see one of those delicately featured, hard-bodied, little mountain girls, done in stone by some real artist, standing up there on the main street of that town.

3. These Are Our Lives

The subtitle of These Are Our Lives *reads: "As told by the people and written by members of the Federal Writers' Project of the Works Progress Administration in North Carolina, Tennessee, and Georgia," and on the facing page is the statement: "The stories in this volume are of real people. All names of persons have been changed, and where there is any danger of identification, places also." Its publication in 1939 was not only the high-water mark but the last wave of an unprecedented tide of government-sponsored creative work by writers, artists, and theater people during the depression years. It would have been simple enough to republish here one or two of the blackout plays written and produced by the Federal Theatre, to its eternal credit, but in light of the special relationship between writers and the government during the thirties, one is more inclined to cite not the playwrights but the men and women who compiled the extraordinary series of guide-*

From *These Are Our Lives* (Chapel Hill: University of North Carolina Press, 1939), pp. 165–179, 235–252. Reprinted with the permission of the publisher.

books to the states and who, thanks to being on the payroll of a generously understanding bureaucracy, were enabled to carry forward their own work—as in the case of Richard Wright, who was writing his searing volume of stories, Uncle Tom's Children. The appearance of *These Are Our Lives caused Charles A. Beard to exclaim: "Some of these pages are as literature more powerful than anything I have read in fiction, not excluding Zola's most vehement passages." From the early efforts of the devoted pioneers responsible for this volume have come—thanks to the tape recorder—the technologically more sophisticated labors of the academic social scientists, the oral historians working at home, and the anthropologists working abroad; but none has surpassed this first volume in simplicity and humanity. Here, in their own words, are the stories of two young men and what the depression did to their lives.*

Grease Monkey to Knitter

Ed Smalley, a well-dressed, bespectacled young fellow, was standing on a street corner when I asked him for a history of his life.

"History of my life?" he asked in a puzzled tone. "What do you mean? What is this? What right have you got to ask me for a story of my life?" His voice and manner were resentful.

After I explained the purpose of my request he became more friendly.

"I don't know if I could tell the story of my life so it would be interesting to anybody," he said, "but I'll give it a try anyway. Let's go sit in my car while we're talking. It's right near here."

He led the way around the corner into a side street where his automobile was parked.

"I am a knitter," he said, after we made ourselves comfortable in the car, "a full-fashioned knitter. I was born on a little cotton farm, near Fort Worth, Texas, August 18th, 1912. I am twenty-six years old, been married three years, and have one baby, a little girl, two years old. Here's her picture, just taken last week."

He pulled a wallet from his pocket and showed me the picture of a beautiful little child. She had a doll in her arms. The doll seemed to be staring straight into the camera, but the little girl was looking down at the doll.

"Go ahead," I encouraged. "I got all that down. What was the most interesting experience of your boyhood?"

"I guess the most interesting experience of my boyhood was a trip into Mexico. When I was about ten years old my father and mother went on a visit to Mexico. One of my uncles lived there, in Vera Cruz. He was a cotton broker or something of the kind. Anyway, he was connected with the cotton business and I guess he made money because he lived in a big house. It was a stone house, built around a little court. The windows were covered with iron grill work.

"My uncle had been in Mexico a long time. Both he and his wife spoke the language. They had Mexican servants. I remember how astonished I was the first day we were there. We were at breakfast and my uncle was talking to my father. Suddenly he turned his head and gave an order in Spanish to one of the servants. I don't know why it startled me so, but it did. I must have been staring with my mouth open, because he and my father laughed.

"That visit made a great impression on me because everything was so strange. The people dressed different, and spoke a different language. Even the signs on the business buildings meant nothing to me. They were in Spanish, and I remember how strange they seemed.

"One time my uncle and aunt dressed in Spanish costumes and took us to a fandango. My mother and father could not dance the fandango, but my uncle and aunt could. They danced with the others. My uncle wore a long red and yellow sash and I thought he cut quite a figure. No one would have suspected that he was not a Mexican himself. My aunt was dancing with a man and when the dance was over she led him to where we were sitting and introduced him to my mother and father. As they came up he spoke to me and said, 'Hello, Sonny,' and I was astonished, for I had thought him to be a Mexican. But as it turned out he was an American, and was connected with the same firm as my uncle. I guess we stayed about two weeks, and I'll always remember that trip to Mexico.

"My mother was raised 'way out in west Texas, near the New Mexico state line. When I was about twelve years old her health began to fail. That was in 1924. I remember that it was just after Christmas because I had been given an air rifle for a Christmas present.

"My father urged my mother to make a visit to one of her brothers who still lived out there. My mother decided to go and see if her health would improve. She took me with her, and of course I carried my air rifle.

"My uncle lived on a ranch, and he had a twenty-two rifle. That is what I recall most about that trip. First, shooting at prairie dogs with a real rifle; and second, my mother's death. Her health did not improve, and while we were there she got sick in bed. She was too sick to make the trip back home. My father came out there, and we stayed until her death. She died March 21st, and she's buried there on the same place where she was born.

"My mother's death was a great blow to my father and me, but it drew us closer together. I was the only child. We returned home and continued to live on the farm. It was just a small place, but my father owned it and it was home.

"My father made a little crop each year. I didn't help him much because I was in school. I had lost a lot of time and my father urged me to study hard and try to make up for lost time. I did study hard, and I passed my grade that year and graduated from grammar school.

"I remember how we missed Mother. Father did not say much. He was a quiet man and a great reader. In the evenings I would study and my father would sit with a book open on his lap, a faraway look in his eyes. I knew that he was thinking of Mother.

"The next year I went to high school. My father continued to farm the place. I know that he didn't make any money, but we had a good living. I helped him when I wasn't in school, and we got along all right. We did all the work ourselves, both the farm and housework.

"In 1927 my father had a sick spell. He managed to 'tend the place but his health was none too good. I wanted to quit school so I could help him but he wouldn't agree. By the spring of 1928 my father was hardly able to be about, so he hired a man to help out. After I finished school I helped with the farm work and we had a fair crop that year. But expenses had been high due to my father's illness and to the fact that we had to have a hired hand. My father borrowed some money that year. He died in February, 1929.

"After things were settled up and my father buried, there was little left, so I rented the place for two bales of cotton. Then I got a job as waiter in a café in Fort Worth. I was paid $6 a week, room and meals. I was hoping to earn and save enough money to pay off the mortgage on the place.

"I had saved a little money, and I sold the two bales of cotton that I had been paid for rent. I was planning to pay the interest on the loan, and what I could on the principal, but in December, 1929, the house caught fire and burned. The place now had no house on it, so I decided to let it go for the debt.

"It's a good thing I did, for in January, 1930, the café where I worked went busted. I was out of a job and I couldn't find a single thing to work at. I was young and had no training, and lots of people were out of work. I had nothing to do all the balance of that winter, and when spring came I was down to $30.

"There was another young fellow there in Fort Worth, Sam Haines. He had an old Ford car and we decided to hit the road in search of a job. Sam was a waiter, too, and we got three other fellows to go along with us. Sam was to furnish the car and we were to furnish gas and oil.

"We set out in April, 1930. We traveled around over Texas—Dallas, Waco, San Antonio, Houston—but we didn't find any jobs. We left Houston heading for New Orleans. In Monroe, Louisiana, 'old Lizzie' gave out. Something went wrong with her 'innards.' She knocked a few loud whacks, then threw off a connecting rod and busted the block. It's a good thing that happened in a town instead of out on the road. Sam sold her to a junk dealer for $5. That was a good thing, too, because we needed that $5 before we found a job.

"We all caught a freight train in Monroe and rode it to New Orleans. There the gang split up. One of the boys got a job on a banana boat bound for South America. The other two struck out for Florida.

"Me and Sam stuck together. We made it to Mobile but there was nothing doing there. We rambled on up to Birmingham and there Sam found a job as waiter. We had just sixty cents between us when we got there.

"Sam got his room and meals and $5 a week. The proprietor agreed for me to occupy the room with Sam for awhile until I could find something to do. I stayed around Birmingham for a week, but couldn't find any kind of job. Sam wanted me to stay on but I wouldn't. He was only making $5 a week, and was giving me a part of that to eat on.

"We had both kept our clothes nice. I had two good suits and plenty of shirts. I left all my clothes with Sam and hit the road light. I only had fifty cents that Sam had give me. I made it to Atlanta in one night on a freight train, but things seemed duller there than they were in Birmingham.

"I bummed around in Georgia and South Carolina for three or four weeks. Everywhere I went it was the same old story— 'No help wanted.' My clothes got pretty dirty and soiled from sleeping out. I could wash my shirt and underwear, but I had no money to have my suit cleaned and pressed.

"But there were lots of people on the road worse off than me. I was young, in good health, and had only myself to look out for. That summer I met whole families wandering around homeless and broke, even women with babies in their arms.

"Between Augusta and Charlotte I met a man, his wife and seven children. The oldest child was only eleven and the youngest was a nursing baby. I guess the baby was the luckiest in the lot because he had something to eat. The other children were all hungry. Some of the little ones were crying for food.

"The family was stranded on the highway. It was late in the evening, and neither the mother or father seemed to know what to do. They just stood there on the outskirts of a little town, hoping. I had nothing to give them so I walked on ahead, trying to catch a ride. Nobody stopped to pick me up and at dusk I walked back to where they were still standing. I suggested that we walk along the road until we come to a patch of corn. They agreed, and we didn't have to go far before we come to a cornfield. Across the highway from the cornfield was a little patch of woods. I told the man to build a fire while I gathered corn. We roasted corn around the fire and we all ate it except the baby. We spent the night there in the woods. The next morning a big truck picked us up and carried us to Chester, South Carolina. There I caught a freight to Charlotte. I never did learn what became of those people; I've often wondered.

"I stayed around Charlotte two days looking for work. I slept in the depot at night and hunted for work in the daytime.

I found nothing there, so I caught a freight for Greensboro. I got off at Pomona Yards and walked on toward town. I left the tracks and went over to the highway. I come to a big service station. A lot of cars were parked in and around the place. Something caused me to ask for a job, and sure enough I got one. It was on July 3rd, 1930, and a lot of people were having their cars washed for the Fourth.

"The manager put me to helping a colored boy wash cars. It was about ten o'clock in the morning when I went to work, and we washed and greased cars until midnight. The boss gave me $2 and told me to come back in the morning as he might have something else for me to do. I hunted up a little all-night café. They still had a plate lunch on. I bought one for a quarter and I still think that was the best meal I ever ate. I was mighty black and greasy but I was hungry, too. I hadn't had anything to eat for about thirty hours. I sure enjoyed that plate lunch.

"After eating I went back to the service station. An old truck was parked on the street nearby and I slept in it until morning. Then I went over to the service station and the boss gave me a job as grease monkey. I don't know why unless it was because I looked the part. My pay was to be $12 a week; my hours from seven to seven, seven days a week. I was to grease and wash cars, clean up around the place, wipe windshields and do other odd jobs. It looked like a hard job but I was glad to get it.

"I had no clothes except the ones I had on, and they were so dirty that I wouldn't have gone to a rooming house to rent a room. I slept around the service station for the first week; just any old place. I wrote Sam to send my clothes and he did. I had them addressed in care of the service station, and the expressman brought them in about a week. That evening when my work was finished, I took a bath and put on clean clothes. Boy, I felt like a gentleman! I hunted up a room where I could sleep for $2 a week. It was not much of a room but good enough for a grease monkey. That was the first night I had slept in a bed in about two months. The next morning I was sore all over from sleeping in that soft bed.

"I didn't like my job much but it was better than being on the road. I decided to make the best of what I had because jobs were hard to find. Lots of people were out of work, but lots of other people had money. That was a big filling station, on a main highway, and in the course of a week I would serve big cars from nearly every state in the Union. Those folks had money—I'd often see a flashy roll as they paid their bill. They were rich folks, I guess. Business people, tourists, and all kinds stopped there.

"A guy had a nice little café just up the street from where I worked. It was a small place, kept by him and his wife, but she was a good cook, and the place was new and clean. They were just getting by, serving twenty-five-cent plate lunches to workingmen in the neighborhood. I ate there regular, but I only ate two meals a day. I was saving my money because I wanted to get out of the grease monkey business.

"One day they had a chicken for dinner, and they gave me a piece on my plate lunch, as well as some cream gravy. It was a fine piece of chicken; tender, tasty, and well-cooked. The gravy was good, too, and I got an idea from that piece of chicken. I suggested that they serve a special fried chicken and gravy meal all through the day for tourists. They didn't think much of my idea, but finally decided to try it. The price of the meal was to be fifty cents, and I, the grease monkey, was to send the tourists along to the café. If the plan succeeded I was to get three free lunches a day.

"As I think this over now I can see the absurdity of the scheme. Imagine a grease monkey, all black and smeary, wiping your windshield and at the same time trying to sell you a chicken dinner. Now that I think of it I can't think of anything more unappetizing.

"But despite its absurdity, or possibly because of it, the scheme went over big. I well remember our first customer. He was a big fat fellow, driving a Lincoln with Florida plates.

" 'Cap,' I said to him as I wiped his windshield, 'how would you like to wrap yourself around some of the finest fried chicken in all this great land?' "

" 'Sounds interesting,' he returned, smacking his lips.

" 'I'll tell you,' I went on confidentially. 'It's some country people moved to town, real Southern folks, and they opened a small place just to have something to do. The woman does the cooking herself, and she can fry a chicken like nobody's business. The funny part is they don't even know enough to charge. They serve a half fried chicken, a big bowl of cream gravy, and fresh hot biscuits, all for fifty cents.' "

" 'Where is this place?' he demanded abruptly.

" 'Just up this street, half a block.' I pointed and he touched his starter and whirred away. I watched him park in front of the café, then I got busy and forgot him. About an hour later a Lincoln drove into the place and honked loudly. The pump attendant ran to his pump, and I grabbed my smear rag. 'Here,' said a voice from the car, and I looked in to see the fat man. He had a big blob of gravy on his shirt front, and a contented look in his eye. He handed me a quarter and said, 'You told me right. Best fried chicken I ever ate, and the gravy, Yum, Yum! I'll be coming back,' he added as he drove off, and the very next week he was back, driving a Packard with Illinois license plates. I've often wondered if he drove all the way from Illinois just to get another mess of that fried chicken.

"Well, our plan succeeded. It was a poor day when the little café did not serve fifteen or twenty chickens, and the folks were well pleased with the arrangement. I got my three plate lunches a day and an occasional piece of chicken.

"I didn't like my job as grease monkey a little bit, but I reckon the boss liked my work all right. The third week he raised my pay to $14. I was only paying $2 for my room and getting my meals free, so I decided to save $11 a week. I guess I did save about that much, for I had $80 in September.

"Along in September, 1930, a guy drove in one day to have a flat fixed. I cleaned his windshield, and as it was a slack time we got to talking. He told me that he seldom had a puncture because he traded cars every year, and that he was a knitter.

" 'Must be a pretty good job,' I ventured.

" 'Oh, it's not so hot,' he replied. 'About forty a week.'

" 'Wish I had a job that good,' I said.

" 'They're taking on some learners over in Merlton this week. Takes about three months to learn, and you don't get any pay while learning.'

"He got his flat fixed and drove away. I kept thinking about what he'd said. I had about $80 saved. I could count on having ninety when I got my back pay. But I decided not to quit. I played cagey. I sort of moped around for the balance of the day, and in the evening I told the boss that I was sick, and asked him to get somebody to work in my place the next day.

"The boss let me off for the next day and I took the first bus for Merlton. I got a job learning to knit at the first mill I come to. They told me that if they didn't have a machine for me when I learned they'd give me something at which I could earn expenses. It was understood that I was to learn three months without pay.

"I hustled back to Greensboro and got my pay. I had $89.89 when I got back to Merlton. I found a boarding place for $5 a week. As I was going to go three months without a pay day I resolved to stretch my money pretty far, and it held out all right. After a learner has worked a couple of weeks he can be of much help to the knitter. My knitter made good money, and he gave me a dollar or two every week. Knitters ain't bad guys. I've learned a couple of fellows myself and I always give them a little something every week.

"I worked the rest of that year for nothing. I got a machine on the night shift the first of January, 1931. I'm still on that same machine, but I'm now on the first shift, from seven in the morning to three in the afternoon. I saved enough money the first year to buy a car. In 1935 I married. My wife is a looper. She worked on for awhile after we married and we bought a lot and had a house built on it. But we've never lived in the house. When it was finished a fellow wanted to rent it. He offered a good price, so we rented the house to him and we lived on at the boarding house.

"Before the baby was born we bought some furniture and rented a little place in the country. Maybe I am just a farmer at heart. Anyhow, I love to putter around in the garden, and my wife does, too. We keep some chickens scratching around. It's only three miles from town and I can be home in five minutes after I get out of the mill.

"Knitting may look like an easy job, but it's not so easy as it looks. For one thing, it is hard on the eyes; for another it's exacting. The full-fashioned knitting machine is a delicate and highly complicated machine. A knitter must keep his wits about him constantly. It's very easy to smash a machine, doing hundreds of dollars' worth of damage and maybe putting that machine out of commission for a couple of months.

"A knitting machine has twenty-four heads and knits twenty-four stockings at a time. Every head has hundreds of needles, and while they only cost one cent there are several thousand to each machine. The needles are fine and easy to bend or break. Moreover, they have a little barb, or beard, finer than a human hair. Every needle must be straight and in exact line, and every barb must be set correctly or they won't work.

"A stocking is knit flat, spread out, and is then seamed, or sewed up. If you want to understand why knitting is such a particular job, and puts such strain on the eyes, spread out a silk stocking and examine the weave, or mesh. Then try to stick a fine needle through one of the spaces in the weave. There are 420 spaces in the stockings knit on my machine. That means that every head has 420 needles, and when a knitter tops a stocking on he spreads it out and slips those 420 spaces down over 420 needles. When a thread or needle breaks it spoils that stocking at the break. The knitter tops it back on and ravels it down to the break. Fortunately, he may knit several dozen without having a break.

"When a stocking is being knit a wide line of needles, 420 on my machine, come up through the mesh at every stitch. The beard on the needles catches a silk thread and draws it down through the mesh, and that is the way a silk stocking is knit. This is a poor description, and you would have to see a machine in operation to understand how it's done. Even then it would be hard to see into because the needles work very fast. But you can see from this that it's hard on the eyes, and that every needle and barb must be in line.

"The silk threads are fine, and the needles are small and slender. Unless a man has very good eyes he will have to wear magnifying glasses soon after beginning to knit. Knitting is a young man's job. You'll see ten times as many knitters under thirty as you will over thirty. A man's eyes were not made for such fine work. The eyes of some knitters go bad after five or six years, sometimes sooner than that. In fact, unless a man has good eyes he can't learn to knit. Some learners fall down the first week on account of their eyes.

"The mills around here teach their own knitters. Some of them have an age limit of twenty years for learners. They prefer young fellows under twenty, just out of high school. I imagine a knitter would have to have very good eyes to last ten years. But knitting pays well, comparatively speaking, and there's no lack of applicants. A full-fashioned knitter is considered to have a good trade hereabouts. The wage is much higher than common. A good knitter can average $40 a week the year round. The work is not hard except on the eyes. The light isn't always good. If a man had daylight to work under it wouldn't be so bad, but that can't always be. Most of the mills around here run three shifts, and some are naturally dark and require artificial light even at midday.

"There's a boom on in the silk hosiery trade. All the mills

around here are running full blast, and those that don't have third shifts are starting them. Many new mills are being built close to Burlington. I've heard that the mills up around Philadelphia are not doing any good. Silk hosiery is a new industry in the South, but it's growing fast."

JOHN H. ABNER

GEORGE L. ANDREWS

I'd Rather Die

Rain lashed the windows in gusts and somewhere immensely high and remote thunder muttered. Inside the pie wagon was bright hot light, the smell of greasy fryings, of dish water, beer, and stale cigarette smoke.

The young man with the dark broad face and heavy shoulders poured his beer. "Might as well go on talking," he said. "Looks like this rain's caught me here for some time. I live a mile from the end of the car line here and I'd be drenched before I could get home. Wet enough as it is." His curly hair dripped and the gray work shirt was mottled with rain.

From the cheap radio above the counter, where Gus the owner of the pie wagon leaned chewing on a match stick, the pant and grunt of a Negro singer came through a hammering beat of orchestration.

> "Flat-ah foot-ah floogie
> "With-ah floy-floy-
>   "Floy-doy, floy-doy, floy-doy."

The young man got up from the table, stepped across, and rolled his emptied bottle down the counter. "For God's sake, Gus, can't you turn that racket off?"

"Sure, Jeems." Gus nodded. He turned and clicked the switch. "These here popular songs gits crazier ever year. Nothing good on the radio no more but the Saturday night barn dance. I keep the doggone thing on all the time for the customers but it's got so I don't no more hear it than nothing. Gits to be a sort of silence, that noise does."

Gus took the bottle and dropped it in a case. Then he shuffled behind the beaver-board partition to wash the dishes left by the supper crowd. "Y'all need anything, just call me, just call me," he said.

Jimmy dribbled salt over the head of foam in his chill-beaded glass. "Well, as I started telling you, I went to work for Travis and Son a few weeks after Dad died. It's an overall factory—Everwear brand, you know. The name Travis and Son doesn't mean anything now. The Travises drank themselves to death a long time ago and the company's run now by Old Dave MacGonnigal and his four boys.

"I never in my life dreamed I'd ever have to work at that place. Of course, Dad was a pattern-maker there and worked for Old Dave over forty-five years. But if things hadn't gone the way they did, I'd never known what he went through to keep us alive all those years. Well, after Dad's death when the bottom dropped out from under the family I couldn't find a job anywhere. Finally I applied to Old Dave MacGonnigal.

"It was the first time I'd ever seen him. He's a tall man, kind of bent over, and with a long face and a long nose. He used to have a mop of hair, they tell me, but now his head's as bald as a brass door knob and just about as shiny. He looks glum and sour all the time and turns his head sideways and snaps at you when he talks.

" 'I'll give you something, boy,' he told me, 'but you've got to work.'

" 'I'll do my best,' I said, just like the boy in the books.

" 'Well,' he said to me, 'you needn't think that because you've got that high school diploma you can sit around on your tail here and talk Latin. We work here, boy. I put on overalls and work like the rest. You soldier on me and I'll fire you like a shot —understand?'

"I stood up straight and looked him in the eye. You're supposed to do that, you know, to show you've got character. I said, 'You can depend on me, sir!'

" 'All right,' he said. 'I'll expect you to report to the stock room at seven-thirty Monday morning. And I mean on the dot! I really don't need you, mind, but I'm putting you on because you're one of Bob's boys. Clear out now, boy. I'm busy.'

"Seemed to me at the time that the job was something handed down out of heaven. I was so happy and relieved I didn't even ask the old man how much he was going to pay me. Rushed on home as fast as I could go to tell Mama.

" 'Work hard,' she told me, 'and Mr. MacGonnigal will certainly advance you. Your father was a valuable man and they'll keep their eyes on you. Wait and see.'

"I promised I would. I guess I was about as happy as I'd ever been in my life.

"I can tell you I didn't feel that way when the end of the first week came around. I drew six dollars and fifty cents.

"But there's a lot before this that I'd better tell.

"I don't ever remember want or any feeling of insecurity when I was little. Dad made good money in those days—say, about fifty or sixty dollars a week. You know, a pattern maker has a pretty important job in an overall factory. If the patterns he lays out aren't right to the fraction of an inch the cutters will ruin a lot of goods. There's a good deal of figuring to it, complicated figuring, and he can't make mistakes. Dad never learned mathematics because he hadn't had a chance to go to high school. But he'd worked out a system of his own with all sorts of funny little signs and symbols. Nobody else understood it. He could take a problem of figuring up goods and have it done in a minute where some of the efficiency experts Old Dave had in from time to time would take an hour to work it. And Dad's would be nearer the right answer than the experts'. The boys in the cutting room told me all about it when I came there to work. So they paid Dad a pretty good salary, though not what he was worth.

"We had our own home in North Chattanooga and we had

a car. My two older brothers and my sister finished high school. My oldest brother, after being a salesman for a few years with Radebaugh Shoe Company, worked his way through Columbia University. I don't guess he could have done it by work alone. But he won one scholarship after another and finally a traveling fellowship that gave him a year in Europe. After that he came back and went into business in Chicago. My next oldest brother got a job on a newspaper after high school. Mother'd wanted him to be a lawyer but he wasn't interested. Sister married and moved away.

"The first hard times I remember came in 1933, when I was in the eighth grade. Travis and Son shut down and for six months Dad didn't draw a penny. Things must have been pinching for two or three years before that because by that time the house was mortgaged and the money spent. I don't know much about the details. Anyhow, my brother in Chicago couldn't help much. He was barely holding his job up there. My brother who worked for the newspaper was cut to practically nothing. He made enough to pay his expenses and that's about all. Then they cut the staff and let the youngest reporters off and he was one of them.

"Then we were really up against it. For a whole week one time we didn't have anything to eat but potatoes. Another time my brother went around to grocery stores and got them to give him meat for his dog—only he didn't have any dog. We ate that dog meat with the potatoes. I went to school hungry and came home to a house where there wasn't any fire. The lights were cut off. They came out and cut off the water. But each time, as soon as they left, my brother went out and cut it on again with a wrench.

"I remember lying in bed one night and thinking. All at once I realized something. We were poor. Lord! It was weeks before I could get over that. I was ashamed to look at anybody and to talk to them. I thought everybody was saying to themselves, 'This Douglas boy is poor.'

"I won't go into all the hard times we had. I hate to think of them. I'll just tell a little. Well, we lost our car and our house and kept moving from one house to another. Bill collectors hunted us down and came in droves. Every now and then my brother or Dad would find some sort of odd job to do, or the other brother in Chicago would send us a little something. Then we'd go wild. I mean we'd go wild over food. We'd eat until we were sick. We'd eat four times a day and between meals. We shouldn't have done it. We ought to have gone easy on it, but we just couldn't help ourselves. The sight and smell of food sort of made us crazy, I guess.

"The winter of 1934 was the hardest time of all. Dad was working again at Travis and Son, but he wasn't making but around ten dollars a week. My brother was selling a little stuff free-lance, but it hardly amounted to enough to pay for postage and typewriter paper. And debts had piled up until we couldn't get credit anywhere.

"We were completely out of coal one time when we were living away out at the edge of town. The weather was freezing bitter then, so at night my brother and I would bundle up and go about a quarter of a mile away to a big estate on the Tennessee River. We made a hole in the fence and stole some of the wood that was piled a good distance from the house. We just walked in and got it. I don't remember that we tried to be quiet about it in particular.

"We hauled that wood through the fields in a coaster wagon and a wheel barrow. Lots of times we made nine or ten trips and worked almost until morning. We took two or three whole stacks of wood that winter, and it's all that kept us from freezing. Mama never did ask us where the wood came from. She always knew somehow when we were going to do it and those nights she went to bed early before we left. I was thirteen then and it was kind of exciting to me. Sometimes I was afraid we'd be caught, but we never were. I don't know why. My brother used to keep one heavy stick of wood in his overcoat pocket while we were taking the stuff. I asked him why he did it and he told me if anybody found us out and tried to stop us I'd see why.

"Another time when we were out of anything to eat and were getting pretty hungry, he went around looking queer. I saw him slip out late at night and he had a foot-long piece of iron pipe with him. I knew he was going to try to knock somebody in the head to get their money. I stayed awake, scared stiff until he came back. He mustn't have found anybody, because he didn't bring home any money. Maybe he got cold feet. I've never asked him about it.

"We sold everything we could except the piano.

"Mama wouldn't let that go. It was a Steinway upright and she said we'd never get another one if we sold it. All of us had taken our music lessons on it—especially my sister, the one who died when I was little. I guess that was the real reason Mama wouldn't let it go.

"After awhile things got some better. My brother in Chicago got so he could send money home and my other brother got another newspaper job. Dad went back to regular work at Travis and Son, though he only got about twenty dollars a week. We weren't over the hard time because of the debts from the bad years. Still, compared to those years we were just sailing.

"I went on through high school and made good marks. In my senior year I had an average of ninety-eight and was elected class president and was valedictorian at graduation. I expected to go to college the next fall. Now, I can't see how on earth I could have expected to. I knew that there was no money for it. But somehow or other it just seemed to me that a way would turn up.

"Mother felt the same about it. She'd say, 'If you want a college education badly enough you will get it. Any boy who is determined can work his way through. Brother worked his way through Columbia and you can work your way through U. T. All great men have had to struggle.'

"Well, I'd think of what I'd read about Lincoln and all those others and it seemed to me I could do it, too. You see, I thought I was going to be a great man."

Jimmy drained his glass. He set it down with a thump. The rain was drumming steadily on the roof. There was a dull clatter of Gus' thick crockery from behind the partition. Gus was whistling You're the One Rose.

Legs extended, hands in his pockets, Jimmy slouched down in his chair. "I was going to be great. I didn't know just what sort of great, but I was going to be a world-shaker." He gave a short dry laugh.

"The first of the summer after I graduated I stayed at home studying—reviewing my high school books. Mother wanted me to do that so I'd be ready for college. She had a notion that my brother in Chicago would be able to scare up the money for my first year in the University of Tennessee. After that, of course, I'd get along on scholarships. I kind of hoped football would help there, too. You see, I'd been a good linesman in high school. And since the football season and the good eating we'd begun to have, I'd been filling out. Gained twenty solid pounds and that brought me up to a hundred and ninety.

"That summer we had a scare. There was some sort of strike at Travis and Son. Seems that after the NRA blew up, Old Dave put the girls in the sewing room on piece work and some of them just couldn't make a living. They protested but it didn't do any good. They rocked along then for a long time, just talking. Then some organizer came and got them to go out on a strike. The men went out, too, and they ganged around the entrance blocking off part of the street.

"Dad didn't know what to do. He walked the floor at home. He said that the girls were right, but he didn't believe they could win out because the mayor had said he'd back Old Dave to the limit. I remember Mama telling Dad, 'Oh, Bob, please don't do anything foolish! We've been through such a hard time. What on earth would we do if we had to face it again? I couldn't bear it!'

"So Dad went to work the next morning. I had some errands to do for Mama so I went to town with him. Old Dave had called up and said he'd have policemen to carry Dad through the strikers. When we got there the policemen were ready all right. They told Dad they'd rush him through. He started out, with me tagging behind. Then he made me go back to the corner and started again. The strikers were bunched up at the door of the factory. They weren't saying a thing or making a move. Just men and women standing there watching.

"I saw Dad stop again. He had an argument with the police. I heard him say pretty loud, 'No, I'll go by myself or I won't go at all.' He said it two or three times.

"The policemen were mad. 'Okay, Cap,' I heard one of them say. 'It's your look-after, not mine.'

"Dad walked on without them, but they sort of edged along some way behind.

"All at once the strikers began yelling and meeowing. Dad walked on. When he was right at them, about a dozen men and women grabbed at him and started tearing his coat and shirt.

"I started running down there and so did the police.

"But right then the strikers got into a free-for-all fight among themselves. Dad had a lot of good friends among them and these friends jumped on the ones who'd grabbed him. They pulled them off and Dad walked on through and went into the factory. He never was bothered again. Old Dave and the others had to have the police to get in and out. Dad came and went without anybody trying to stop him.

"So the strike petered out and the strikers were out of jobs. Some of them came to Dad and he tried to get them back on. But Old Dave said he wouldn't touch a one of them with a ten-foot pole.

"One night late in July Dad didn't come home at his usual time. Hours passed and there wasn't any sign of him. Mother and I were worried to death. We didn't have a 'phone then and at first Mother was ashamed to ask the neighbors. Finally, around seven o'clock she did, though, and called Old Dave. He said Dad had left at the usual time.

"So Mama told me to walk to the car line and go to town and see if I could find Dad. 'I just know something terrible has happened,' she said. 'Bob has never been late. He wouldn't be if something hadn't happened.'

"I started out from home running. It was a mile to the car line, so I took a short cut through the woods. When I came out at the end of Terry Road, still running, I saw a man coming down the last hill. He was sort of weaving as he walked, taking uneven steps, and stopping every third or fourth step. Then I recognized his brown suit and I knew it was Dad.

"My heart almost stopped. I'd seen men walk that way before and I knew what it meant. I kept on running.

"When I got to him, he just stared at me for a minute. His face was as white as a sheet. He looked awful.

"He said, 'Jimmy!' Then he caught my arm to keep from falling. And when he was that close to me I could tell that he hadn't been drinking. I knew he was a sick man.

"It took us more than an hour to get home, because we had to stop and rest so many times. A little at a time Dad told me what had happened. He'd been waiting for a street car uptown when all at once he felt dizzy and had to sit down on the curbing. Every time he tried to get up things whirled and dipped so that he had to sit back down.

" 'People laughed at me,' he said. 'Must have thought I was drunk. I tried to say something but I couldn't get a word out. I sat there I don't know how long. A while ago I felt steady enough to catch a street car and come on. I've never felt like this before. Just don't know what it could be.'

"Well, it was death coming on. Dad knew it, I believe, but I just couldn't imagine such a thing and Mama couldn't either— even when he had to go to the hospital and any fool on earth could see he was sinking. Yet I just couldn't get it through my head until Dad was gone. Then I felt like somebody had hit me with a hammer. I wanted to run, not anywhere, but just run till I dropped. I wanted to fight something and beat it with my fists and tear it to bits with my fingers. Never will be anything that can hurt me like that.

"The doctors never did know what was wrong with Dad. He was sixty, but there wasn't anything like cancer or tuberculosis. One of the doctors at the hospital told me that he was really just worn out completely. I guess he was right."

Jimmy Douglas called for his second bottle of beer. He drummed on the table and stared at his fingers while Gus was getting it. He didn't pour the beer in his glass this time. He drank from the bottle and didn't set it down until it was empty.

"Dad's insurance had lapsed during the hard time," Jimmy went on. "We had the funeral expenses and doctors' and hospital bills to pay. Now I know that the funeral ought to have been just as simple as possible. That's the way Dad would have wanted it. But at the time I didn't have any sense. Mama wanted the best and that damned undertaker was smooth. Every time he'd point out a casket and say, 'Now this is a fine piece of merchandise,' I felt like choking him. I was glad when Mama picked out a casket that cost four hundred dollars. She told them Dad had insurance so she could get it.

"I'll skip a lot now. I've already told you how I looked for work and couldn't find it and finally got put on as stock boy at Travis and Son.

"The job was hard. Not on your mind but on your back and legs. You see, the stock room is in the basement. I have to load lays of overall goods—I can tell you that stuff's heavy, too— into a big wheeled push-truck. Then I man-power that truck up a slope of concrete to the elevator door. The elevator takes me up to the cutting room where men cut the goods by pattern. In the cutting room I get the stacks of cut-out goods and take it up to the sewing room and the girls sew the stuff into overalls. From the sewing room I haul the finished overalls down to the shipping room. Between times I unload lays of goods from trucks outside and haul it into the stock room or help load boxes of overalls to be shipped out. Never a minute of rest.

"The cutters and the girls are on piece work, so they are always crying for more goods. Jimmy! Jimmy! Jimmy! Until I feel like I'll go crazy. I didn't think I'd ever get through that first week. When I came on, Fred, the other stock boy, let up and shoved a lot of the work he should have been doing on me. But I didn't know enough about the work to see what he was doing right at the beginning.

"When I started to work I laid out a schedule of what I wanted to do. I was going to keep up my study at home so if my brother in Chicago could help me I'd be ready to go on to college. He was already sending money home to Mama and my other brother was helping as much as he could, but he'd got married about six months before Dad died and had his own family coming on. Well, I was going to study. But I was so dogtired every night when I got home that I just dropped in bed after I'd eaten, and went to sleep. It wasn't sound sleep, either. I had nightmares of trying to buck a truck of goods up a steep slope, and the truck was as big as a house and the slope as high as a mountain, and Old Dave yelling and all of them yelling at me to hurry.

"So I said I'd study Saturday afternoons and Sunday. Sunday, anyhow. We hadn't gone to church for years, so Sundays were open. But I didn't do it. I had to do work around the house on Saturday and on Sunday I just couldn't make myself get up until almost noon. I'd read the Sunday paper and go to sleep lying on the sofa in the afternoon. I found I couldn't get anything out of reading. I used to like to read, but now I was always so tired—tired down to my bones—that I couldn't get any sense out of a book and I'd go to sleep trying to read it.

"All that winter and next summer I was hard at it. Got to know all the people at the factory and liked some of them pretty well. But I'll tell you I never before knew that such people existed. Most of them had come in off of the mountains somewhere and they had such a funny way of talking that plenty of times I wouldn't know what they were saying.

"The girls were usually either sloppy fat or thin and dried up. Their hair all hung in strings and a good many of them dipped snuff and spit all the time. They wore the doggonedest clothes I ever saw, with their stockings wrapped around their legs in folds and full of holes and their heels run down. They told each other the slimiest jokes while they were working and they'd say things to you that would make you want to throw up. I've seen them have fights, pulling hair and scratching and biting.

"Some of them made as little as fifty cents a week. No, I mean it! Fifty cents a week! I've seen their pay checks. You see they were on piece work and hoped to get experience enough to make more. Others of them, the fast workers, made up to sixteen and eighteen dollars. They set the pace and every-body else had to measure up. The sewing room was right under the roof and in summer, too, and I was good and glad that I did some of my work in the basement. It reached a hundred and twenty degrees on hot days in that place and the girls would keel over on the floor. Got so hot in July that Old Dave shut the factory down during the day and had us work at night instead.

"I didn't have as much to do with the girls as with the men. They were funny people and there was only one thing that would make any impression on them. If they didn't think you were tough, they'd pick you to pieces. I got in my bluff as soon as I saw how they were. I'm big and I can make my voice sound like a big dog growling. So I told them I'd studied boxing and how I'd knocked a lot of fellows out. They believed me and sucked up to me then—even those that had been in jail and always carried knives. Anyway, most of them were awfully measly looking men. Not a beefy man among them.

"But they were tough. Always getting in knife fights on Sat-urday night out to Fount Dillon's joint and being thrown in jail. But my bluff worked and they left me alone. Some of them who hadn't gone on the strike had known Dad and they were always nice to me, too.

"All of them were afraid of Old Dave and hated him. They used to sit around at lunch eating their fried pies and egg sandwiches and talk about all the things they'd like to do to him. When he was around they just yes-sired him like a bunch of niggers.

"He'd told me that he worked just like anybody else. Well, he does put on overalls and prowl all around. First he'll pop into the sewing room and then in the cutter's room. You can't tell when he'll be in a dark corner of the basement. He's always trying to find somebody loafing. It looks to me like it makes him happy when he can spot somebody and can bawl them out.

"Old Dave never has a pleasant word for anybody. When he's in the stock room it's 'Boy, get that truck moving! You look like the dead lice are falling off you!' And, 'Damn it, you lazy no 'count young-un, get those lays loaded—hear me?' Work your head off and he won't give you the least little praise. Stop to get your breath and he's all over you.

"They say he's worried about conditions and that's what makes him so mean. The way I look at it, that's no excuse. Dad had a hundred times more worry than Old Dave, but the more worried he got the politer he was to you. And another thing— Old Dave's a big man in the church. You see his picture in the paper every once and a while. But you'd never know it at the factory.

"The five MacGonnigal boys work in the office. I mean they're supposed to work there. I've never seen any of them but John do a tap. John's all right. I'll say this for him—he does keep pretty busy. The other four just sit around and read the paper or some magazine. They come in late and go out to lunch early. They stay out two hours and hang over the telephone talking to girls in the afternoon and leave before quitting time. Old Dave raises the roof but they don't pay much attention to him. One thing, though. They all draw good salaries.

"I was saying that Old Dave didn't exactly choke you with praise. He dingdonged at me so that one day I got good and mad. For a minute I didn't know whether I was going to jump on the old man and then go upstairs and clean up with his boys or whether I'd quit the job. But I didn't do either one. I said to myself 'All right. I'll show the old son-of-a-gun. I'll work so hard he'll have to say something.'

"I did it. I worked until I thought I'd kill myself with it. Fred, the other stock boy, told me I didn't have any sense. I worked a whole week that way.

"So when Saturday came Old Dave called me off and said he was going to raise my pay. There were two extra dollars in my envelope."

Jimmy laughed until his body shook.

"Yep—two extra dollars. And Fred got fired and I had all his work to do as well as mine. Boy! Was I the bright one, though!

"I was so mad I couldn't get to sleep for hours that night. I did everything imaginable to Old Dave—all the way from just knocking him down and stomping on him and burning the factory to cutting him up a little at a time.

"Well, I waited for a chance to get back on him. About a month later there was a big rush of orders and things were humming and they had me hopping trying to keep the cutters and the girls in enough goods. So I caught Old Dave in the hall. I said, 'I want a raise, Mr. MacGonnigal.'

"He looked like he was going to bite my head off. 'You get back to work or I'll fire you.'

" 'No you won't,' I said. 'I'll just quit right now.' I started off, untying my apron.

"He grabbed my arm—see, he knew they couldn't break a new boy in right in the middle of the rush, and he knew he wasn't likely to get another one that would work as hard as I did.

"So he grabbed my arm and said, 'Two dollars.'

"I said, 'I'm worth fourteen a week.' That was almost double what I was making, but no more than he'd paid for both Fred and me. It looked like he was going to try to hit me. I kept on walking off, dragging him along because he still had my arm.

"Then all at once he turned loose. 'Twelve dollars. Take it or leave it.'

"You could tell he meant it. So I took the twelve. That's what I'm making now."

Jimmy got up and went to the window. The rain was little more than a misty drizzle now. The tires of the cars that flashed by on the highway sang against the wet asphalt.

"I'd better get going now, while it's slacked up," he said. "But first let me tell you the other surprise I've got for Old Dave.

"I'm quitting next Saturday. My uncle in Florida is sending for Mama to come and live with him. I've got enough money to pay my fare down there and when I get there he's got a job for me. Before I'd work in a place like this again—why I'd rather die first.

"Boy, will I tell Old Dave what I think of him! No, I don't really guess I will. What's the use in it? Anyhow, it's fun to keep on thinking that until the time comes. I can go to sleep grinning like a 'possum."

JAMES R. ASWELL

4. The Land of Plenty

ROBERT CANTWELL

After a year of college, Robert Cantwell (1908–   ), native of Little Falls, Washington, dropped out and went to work—in a veneer factory, in a California wholesale house, on a Texas pipeline construction crew. At twenty-three he published his

From *The Land of Plenty* (New York: Farrar & Rinehart, 1934), Chap. IV, pp. 75–98. Copyright 1934, © 1962 by Robert Cantwell. Reprinted by permission of Holt, Rinehart and Winston, Inc.

first novel, Laugh and Lie Down. *More remarkable than this precocious effort, however, was the rapid growth that enabled Cantwell, only three years later, to publish a book which was a genuine* tour de force. *In* The Land of Plenty *the young writer presented his sash and door mill as a microcosm of depression America; when the lights go out, the night-shift workers, brought together by the sudden power failure, decide to strike against intolerable conditions. On the strength of this impressive work, Cantwell made his way in the New York radical and literary world, contributing to a wide variety of magazines. Almost thirty years later Malcolm Cowley remembered him as he was then: ". . . working part time for the* New Republic, *and reading Henry James, though he was also reading Marx. He was a slight, sallow, hungry-looking young man who dressed neatly in dark suits that were always too large, as if he had shrunk since buying them, and who stuttered with excitement—which he passed on to others—as he explained the dramatic value of a strike or imagined the secret maneuvers that went on in a crisis." ("A Remembrance of the Red Romance,"* Esquire, *March 1964.) Cantwell became an editor of* Time *magazine and thereafter fell silent; but his novel of people talking and learning in the dark remains brilliantly effective, as this chapter, seemingly aimless but heading toward a climax, makes clear.*

Winters

Listen, the voice said dully and he said, I'm listening. I don't want to argue, the voice said. I want to tell you the truth.

Don't listen to that goofy bastard, the other voice said.

Goofy, the first voice said coldly. Goofy, you goofy son of a bitch, you're goofy.

What?

I'd like to get that guy here. I'd like to have him juggling them hundred-fifty-pound irons on the press for a week. I'd give him his three weeks in six weeks and let him look at forty-six ahead of him.

Listen, the voice said. See if I'm right.

Winters said, Why? What are you arguing about?

A match flared somewhere down the wall. On the harbor the string of channel lights and the intermittent flash from the lighthouse of the jetty. No wind on the slate water. It's cooler, he thought, and then he thought of the hot room where the fan swung and Ann gasped for her breath. *Open the window!* Blind in the heat and the fan humming like an insect and the sweat on her face and the muscles in her throat like wires. *Ed,* she said, *open the window!* and the girl wiping her face and the fan reaching the end of its swing and starting back.

Don't listen to him, the voice said with dull passion. His ass is out.

Tide in, the tugboats headed for the bar-bound ships. Forget it. Somewhere down the wall a match flared. *Listen.* Cool on the still water, the fresh air she'll never taste.

What? he cried. What is it?

We're having an argument.

Argument hell.

Listen, Winters.

Let me tell him.

So all right I can't stand it and her eyeballs turned back in her head. I can't stay here. I can't stay here. Hands clench and unclench and the girl reading and the fan buzzing like a fly. Stopped now. I wonder.

Believe it or not the voice said. You seen the cartoon. You know Ripley, them believe it or not cartoons, he had one proving that if you worked twenty-four hours a day you'd only have to work three weeks to work as many hours as you do in a year working eight hours a day. Three weeks! I looked at that, I said, if you was here you'd learn something, baby, besides how to draw cartoons.

Tell me this.

He says you work three weeks out of the year. If you work twenty-four hours a day. Three weeks! How does he get it? He figures five and a half days a week.

Forty-four hours.

You're nuts, the voice said. Nuts.

I didn't say it! I'm telling you what it said in the paper!

Forty-four hours. Fifty-two weeks.

It still makes better than three months. And he figured you got Hallowe'en off and a week for Christmas and two weeks' vacation and ten days besides.

He did it by days.

I don't give a damn how he did it.

He said, I don't get it. I don't see what you're driving at.

Listen, the voice said. We're having an argument.

A voice corrected him. His idea of an argument.

Listen, the voice said. You see how he got it. Three hundred and sixty-five days. Take off fifty-two Sundays.

Yeah.

Take off twenty-six Saturdays.

Yeah.

Take off fourteen days' vacation and ten days for holidays.

Ed? a voice said. Ed?

Connor's voice.

Yes.

What's up?

I don't know. They're having an argument.

Connor moved up by him, kicking through the long grass that grew beside the building. The sound of his feet in the grass like water. The voices moved down. Here in fresh air no deep enough breath. Connor grunted as he eased himself against the building. "Christ, I'm tired," he said. He rummaged through his pockets, squirming his large body as he searched.

"I believe what I read, Winters," he said. "If they say no matches I don't carry any."

"I haven't got any."

Connor went back to the group, saying "Matches? Who's breaking the iron-clad rules?" The match flared, revealing his square clean face, the high forehead and light hair, the figures grouped around him.

"Ditch it," a voice said. "He could tell who you were."

The cigarette glowed as he returned. Red beneath the fragile ash. No deep enough breath. Like a deep mounting pain in his chest that no deep breath could answer. The drenched bed and suffering.

"How is she, Ed?"

"No better."

The warm voice touched him. Mounting through pain like staying too long under water, the lungs begging for air. He took a deep breath. The drenched bed, the sweat on her face, the fan buzzing like an insect under the sick orange light.

Silence. Connor cleared his throat, gravely thoughtful, drew at his cigarette. Doesn't know what to say, Winters thought. He wants to say something.

A voice said bitterly, "If he worked here he'd find out you work longer than three weeks."

"She suffering?" Connor asked.

"They keep her doped up." Then he said with an effort, "She's got a good chance. It ain't hopeless . . . I couldn't stay home! I thought I would but I couldn't stand it. Besides they won't let me see her after five."

"They won't let you see her?"

"Not at night." He spoke with a gauging calm. "Besides, she don't know me."

Silence again. Walt stirred restlessly, said *Jesus!* and drew at his cigarette. Farther down the wall the voices died away, became only slow lazy sentences broken with occasional sharp cries of doubt or indignation. Winters listened, trying to keep his mind here on the factory and the tideflat, but stirred and deeply moved that Walt had looked for him and asked him how she was. Think of something else, he thought, force myself, and brought his mind back to the tideflat, to the hot factory, to Walt and the words of the men. *I can't live on it,* he heard. *How do they expect?* And he thought, They won't take it. That's one thing. Very slowly he drew his mind back from the thought of Ann, slowly and patiently, as though making a physical effort that took all his strength and left him exhausted. "She'll get all right," Walt said awkwardly, and then, as though conscious of the awkwardness and hollowness of what he said, went on hurriedly, "I was supposed to be looking for Hagen. Carl sent me and they told me he was out in the fireroom but I couldn't locate him."

"He was looking for Carl. Up by Carl's desk."

This brings me down to three bucks a day. Last year I made four and a quarter and there's only three of us left on the crew. Last year there was five. We do twice as much.

They won't take it, Winters thought. They won't take that last cut. The knowledge pulled his thoughts back to them and he thought of going to them and joining in their talk.

Walt said, "He sure must be taking his time."

He heard the indifferent complaint, impatience, a sort of smothered accusation. Why? Walt ground his cigarette under his heel. "I yelled all over for him. Then I thought, to hell with it. Why should I be doing his work? Carl's sore as hell."

When I looked at the check I said, Listen, I said, when are you guys going to begin paying us off in buttons?

He roused himself again. *Forget it!* he thought. *Forget it! Does it do her any good?* The long spears of bulrush crumpled in his hand. Someone moved out on the tideflat, wading through the grass that reached to his knees. He threw the broken spears of bulrush away, irritated with himself that he had held and broken them without knowing it.

"I think Hagen's done for," Winters said. "From now on, Carl won't give him a chance. He'll pin this on him. See. He'll find some way."

They think they're a bunch of missionaries. All they need is a string of beads and some strips of red calico. I looked at the check and Jesus, I said, how you throw away money.

Walt said uneasily, "Hell, be fair. He ain't so bad."

"No?"

You'll learn, he thought. Wait till you been here another year. He thought of Walt coming into the factory, looking over the crew with a college-boy uneasiness, getting in the way and trying to brag about school while he worked.

"It's Hagen's fault. Carl tried to make up with him. He told me himself. He went down to Hagen and said he'd put his cards on the table and Hagen wouldn't even talk to him."

"Yeah. He wanted Hagen to suck around."

Walt stirred uncomfortably. "It'd be all right," he began vaguely, "if all of the guys. . . . But that Polack I work with. He shoves off everything on me. . . . Hagen's sour. He can't get along with anybody. It makes a lot of trouble. . . ."

The tightness returned in his chest. I'm tired, he thought, with a dull surprise, how long since I slept? Arms and legs heavy, a weight in his lungs that a deep breath did not lift. By Ann's bed, still tired, watching the fan swing while she slept. Only her heavy breathing and the buzzing of the fan. The smell of antiseptics and the sick smell from her bed and the girl reading, the fresh ink smell of the magazine as she opened the pages. THE CASE FOR FROZEN FOODS. WHAT PRICE COMPLEXION? The sweat on her ravaged face.

What good does it do her? If I sit here eating my heart out?

He opened his eyes and looked hard at the shadows beyond his feet. Think about it. He could see his own feet and the faint outline of Walt beside him. Walt's new overalls, his clean white shirt. Beyond, the empty flat and the few lights on the harbor and the faint gray reflection of the lights in town. Low sky, smoke from the fires.

"I don't blame Carl," Walt said. "Hagen don't try. He's been here so long he thinks he owns the place."

"That's what he'll say."

"Who?"

"Carl."

"I don't blame him."

But why try? Oh, why, why? The waves of grief rolled over him. What I could do, he thought, all I could have thought of! In the narrow room she watched him, crying, and he said it: *Christ, I didn't want to marry you. I'm sick of your God-damn whining.* Her face gray and her eyes clouding over. Say it, say it, no excuse. In the narrow room, the rain outside and the window shade torn and Ann sitting on the bed, her face swollen and her mouth hanging open watching me. *Nobody else would have you. Nobody else would have you.*

Why I said it. The dull urge of no reason. Oh, Ann! Racked and tender; listen, darling, listen!

He got up and walked blindly to the group down the wall.

"He won't work together," Walt was saying, quietly, so the men could not hear. "When a man's that sour. Why do you put all the blame on Carl? He's all right if you get to know him."

A voice said passionately, *What did they do with the glue crew. They put them on piecework. All right. They made good money. They worked themselves to death. Whenever we got bad stock they'd all get sore at us—they'd say we weren't giving them any stock. So what happened? As soon as they found out how much the crew could do they cut out the piecework. They'd give them a cut and then sweeten it a little if they squawked and then cut them again and now they're doing twice as much as they did before they went on piecework. Now with this they'll get ten per cent less.*

"Listen," Walt said. "What's the matter?"

"What?"

"What's the matter. Jesus, I just said. . . ."

He looked around, seeing the white shirt and the blurred outlines of Walt's face. The voice sore and puzzled. "What's eating you?" Walt said. "Just because. . . ."

"Nothing."

"Well why. . . ."

Whatever they do we get the dirty end of the stick. To hell with it. I've had enough of it. Ten per cent. That means thirty-five cents for me and multiply that by a thousand and you see what it means to them. Three hundred and fifty bucks a day. Right here in this one plant.

Because I walked off. Thought I was sore. "No," Winters said, "I was thinking about something else." He waked up slowly to Walt's puzzled resentment, tried wearily to think of something to say. *I won't take it,* the hot voice said. *I'll go down the road before I'll take it.* Walt moved about uneasily, wading through the long grass, mumbling something that he could not hear.

"Hell," Walt said. "He has to earn a living. Like anybody else."

A skyrocket sailed over town, exploding into thousands of green and red balls of light. The sky turned the color of milk. He could see Walt's square face, questioning, distrustful, young, and he came back to earth, driving the thought of Ann out of his mind, feeling ashamed of himself because he had forgotten what he was doing. Sticking up for Carl, he thought. You'll learn.

The muffled chatter of the skyrocket reached them: an explosion and then a rush of diminishing sound, a ball rolling downstairs.

They got it worse at the Superior, a voice said. *Fifteen per cent.*

Yeah, and they won't take it. They're talking strike and they won't talk anything else.

He took Walt by the arm. "For God's sake don't swallow that stuff," he said. "You start sticking up for that son of a bitch and you got your hands full. The hardest guy to stick up for I ever run into." They walked toward the door to the factory. He felt the effort of talking and tried to keep away from an argument; he felt a vague irritation that Walt was so stupid and at the same time a friendly response to Walt's own friendship for him. "You haven't been here long enough," he said. "Wait till you been here another year. Wait till he makes you work yourself to death and then turns around and gives you hell for doing what he said to do."

Walt said, "Hell, they all jump on him."

For God's sake! "Listen," he said sharply, "do you stick up for every son of a bitch you see just because he's a son of a bitch? Do you know what that guy's here for? Fifty men have lost their jobs since he's been here. We've all got two cuts. What do you think he carries a stop watch for? A race! You think he's going to time a race?"

Walt said unexpectedly, "I get along with you but these guys make me sick. They never do anything but beef. You're the only guy I ever worked with I got along with. That Polack I work with now drives me nuts. He gives me the heavy end of every truck and whenever I crab about it he says we're all members of the working class."

Winters laughed. Walt rushed on, confused and aggrieved by his laughter, "You don't believe me. I'm telling you the truth. He does it every night. And when I was working with Frank Dwyer he used to give me every dirty job that came along. He'd make me clean up the crap under the kiln when the heat was on, just for the hell of it. They got it in for anybody that's got any education trying to get along. It's no way," Walt said bitterly. "No way to treat a white man."

What do we stand to lose! the voice cried. *We can't live on it! Nobody can live on it! I don't want any trouble but I'm so damn far in debt now I'll never get out.*

"Listen, Walt," Winters said.

"If I hadn't got along with you I'd think it was my fault. But we worked all right. Just because a man has a college education. . . ."

Even then I did your work, Winters thought. I tried to break you in. "Take it easy," he said. "They all got all they can do. Dwyer's got his hands full. . . ." He was listening to the harsh passionate voices of the men, their anger evoking a stir of elation, breaking the numb despondency that had paralyzed him. "Listen!" he said sharply, when Walt started to answer him. *I'll go out*, a voice said. *Any time anybody says the word.*

Say the word, a voice repeated. *Just say the word.*

"Then they wonder," Walt said bitterly. "They act like that— then they wonder."

Are we going to take it? Is there a law we have to take it?

Wake up, he said silently to Walt. Wake up for God's sake. He saw the white blur of Walt's face and sensed his anger and bewilderment, feeling an irritated friendliness. He doesn't know what it's all about, he thought, and touched Walt's arm briefly. "Come on inside," he said. "Let's see what's up."

"Why?" Walt said.

"Come on," Winters said impatiently. "I want to talk to you."

There was a moment of silence.

"No," Walt said. "I'm going to wait here."

Stubborn, Winters said silently. Wake up. "O.K." He walked toward the door.

Say the word! the voice said. *Just say the word!*

Wake up, he thought.

He got inside a few moments before Carl and Hagen quarreled. He heard the passionate voices as Carl sent Johnny after Frankie and then, when Hagen called him, when he told Carl to pull his card, his heart began to pound with excitement; here it is, he thought, and he knew that if Hagen left he would leave too. The men began crowding around him. *Fight!* somebody said exultantly. He boosted himself up on a pile of lumber. In the dim light he saw Carl glance nervously at the crowd, worried, indignant at this fresh worry, the ground slipping out from under him. Then Hagen called his bluff and

Winters got ready to jump down, never thinking of anything but of walking out when Hagen walked out, and then he saw the fleeting panic on Carl's face, heard him stammer hotly, his voice loaded with contempt, *I'm not pulling anybody's card. I just want to say . . . I'm trying to get the lights back on. I ain't got time to screw around here all night with everything else.* He watched Carl and Molly wade off into the darkness, saw them diminish to a little blob of light and disappear. Hagen switched off his flashlight. There was a vague stir in the darkness.

Hagen said flatly, "I won't take anything more off that son of a bitch."

Someone said skeptically, "What'll you do?"

"I don't know. But I know this: I'll drive that son of a bitch out of here. Or I'll get out."

Winters was stirred; he was impatient when the same voice said again, wearily, "What the hell difference does it make? If it ain't Carl it'll be somebody else. Why worry with him?"

Hagen said sharply, "To hell with that. That's what I used to think." He lifted his voice. "I worked here ever since they built this place. I've seen twenty foremen in here. But we never had anybody as bad as that fat little bastard. I mean it. Never been anybody in here like that little son of a bitch."

When Hagen settled back against the wall, someone said briefly, "He sure gave your kid hell."

"To hell with him," Hagen said. "I don't care about him bawling out the kid. But he's so damn useless. He can't walk around without falling down. I spend half my time pulling Molly out of a conveyor. He couldn't even operate a flashlight. I gave him a flashlight and he didn't know how to turn it on. Asked me if a fuse blew out. For God's sake. A fuse. Look. Mike sent a kid in here to ask Carl if he ought to pull his fires. Now you know God-damn well that Mike knew he ought to pull his fires. But he had to send the kid in here to tell Carl to protect himself. And what did Carl do? He flew off the handle, raised all kinds of hell, and finally sent the kid back to tell Mike what Mike told him. *We can't do our work as long as that guy is here. He gets us in one mess after another!*"

A voice said, "You can't tell me anything. I remember one time when I first came to work I showed him where the floor was loose and somebody was liable to fall through and break their God-damned neck, so he better get it fixed. The next night, *the next night!* he came along, he said, 'Look here, Madison, God damn it, you better watch this floor,' he said, 'you better watch this floor or you're liable to fall through and break your God-damned neck!'"

There was a silence. Presently another voice said thoughtfully, "Son of a bitch takes credit for everything."

Hagen asked, "Why do we have so much trouble on the night shift? Because he's always got his nose up it. He tells you one thing and five minutes later he turns around and tells you something else. Then he gives you hell for not doing something entirely different. If we get anything done he thinks it's because he did it. Then when we have any trouble he thinks it's because nobody did what he told them."

Someone pushed Winters aside. "Move over," a voice said. "I want to lay down and I hate to lay down on the floor because I get grease in my hair if I lay down on the floor."

Winters shifted over on the pile of lumber. The newcomer stretched out, grunting and sighing as he tried to get comfortable. "I'm stiff as a board," he said. "I had to get up at six o'clock this morning and reline the brakes on my car. Took me all morning. Finally I got them relined."

No one said anything. The newcomer yawned, exhaling a series of mournful, wordless sighs. "Oh, I got the yellow dog," he groaned. "I think I'll die. . . . Hagen, you big bastard, if you turn the lights on again, I'll kill you. They been pounding me on the tail so hard I didn't know what I was doing. When the lights went out, Jesus, I put my hand on my forehead, Jesus, I thought, my eyes are sure getting bad."

Hagen said bitterly, "When he first came here he used to carry a stop watch around, little bitty rig, fit right in the palm of his hand. Then he used to follow everybody around, see how long it took to do anything. If you went to get a drink, there he'd be, working his little clock. If you wanted to take a crap, there he'd be. It gave you the creeps, having him stick that watch up against the back of your neck like a gun. Took twice as long to do anything."

"You know what he did before he came here?" a voice asked. "He used to sell shoes. I run into a guy that knew him. He was a dick for the company. He'd go around, checking up on all the clerks to see if they was getting a rake-off. Then he'd see if the clerks was wearing the same kind of shoes they sold in the store and if they wore new shoes."

"How can a guy work if some son of a bitch has got a stop watch pointed at him?"

"Yeah," the voice said, "this guy told me Carl knew all the stock so he'd find out if the clerks knew the stock by asking for some funny-sized shoe. All the clerks was supposed to try to sell some high-priced shoe—if you said you wanted something for five dollars they was supposed to sell you something for six. So when Carl would go into a store, letting on he was a customer, he'd ask for something for five dollars and if the clerk didn't show him something for six he'd turn in a report and the clerk would be bounced."

"I believe it."

"Yeah. So this guy told me that when Carl would leave one of the stores there'd be shoe boxes all over the place and all the clerks would be run ragged and they'd think they'd been selling shoes to some poor loony bastard that didn't know what he wanted. And all Carl would do, he'd take the shoes back to the main office and turn them in and they'd go right back on the shelves. Then Carl would turn in a couple names to show he was working, the guys would get fired, so then he got to be an efficiency expert."

Somebody said, "Hell! You know what he did to me? He never could catch me ———— the dog, so you know what he did? He used to stop me when I was working, ask me a lot of dumb questions and start chewing the fat, and all the time he'd be working that God-damn watch! When I found that out, I could have killed him."

The man who was lying beside Winters lifted his head. "What are you guys beefing about?" he asked. His voice was mild and inquisitive. "What now?"

"Carl," Winters said soberly.

The newcomer began groaning with vast contempt. "Oh, my God, my God, get something new. Won't you ever wear it out? A whole year now, and I haven't heard anything but crabbing about Carl. Here in the old days you used to crab about everything, now all you do is crab about him. Jesus, show some imagination, get a new subject, give us a rest. Why don't you crab about Hagen here? He's behind it all, don't you know that? He's the guy that turned out the lights—he's in cahoots with the power company."

No one answered. The newcomer settled back again. "I get tired," he complained, "of the same old crap all the time."

Winters shifted away from him in annoyance. Someone from the crowd—the man who had asked Hagen what he was going to do—fumbled his way through the darkness and sat down beside the newcomer. "Hello, Jug!" He threw himself heavily on Jug while Jug was stretched out and snoring. Jug began screaming, "Oh! Oh! Oh! I'm boogered! I'm boogered!" and they began to thrash around on the pile of lumber. Winters could not hear what Hagen was saying, and after a moment he got down on the floor.

"I have to stay right here," Hagen was saying. "If I don't, he'll come back and say he had to spend half the night looking for me. He'll say it anyway. I don't give a damn, but I won't give him any excuse for it. Then look. He sent my kid up to tell Dwyer to watch the heat. What does he think Dwyer's here for? Dwyer's been watching them kilns four-five years now. He was watching the heat when Carl was still selling shoes. When he's asleep he knows more about the heat than Carl will ever know about anything. You think that makes any difference? Hell, Carl can't tell the difference when a man's doing his work and when he's going through the motions. If a man just sweats enough and runs around enough and blows off enough steam and get so God-damned rattled he don't know what he's going—then Carl thinks he's working."

Winters listened. How many of us now? He could name most of the voices, grading them roughly by their harshness: Sorenson and Prent Fisher and Bullett and Gil Ahab, the religious nut, the *Millions Now Living Will Never Die!* man. All over the factory and on the tideflat, some of them making some mild and general complaint and some of them furious as Hagen himself. He sat back silently, somewhat behind the others, his hand moving nervously over his face, peering through the darkness at one speaker after another. In how many groups are they talking like this? Hagen and Sorenson and Ahab—they hated Carl because he interfered with their work, because the factory could only run when they disregarded what he told them to do. But the rest of them hated him because he drove them, drove them endlessly and senselessly even when there was nothing to do—or most of all when there was nothing to do—drove them in a fever of activity to do something that would have to be done over again tomorrow, or drove them like mad on some insane job they would have to spend the rest of the week, at the same sweating pace, undoing. Oh, how bitterly they hated him! There were no words that could get down deep enough to say what they felt, and they fell back on savage monotonous curses, never describing him except in terms of filth, of excrement, as though his very name suggested only some nauseating mess.

I don't care, a voice said. *I can take anything. I've worked in some of the toughest jobs on this coast, and when I worked on the Milwaukee, putting it over the mountains, the section boss carried a gun and would rather shoot you than talk. I could stand it. But I won't work for a guy that's nuts.*

"You think Carl's crazy," Bullett said. "Hell, I'll tell you about a guy we used to have at Claiborne-Kelley out of Vancouver— what a nut! Oh, he was dizzy! He made Carl seem like a God-damned sage. But up he went. I remember I was working in the yard, and when I first went there he was nothing but a yard boss. Then they made him foreman of the graveyard. Jesus, he gave you the creeps. You'd look around, there the son of a bitch would be, peeking around a pile, grinning like a God-damned baboon. *Yowie!* What a guy! Finally son of a bitch went stark, raving mad. Same day they made him general superintendent." He paused for a proper effect. "There he was," Bullett ended solemnly, "right in the middle of the street, waving it at the girls."

For a time no one said anything. Winters glanced toward Bullett; he was afraid that the conversation would veer off Carl and get lost in a welter of miscellaneous reminiscences. "What of it?" he asked.

"What of it? Nothing! I'm just telling you, what do you guys expect—I'm just trying to show you Carl ain't as bad as some of them."

"He's bad enough."

"Sure he is. But what the hell of it? What are you going to do about it?" Then Bullett poured a little salt into the wounds. "You guys make me sick, all you do is beef about that poor little sucker. Why don't you get a new subject? Jesus, I'm sick of hearing about him."

"I'm sick of seeing him," Winters said.

"Christ, go down the road! Nobody's keeping you. You don't have to see him, this is a free country."

Winters suddenly tightened up inside. "You just been telling us they're worse everywhere else," he said bitterly. "Free for what—to break my neck for some son of a bitch like Carl?

No. We can get him out of here. Don't tell me we can't do it. Three hundred guys on this shift hate that sucker like poison. Why can't we get him out? What's to stop us?"

There was another silence, and the men stirred uncomfortably. Winters sat back and waited. His heart was pounding; he was afraid that now, because of the sense of discomfort that had settled over the men, the subject would be dropped, or the group would break up. But Bullett too backed down; he settled back with another loud groan of despair. "Jesus, you'd think *I* was keeping him here. I didn't hire him! When he first came here, I said somebody ought to drop one of them hundred-and-fifty-pound irons on his thick skull, but nobody backed me up—besides, it probably wouldn't have done any good, his head's so thick he wouldn't have felt it anyway."

Beside him Fisher spoke up with his whanging Southern voice. "You ought to do what we did with a fat old boy we had when I was working for the E. I. Pristley Sash and Door in St. Louis. We took that old boy out and we just beat the living Jesus out of him." As no one answered him, he turned to Bullett and began talking to him in a low voice.

"These guys make me sick," Bullett said wearily, "they crab their heads off, but they never do anything."

Presently Hagen said again, "I'll get that guy out of here. I'll get him out or I'll get out. I've taken enough off him. He gets in the road, he can't do a damn thing, he's got his finger up everything."

One of the old men said vaguely, "When he first came here, I remember there was some talk of getting up a petition. I don't know that anything ever came of it, but I remember there was a good deal of talk about it at the time. I never signed it; they never brought it around to me; but if they had brought it around, I'd have signed it."

Someone explained, "That was the shipping department. They were getting paid by the hour, and Carl put them on a straight weekly rate. They were working a lot of overtime—

it was when all that stuff was going to Australia. So they kicked. But it was just in the shipping department. Nothing came of it. The shipping clerk took their petition in the office and that girl in there—Miss Hazen—she put it away in a drawer. She said it would make MacMahon sore if he saw it."

"What happened?"

"Well, I don't know—they kicked about it, and a couple guys quit, and finally after that big Australia order was finished Carl came around. He said he heard they was beefing about not getting any overtime, so they'd put them back on straight time. But then there wasn't any more overtime, and pretty soon the poor bastards only worked three-four days a week for about six months. They were sore as hell for a while, and four-five guys quit—they got a whole green crew out there now."

"You can't go by the shipping department," Bullett said. "Those poor bastards are nuts. They're all nuts. They wouldn't be out there if they wasn't nuts."

They were interrupted. Three girls were feeling their way through the darkness to the ladies' toilet. They were holding hands and crying out in little suppressed giggles whenever they bumped against some substantial portion of the darkness. Winters could hear them breathing and hear the rustle of their clothing as they approached. One of them whispered, *Oh, kid, be careful!* and another replied, *What do you think I'm being?* They passed behind him so close that their overalls brushed against his back. Someone asked, "Where you going, girls?" and they laughed vaguely in reply. Winters could hear them as they found the pile of lumber and turned to pass by it. One of the girls suddenly screamed. The others stopped and after a moment screamed with her. Hagen switched on the flashlight. They stared at it blindly, their eyes widening in happy alarm as they backed against the whitewashed wall and huddled together.

The screams had reached the other end of the factory. Someone shouted, *"Let her up! Can't you see she's tired!"* Bullett and Fisher began laughing raucously, and Hagen switched off the flashlight.

The girls started on again. Winters heard one of them say, "What did he do? Did he do anything?"

"I put out my hand. . . ."

Bullett and Fisher were rolling around on the pile of lumber, laughing over something the rest of them could not hear. The girls went on, the little suppressed giggles and warning plaints and whispers marking their progress. Winters stirred restlessly; he had a sick feeling that something was lost, that some gain that had been made was threatened. They're breaking up, he thought, hearing some of them stirring and moving out toward the tideflat. For a moment he thought of giving up too, drawn by the cooler air and the quiet voices and no interruptions of outside. But then he remembered the way Hagen had turned on Carl, and the faked, hollow resolution when Carl said *I'm not pulling anybody's card!* and the way Carl had mumbled to himself, stumbling out of the factory, the way his own heart had suddenly lifted!

"Walk out," he said suddenly. "Who'll walk out?"

For a moment there was no answer. Someone who had started outside sat down again. He could feel the words going through them, the question sinking in, stopping them and holding them. He was nervous, and his nervousness surprised him, and he waited, his heart beating more rapidly, afraid that no one would answer or somebody would say, you're nuts, forget it.

"I'll walk out," Hagen said. "I won't work with that son of a bitch any longer."

Bullett said, "You can't make these wooden-heads walk out. You couldn't drive them out with a club."

He turned on Bullett. "Will you walk out?"

They waited.

"Me?" Bullett said.

"Yeah. Will you walk out?"

"For God's sake! Why not? But why chew the fat about it? They won't move. You couldn't blast them out. But why jump on me? If Carl ain't jumping on me one of you guys jumps on me.

"Jesus," Bullett said, after a moment, "I get sick of it."

"They're picking on you, Jug," Prentiss Fisher said. "That's all they're doing."

"You mush-mouthed bastard," Bullett said. Fisher suddenly yelled and began thrashing around in the dark, *Oh he's got me by the!* . . . . They began wrestling again. When they stopped Bullett said with an air of surprise, "You know this son of a gun ain't got good sense. He can't talk English. He says *whop.* '*Ef I fight ye,*' he says, '*All sure's hell whop ye.*'"

"I'll walk out," somebody said. "Any time you're ready."

"I'll walk out."

"They're talking strike at the Superior. They got a fifteen per cent cut."

"I'll walk out."

Somebody said in excitement, "I'll walk out! To hell with them!"

Hagen got up suddenly and walked toward the head end of the mill. The light went on. Somebody was calling him. He called out *What?* and turned back to the men, "Shut up you guys."

Prentiss Fisher said, "They coming back on?"

Bullett said, "Leave them off, Hagen! Give us a rest!"

"*Shut up!*" Hagen said again.

Someone was calling him.

Bring it here! Bring us the light! Sharp, a panic voice.

Hagen started off toward the head end of the mill. There was a rustle of movement in the group lined up against the wall and pile of lumber. Most of the men stood up. Winters walked over to see where Hagen was going. Sorenson and one of the sawyers followed him. Hagen was already hurrying down the corridor. The light sent back wavering reflections as he passed behind the machines; the shadows washed backwards, enlarged, dissolved into the darkness. Sorenson said, "What is it?" noncommittally, not expecting to be answered. Then Winters could hear the questions spreading out, *What happened? What happened?* the waves of questions spreading out as ripples spread when a rock is dropped into a pool. He started out after Hagen. The two men beside him hesitated a moment before they followed him. The light was already a long way ahead, and they could barely see the larger obstructions in their path. This part of the mill was unused. Some of the worn-out machines were stored there, and the floor was covered with small chunks of bark and the fine, powdered sawdust that was not drained off by the fans. The discarded machines were stored against the wall, gradually being pulled apart as one piece after another was used for replacing broken parts of the machines that were running. At the entrance of the storeroom there were barrels of oil mounted on racks, and bulging sacks of waste looming up, transformed and unreal. As Hagen hurried on, the light leaped from the floor to the empty darkness ahead and then dropped swiftly back to the floor again. One of the men stumbled on a pile of discarded chains and sprockets that littered the corridor. Winters heard him stumble and heard him draw his breath sharply. "Damn," he said. "God-damn thing."

Some distance ahead of them Hagen met someone. The light touched him for a moment. "Jesus Christ!" a voice said. "Didn't you hear me!" There was a moment of talk before they both hurried on.

Sorenson said, "Somebody's hurt."

"How you know?"

"I can tell," Sorenson said. He was panting along beside Winters. The sawyer was following them. "Why don't they clean up this place?" the sawyer said. "God, I broke my leg."

The log deck opened out on a platform over the line of vats; the floor of the platform was almost on a level with the roof of the vats. Between the vats and the platform there was a canyon, twenty feet wide and ten feet deep, the track at the bottom of it. The logs were taken from the vats to the track and then hoisted to the platform. Hagen and his companion had already climbed down to the track when Winters reached the platform. The light from his flashlight streamed up over the platform; Winters could see the steam escaping around the doors of the vats and rising slowly from the log. When he looked over the edge of the platform he could see nothing at first, nothing but the scattered rays of light and the shadowy bulk of the log. Off at one side, leaning against the door of the nearest vat, a man was holding a torch, trying to get the dim flame started by holding the wood down and letting the flame lick up the side of the wood. Hagen had crawled under the factory, directing the flashlight into the darkness under the log.

While Winters looked over the edge of the platform, Sorenson swung over the side and dropped down one of the posts. The sawyer asked senselessly, "Who's hurt? Who's hurt?" Winters shook his head and walked away. A sudden sickness and weakness almost paralyzed him. The log looked swollen and distended in the dim light; he could feel the heat of it when he leaned over the platform. For a moment he walked around blindly, all his senses tightening with revulsion. The sawyer too crawled over the side of the platform. For a time he held his head and shoulders above the floor, his weight resting on his elbows, his feet scraping for some support on the post. Winters glanced over the edge again. He did not know this end of the factory and he was trembling too violently to trust himself to drop over the edge. He walked back and forth across the platform, looking for a way down. Hagen moved the light a little, and Winters could see the supports that branched up from the posts. He let himself down slowly, his foot clamping and twisting in the crotch where the brace was fastened to the post, his hands scraping over the splinters in the floor. Then he crawled down the post, wrapping his legs and arms around it.

The man who was holding the torch suddenly dropped it and stamped on the flame. "It's no good," he said, almost apologetically. He ground the wood into the damp pulpy earth between the tracks. "It won't burn."

"Who is it?" Winters asked.

"The hoist man."

They looked at each other nervously. The man stamped again on the torch. "Log rolled," he said. His voice was hard, almost self-consciously calm. "It was about half up when the power went off. So it stayed there with all the pull on it sideways and finally it gave way and swung. While he was waiting." Winters nodded. He tried to remember who the hoist man was, or what he did, but he did not know him. He looked at the steamy bulk of the log. It was resting on the track and against the pilings that made up the foundation of the factory. The curve of the log was now a tunnel of light as Hagen was under the factory. The men were crowded around each end of the tunnel; it was impossible to get nearer.

Winters asked, "What can you do?"

"Nothing. We called the hospital. Broke in the office."

Winters could see other men wandering around helplessly in the canyon between the vats and the platform. It was quiet except for the muffled voices and heavy breathing of the men around the log. There was a steady hiss of steam escaping from the closed vats; an occasional rattle as the steam pipes trembled under the pressure. The man standing beside Winters suddenly said *Ah, poor bastard!* in a racked voice, *Ah, poor bastard!*

Winters ran his hand nervously over his face. The bark splinters from the floor of the platform had stayed in his hands; he felt them on his cheek with a kind of dazed awakening; he felt the dirt stay on his face and forehead. Unconsciously he walked to the log, standing on its dark side and listening to the muffled voices beneath the factory, the words tense and indistinguishable, broken by the heavy panting as the men worked in the cramped space beneath the factory. Someone had made a foolish attempt to free the log by tearing up part of the track. A peavey was stuck in one of the ties. Winters pulled it free and carried it out of the way with a kind of senseless, mechanical orderliness; he leaned it carefully against the door of one of the vats, thrusting it deep into the earth to hold it upright.

When he walked back there was a stir among the men grouped around the log. Someone crawled backwards from under the factory. As they broke away Winters got a glimpse into the narrow tunnel of light; he could see Hagen's face, red and sweaty, turned sideways in the narrow cramped space; he saw the hoist man lying on his side, his shoulder jammed up high against his cheek, almost over it. "*Hagen!*" someone said. "*You're too big! Let me under there!*"

Hagen crawled out awkwardly, his shoulders forced into a knot as he pushed himself free. He put his weight on the flashlight clasped in his hand, and it dug into the mud; the steam and the water draining from the log had soaked the ground. He held it up stiffly, shifting his weight to his other hand. "*Take it!*" he said. Then he crawled out, breaking free of the men clustered around the log. Someone else dove under the factory with the flashlight. Hagen grabbed one of the men by the arm. "*There's a pair of jacks in the fireroom. Take somebody with you.*"

The two men started off down the track. Winters had crowded up to Hagen again, and Hagen saw him. "*Winters,*" Hagen said, "*get Carl's light. He's in the office.*"

Winters climbed back up on the platform, suddenly released from the sense of helplessness that had paralyzed and sickened him; he felt his hands hard and firm on the post; he was conscious of his strength as he lifted himself up on the platform. He could hear them talking behind him as he felt his way swiftly along the wall. *"Get some blocks for the jack,"* Hagen was saying. *"Anything. Anything."* Then as he left them behind even the weak reflected light of the flashlight was lost, and he stumbled along with his hand touching the wall to guide him, lifting his feet high to clear the barriers in his path. He remembered the man holding the weak torch, standing by helpless and harassed, the flame barely creeping up the grimy wood —*Ah, poor bastard,* he thought, *poor bastard,* and broke into a run.

5. Variations on a Baedecker

STANLEY BURNSHAW

A native New Yorker, Stanley Burnshaw (1906–   ) had graduated from the University of Pittsburgh, taken a master's degree at Cornell, and involved himself in contemporary poetic movements by the time the depression broke. Although he made no bones about identifying himself with the far Left— he contributed frequently to the New Masses *and was associated with the Communist-front cultural organizations—the depth of his poetic commitment and the breadth of his intellectual concerns precluded any possibility of his being left high and dry when revolutionary fervor had subsided. He went on after* The Iron Land *to publish distinguished fiction, verse drama, and poetry, including* Early and Late Testament *and* Caged in an Animal's Mind. *His international anthology,* The Poem Itself, *has won particular acclaim for its originality and usefulness. He was for many years president and editor-in-chief of Dryden Press, and is now associated with Holt, Rinehart &*

From *The Iron Land* (Philadelphia: 1936), pp. 81–83. Copyright 1936 by Stanley Burnshaw. Reprinted by permission of the author.

*Winston. It may be of use to quote from Mr. Burnshaw's own
note "To the Reader," which prefaced* The Iron Land *in 1936:*
"The Iron Land *tells a story of a contemporary steel mill seen
with the eyes of a young middle-class white-collar employee. It
records his personal growth through workaday experiences . . .
as well as through personal doubts, deliberations, escapes . . .
into a new-world directive."*

Five-past-six of a November dawn.
Penance for reaching Liberty too late:
I ride the tramcars dreaded by all workers,
The chill grey cars that move
Like roving ghosteyes through the black mill-towns.

Past the hard mile of sheds,
Alongside miles of freightyards, steadily
We travel while the heavy morning mist
Layered with the dust of coalsmoke, swims inside
Through broken windows of the shabby car—
Now all empty save for a few faces
Of other workers late on their way, like me,
Staring out of the dirt-streaked windows, wondering
If this before our eyes
Can be a place or some crazed mourner's phantom.

Flanking the freightyards: alleys, wooden shacks,
And hovels: a grim battalion
Of crouching rats covered down by the waters
Of fog that trickles down their slimy backs.
Near these: the blackened sheds
Of foundries, smelting furnaces,
And forges flanking the grey backs of the river
That stares so blankly this November morning.

We cross the bridge from Waterside then wind
Slowly through Clarksburg's ragged streets and alleys

Where sleek black chimneys leap
To spew their floods of orange smoke up, up
Into the low grey sky . . . showering the river
With sooty grime and slag . . . mixing new poisons
With those from other mills,
That change this stream into a torturing temptress
For children leaning from banks in blazing summer,
Longing for cool, green waves.

We wind through musty alleys and broken streets
Where freighters clatter by all night, all day,
Where lumps of children gaze from the steps of hovels
In a dead stare they learned from watching freightcars
Roll by before their eyeballs all year long.

Threading the streets at intervals a handful
Of whole or crippled children dressed in rags,
Playing together in greyness,
While some of their mothers labor in the hovels
With the new child to come—one more body
To keep from playing near the rails—or shiver
With wondering if the workwhistle
Will send her a man half-mangled or once more
A strong mate roaring for his evening meal.

Along another street: A Hun, his wife,
And children staring blankly at the roads,
Asking if they should turn to some other mill-town
Where he might pick up work enough to keep
His brood from starving through the nearing winter.

Hearses along some streets, taking the bodies
Of men who failed, who were not cunning enough
To dodge the swift wheels in the sheds; and the widow

And fatherless children wailing now inside,
Stunned in the grey, long morning.

And as we clank by I remember how once
On a hill across the river
A poet-teacher and his poet-pupil
Stood gazing down on Clarksburg through the fog;

Thinking they saw this phantom-land, and dreaming
What things they could not see . . . But as I stare
Among these streets, I know
That all their vision and their farthest dreaming
Could never tell them of the heart I see:
The blood's unvoiced rebellion brooding under
This sorrow, this despair . . .

PART TWO

Farmers; Sharecroppers, Tenants, Migrants:

IOWA, NEW JERSEY, OKLAHOMA, ARKANSAS,
ALABAMA, GEORGIA, MISSISSIPPI

6. The Executioner Waits *and* Rope of Gold

JOSEPHINE HERBST

Of all the imaginative and rebellious writers of the depression decade, Josephine Herbst (1897–   ) has been perhaps the most seriously underestimated and surely the most actively adventurous. Like a legendary reporter, she had the knack of being in the significant place at the crucial moment, and of being on a footing of comradely equality with many of the most important figures of the day. With the exception of John Dos Passos, no other writer at work in the thirties had even attempted a fictional reconstruction of American life as sweeping and ambitious as Josephine Herbst's trilogy, Pity Is Not

Enough, The Executioner Waits, *and* Rope of Gold. *Drawing on her family background and her own tumultuous life, Miss Herbst undertook a portrait of the decline of an American family from the Civil War down through the 1930's, intercut with vignettes of farmers and workers during the depression, of which those that follow are typical. She herself had worked her way through the University of Iowa and the University of California, after which she went abroad with only a few hundred dollars and remained there for some years. She lived the life of the expatriate in Paris, along with Hemingway and all the others, visited the Soviet Union, lived in Nazi Germany shortly after Hitler took power, was in Spain in 1937 with the Loyalists, spent a year in Mexico, sailed a ketch down the Maine coast, fished in Key West, sat with farmer pickets on the roads of Iowa, sent back exclusive dispatches from the mountain hideouts of Cuban strikers. It is no wonder that the publication of her memoirs, on which she has been at work for some years, is eagerly awaited.*

The Executioner Waits

Bunker Hill, U. S. Route 20. 1932

The old man stirring the ground with a stick was the first to lift his head. "There she comes," he said. Six of the big fellows got up slowly from the earth and taking hold of their sticks moved toward the road. The one man left behind put another chunk on the fire and shivering held out his hands. It was cold in the cut the way it gets sometimes at the full of the moon with one of those clean blue skies that are as blue at night as in the day. The tall corn growing almost up to the road made a good windbreak for the fire. The flames were steady. The big guys stood ready by the road swinging their sticks gently as the whine of a motor coming up grade hummed through the cut.

"That ain't no truck," said the man by the fire. It sounded to him smaller than a truck, a car maybe, but coming up it had an ominous get-ready noise like during the war when a shell was about to crash. He couldn't get out of the habit of cowering inside at that kind of a noise. "It ain't a truck, I tell you." A big car nosed through the cut, slid gently down hill toward the boys. The old farmer backed up and was first to sit down again by the fire.

The car slid down by them, passed and stopped. The men by the fire squatted and paid no attention. As someone came toward them, the old fellow turned, said softly, "Oh it's *Him*."

He came toward them humbly, with the crawling timidity of a yellow bitch dog who knows the feel of a stone.

"Hello boys," He said, making his voice loud and jovial.

"Hello," said two of the boys.

"How're things going, boys," says He.

"First rate," says the old man, scowling.

"Now listen boys," He says, edging toward them and beginning to talk fast. "You can take me out in them fields and beat me up with a rock, by jesus, if you can't, if you think I had anything to do with the other night. Listen boys, I'm regular, not special. Those deputies that was out here slugging around didn't know you boys. Why I'm with you, heart's blood. You know that, don't you, boys?"

"Why don't you throw that badge you got hid under your lapel in the fire if you're with us," says the old man.

"Now boys, you know me, listen I'm here tonight with my old man. He's back there in the car, I had to bring him he's so lonesome. You know what tonight is? Why I lost my mother just a year ago, this very night, and I've got my old father, he's seventy-six year old, back there in the car. You'll lose your fight boys, but I'm with you, heart's blood."

"How'd you know we'll lose," said one of the boys getting up to his six feet and looking down at the little whiffet. The deputy backed a little uneasily and said, "Of course you'll lose, you know that. You got everything against you. You can't go shutting off food from the babies like you're doing. The whole outfit in town's against you, you're choking off trade too. Why they're not routing cars to the Black Hills anymore through Oxtail, all on account of you fellows. You can't win, boys, but I'm with you and I don't want no hard feelings, I just want to explain. That's why I came out here." He leaned down peering into the faces of the sitters with his own foolish flushed conciliatory face.

"If you weren't with them the other night, why didn't you tip us off instead of letting them slide in here by surprise?"

"Now boys, I didn't know a word about it, honest to god I didn't. You can ask my old father, he'll tell you. I was eating supper with him that night and afterwards him and me took in a movie. That's because he's so lonesome, he can tell you. We lost my mother just a year ago tonight. You boys got this thing by the wrong leg. Keep the farmers off the road, then you'll not have any trouble."

"No," said the old man. "I expect not. The packing house will get our nice hogs that costs us money to haul in to them, the Rogers Brothers will get our good milk to distribute and fatten up on, sure we get you."

"Boys, they'll hook you for every hook in the road if you talk like that, I'm warning you, I'm your friend."

"Say, they've hooked us already. And we've got too many friends like you," said the shivery man. "The woods is so full we can't see the trees. Get me, we're helping ourselves. Would we be here if our backs weren't to the wall? You belong with the Chamber of Commerce outfit, go back and tell them to mind their business and not go sneaking to the governor asking for gunmen and we'll mind ours."

"Boys," He said in a weepy voice. "There's plenty sons of bitches trying to do you dirt, I'll say that, but I ain't one. I'm with you and I had nothing to do with that dirty raid the other night. I swear to god, I'm with you. Well, I got to take my poor

old man home, but I'll see you soon, maybe bring you a dish
of oatmeal in the morning." He laughed nervously, plucking at
a string of hair that dangled little boy fashion over his nose.
"I'll help any way I can boys, don't forget I warned you. So
long," He got in his car, started her and turned, the car went
up the hill, whimpered through the cut.

"He's tanked up," said the old man, "and guilty as hell. He
pushed the whole bunch of deputies on us, I know by the
green look he's got, can't look you in the eyes. Say, he's scared
we'll beat him up. And let me tell you, we can do it. They ain't
the only ones who can get guns either. That corn ain't growing
tall for nothing. If we can hide there, we can shoot there, I say.
It's been done before."

At the word shoot, the shivery guy held out his hands to the
fire. A log fell and sparks spit out and the men drew closer
around it. They sat there talking quietly, wondering if the other
roads to town were being guarded too or had they double-
crossed the boys by telling them it was all up, picketing was
over.

The town of Oxtail, Iowa, lay on the other side of the cut,
hid by the yellow hills. A glare in even that white moonlit sky
showed where it was, drawing the roads to it, sucking the
country in.

"The damn old spider," said the old man, his eyes on the
glare. "We fed it long enough."

"I heard big news tonight, forgot to tell you," said one of the
boys. "One of the Meyer Brothers shot himself, I think it was
Henry. He shot himself because that business is cracking up so
fast that if they don't get some insurance it's all over. The other
four brothers will get the insurance for the business. That's
what they say."

"Is that right? Are they going downhill that fast?"

"Sure, they're on the toboggan, they are all on the slide and
they want us to plug it up with hog meat, that's the way I see
it."

They stirred their sticks softly in the soft dust, and now and then town noises sounded far off and faint. The town had swelled during the up-and-up years. It had swallowed little farms, turned country into swanky additions and golf courses for the town boys. Now it was strangling on its own cud, it lay there like a sick cow, choked with what it had eaten, its life drained to the eastern seaboard, its substance sold out and its citizens, frantic, passing the buck to the farmers. "Look at you, what you're doing, bringing us more bad times, keeping away our trade."

Oxtail lay, as always, between the Big Sioux and the Missouri. Ruin had fallen upon it. The white lights on the downtown streets had given way to the cheaper red neon. A rocking chair contest went on in a Pierce Street café. Rock, rock, rocking in your rocking chair. The Meyer Brothers, now four, solemnly stood by the bier of their brother in the funeral parlor. His insurance was large enough to stop a gap but not enough to dam a river.

They remembered the pushcart days and how Henry had been the boldest of them all. Now they were floor-walkers in their own mongrel store, the shoes sold out to Minno of New York, the women's wear to Baumfeld. The mortician hovered anxiously near the brothers. He felt he had done a fine job and he was upset not to be congratulated on his work of art. The corpse lay in a natural way with hands crossed upon its breast and a faint red color painted on the stiff gray cheeks.

This was no time for the Meyer boys to be so snotty. They ought to give credit where credit is due, especially considering a bullet always makes a nasty job for any man, even a skillful mortician like himself.

Iowa Farm 1932

"Now boys, take it easy. We don't need guns but guts."
"Got plenty of them, Charley."

"We meet tomorrow at six at Jake's place. Detour in a body to Oberholzer's farm and stand by. The bank or the insurance company will have a bidder but if you bring along a rope, Sam, and sort of dangle it inconspicuous, maybe he'll take the hint. No bids over a dollar. We don't want to lay out cash. It only goes back to the bank boys, and they chewed us up long enough. They're laughin' up their sleeves at us, we're such nice easy marks."

"They got Mellon and Mellon is president. You thought you voted last time for Hoover, but no boys, it was Andy Mellon. He sees that his pal Charley Dawes doesn't get into trouble. Hands out eightymillion for poor downtrodden Charley. But we can't get two cents for hogs. Corn ain't worth taking in. I says, I says I'll feed the corn to the hogs and see how big a hog can grow. Got one nearly 700 pound now but what for should I take it to the packing house? To feed them packing house kings? No, sir. I'll feed my stock and eat my own victuals. Let the rats eat the corn. I got my electricity turned off, no phone.

"But boys, this is the breadbasket of the world. We're living right in it. Folks can get along without neckties, they can do without hats. It's not so hard to let your hair grow if you need a cover. But by god, you can't do without food. We're feeding them bankers and politicians and what are they doing to us? They got us lined up against the wall. They got the wooden shoes all laid out ready for our feet. Boys, they don't care if we lose our homes or if our kids can't go to school. If things don't go right with them, they take a bank holiday and we pay for it. They let our savings be gobbled up and we ain't got no kick. It's the law. The law's all for them, boys. We get the promises. For twelve years they ain't kept one promise they made us. I'll eat a bale of hay for every promise they kept.

"The mayor of Oxtail is a double crosser. Take a delegation there and he'll smile and rub his hands and say ain't it a pity but they're doing all they can. But what goes on behind our backs? What?" He paused and glowered at the mob of farmers who stood solid as if they had been planted and grown there. Nobody spoke.

"He skedaddles off to the governor, him and the big guns, and they ask for outside militia. He knows he can't get our local boys to shoot you down boys. They won't do it. They know what it is we're up against. Then he gets a promise and he comes back and scares our leaders off. 'Boys, you don't want no bloodshed, do you boys.' He tries to make out as if the pickets was paid. PAID. Ain't that good boys, paid. Why if we had a nickel we'd pay ourselves. We don't need no agitators he's talking about. We're all agitators ourselves. We're agitating for our rights and our freedom boys, and tomorrow is a showdown. We ain't got the *Daily News* back of us no more, the mayor scared off that fellow too, said he wouldn't get no more advertising. But boys, we got our own two hands. They ain't licked us. We'll show them it's tough to swallow an elephant. Now boys tomorrow when some slicker wearing good clothes while you and me can't buy overalls steps up pretty as you please to say his piece, stand together. Shake the rope, Sam. And now for the vote, just to be regular." He grinned turning his big head slowly, his legs stiff in the old overalls, his lean hand rubbing his unshaved cheek. His eye roams around, back of the mob of overalled men to the barns, the full corn crib, the dilapidated machinery, the rich fertile fields that have pitched him into poverty; he counts the hands, raised high up at the end of stiff blue jacketed arms, all hard-working hands whose industry has brought them only trouble.

"That's right, boys," he says, in a quiet voice. "I make it unanimous."

Summer in Many States 1934

The government expert was trying to explain. "Now you farmers are just nervous. There's no use in looking so far ahead. A step at a time. We're getting relief in here fast as we can."

"You're not paying us relief," said a farmer. "You're paying the banks relief."

"I don't understand you," said the expert, smiling nervously and looking at his assistant, a young man who was hoping to get through with these people so he could get on to see his girl. "You're getting two dollars for your sheep and goat skins."

"I get you," said the farmer rising and presenting one of those bull necked fronts so antagonizing to a well-meaning expert. "The government pays us two dollars for a skin. We got to sell because the drought kills the sheep and goats. They got no feed. First you told us we had too much. Now we ain't got any. So we have to kill. Who gets the two dollars? Is it us that took care of the flocks? Right off the bat the banker gets a dollar that we never even see. Then on that other dollar, we don't get more than thirty cents because by the time we skin them and take them to a point of shipment, it costs plenty. So when this feller Richberg tells how he puts two billion up for us farmers, he's talking through his hat. He's handing over one billion to his buddies, the bankers, first of all. Then we get about thirty cents, see."

"Well we can't go into that," said the expert uncomfortably, looking frantically for a friendly face. "But if you have any suggestions of any better plan, I'll be glad to hear them. As for debts, I'd be glad to get rid of mine that easily." He tried to chuckle, gave a halfhearted imitation and stuffed his watch in and out of his pocket, his eyes shifty beyond the door to the hot land. He'd got hold of a tough set of farmers this time and no mistake. He began to see why the small-town storekeepers were afraid of them.

When he was whirling off in his car to the next point, he continued to feel the cold arrows of that farmer's speech. He felt as if they were at his heels, with their cold determined eyes. The worst of it was, they were right. He groaned within himself, wishing he had never taken any courses in sociology and had stuck at something simple, easy to understand, if there was such a thing nowadays. The bleak horrified countryside turned up its stiff bones of dead grass, crucified corn and wheat beaten savagely to earth by heat. His very flesh crawled and he longed for fresh green country to the east. This landscape was swept bare as a stage and maybe the small-town store-keepers were right. The farmers would refuse to starve, they would come in droves, they would pick the cans from the shelves, they would fill their old cars with flour and tins. They would be at each other's throats, storekeeper and poor farmer and now another cog had been found to throw into the machinery, the poor farm hand, his threat to the farmer with his strikes won on big farms for higher wages. The trick was to keep them apart, to keep them fighting, let dog eat dog.

The poor fellow, still human, groaned but he could see an implication when it stuck out like a sign post. My God, if they ever realized they were in the same boat, if they ever quit tearing at each other's throats, if the little storekeeper ever got it into his head that his friend, his only friend was the poor farmer, not the rich banker, where in hell would the system be then? I ask you, where would it be then, and where in hell would his job be too? So let the feuds brew and the nightriders ride, let them go to it.

Oxtail 1934

"You'll have to get someone over here quick Mr. Purdy," said old Miss Peck into the mouthpiece, her hands trembling so that her words came over the wire in gasps and splutters. "Hoodlums are at the very door. By the million." She listened to the strong male voice over the wire and dropped the receiver as a brick crashed through the window. Oh they would kill her. She'd die and never get a chance to scrub Papa's tombstone as she did every Decoration Day for years on end. Something was tied to the brick. She crawled from behind the filing cabinet and reached out a hand. Mercy, suppose she couldn't get away. Whatever would they do to her? Stories of Huns and barbarian hordes swept terrifyingly, refreshingly through her parched mind.

Lord help me, she prayed as she tried to read. The words shivered. Demand. They were demanding again. Always demanding. Never a pretty please. No manners. Demand. Demand. Poor people should take what they can get and be grateful. Why should they have cash? They no doubt spent it on drink. All poor people drank or wanted to. They guzzled it away. Well they could shout and howl all they wanted so long as that door at the foot of the stairs held. Maybe Mr. Purdy would get here. Or she might try getting out the back way. Shouts came from that entrance also. What if those beans were mouldy? What did they want for nothing. Don't tell her. She'd suffered. She'd walked the streets more than a year looking for work until she was in tatters. But she guessed she knew what side her bread was buttered on and had sense enough to be grateful when a job was made for her.

The whole town was suffering. Nice people, educated people with sensitive feelings were suffering. Why poor Mr. Brackwood had lost his business. He had shut up his fine big home. Folks said his creamery was run from New York now and he was only manager. Think what a comedown and how painful. She sighed at the pain of poor Mr. Brackwood and tried to keep calm. A boy stood on the burning deck eating peanuts by the peck. Oh why couldn't she think of some fine strong quotation. Not even the Bible. The verses all slipped from her like water tumbling down the hill. They were coming up the stairs. Oh oh. They were big noisy louts and dear knows where they would stop. The phone rang and she edged toward it. "Yes, Mr. Purdy. Yes." She heard the command of her master's voice and it was do or die. The books out of the safe, the money; now for the fire escape. How thoughtful of dear Mr. Purdy to have a car waiting at the foot of the fire escape. Maybe the police were handling the crowds from below. It had become quiet for a minute. The buzz of voices, feet, shouts, kicks, seemed to have been suspended. But only for a second. *One—two—three. Ready* someone was ordering and *All together now*—and yes the very door was quaking and bulging and Miss Peck ran, scuttling down the fire escape oh shocking, terrible if a Man should be below and look up when her arms were full and she couldn't hold her skirts. No, she was down, safely, so nice of Mr. Purdy, she smiled, as from above a great crash like the side of a house falling made the man at the wheel step on the gas and nearly shoot through the brick wall. So nice, murmured Miss Peck but she could hardly wait to get inside her own little house, to lock the door, to stand panting, gazing with tears at the dear goldfish that she had thought for a minute, yes really, never to see again. She wiped her eyes and called up dear Mabel. "Oh you'll never guess. Yes, just hoodlums. They're mad because the food wasn't A 1. Why should it be? But Mabel the real thing they're sore about is that last night you-know-who took that fellow out of jail and beat him up and dumped him across the river in Dakota. He was the ringleader and we think came from Minneapolis. Our town wouldn't grow his kind, Mabel. Yes sir, and if the farmers would keep their noses out of what isn't their business, things would be all right, but they brought that fellow back to town, I say they brought him back and dear knows who all is outside my office. Mabel, it was just like the war. I tell you I never heard such a racket. I never seen the like. I thought I'd die, Mabel, I thought I'd die.

In Many States 1934

Every Christian ought to observe Rogation Days, since such observance helps to increase the sense of dependence on God. I wish everybody could be in Spain on a Rogation Day and be fascinated by the charm and the beauty and the poetry of the processions that go out from the little villages. Writers with a good deal of truth call attention to the monotony and drudgery of American farm life. I am sure the festivities of what in Eng-

land they call "gang days"—the processions into the fields—
would do a great deal to relieve some of this and would add
the picturesque, certainly the needed element in the farmer's
life.

"Turn that damned thing off, turn it off," and the little boy
scraping his bare toes along the floor turned off the radio, the
only thing that was any fun any more. "Turn it off, I say," and
he looked up frightened at his father, rubbing his hand in his
eye. "I turned it off," he said. "What's the matter here?" The
mother frowned at the father. He was trembling all over,
putting his trembling hands into his overall pockets. "I told him
to turn it off, if I hear another crack out of that thing," he
raised his hand as if to strike.

"Now shush, it ain't so bad. Why there's been a big black
cloud back of the barn all morning. It's apt to rain any minute.
I was out sniffing the air, and it doesn't smell so dusty. Seems
kind of clear and fresh."

"I tell you if rains don't come tomorrow, I'll shoot them
cows," said the husband, glaring at his wife.

"Oh come now, it'll rain maybe. Don't let's talk of it. I got a
nice pie I'm making."

"I don't know whatever of," he said.

"Well I ain't decided yet. But I remember my mother telling
about pies she made on the Dakota prairies. Out of any old
thing. A molasses pie is the tastiest pie I ever saw but I ain't
got no more. A brown sugar pie is nice. If I had dried apples
even I could make a wonderful pie."

"Once we had strawberry pie," said the boy.

"You remember that pie? I'll make you another, don't cry,
I'll make another someday." They had moved out to the back
door, slowly inevitably as if pulled by magnets. The great cop-
perish fields were pulling them, they were lying bald and angry
with tufts of sour dust whirling in spikes of revengeful horns. A
long painful moo weak and blasted made an echo that sounded
like a horn blown a long way off. The three listened to it, look-

ing around a little wildly but there was nowhere they could go to escape that cry. The wind would carry it straight to them on any part of the farm. The wind was blowing off the fine top soil, it had blown away the seeds, blighted with wrath all the turnips and garden greens. When it got through with the soil, it would begin with them, and no one would prevent it. It was helping the powers that be. It was destroying crops, animals, life.

"You put that radio on again and by god," but the father did not mean to strike his boy. His hand just fell to his side. The kid looked up sniffling a little. The bare foot of the boy touched the bare foot of the father. The father turned and started to smile. He'd worked that land and plowed it and tended it like a baby. Now it was being scorched in an oven. The crops were frying like eggs. All over the west the pebbles were hot as baking stones. You could cook in the naked grass. The birds were deserting. They were deserting in clouds to make room for the grasshoppers.

"Don't you worry," says the missus, "I'm going to make you a pie, I don't know out of what but out of something."

"You're damned right I ain't worrying. This land will raise us a crop or we'll know the reason why. We ain't going to starve. I'll guarantee you that. There's money in this country, we been sending it east out of the west for a long time. Let them bring out the food, if they got so damned much of it. They got so much they didn't want what we could make. Don't bother, they says, we got enough. Plow it up. Kill them pigs. We got too much food in the world. All right bring on your too much, is what I say. Let them fill our bread basket, as they seem to have so much in their own."

"I'll make you a pie with tomatoes in it," she said. "They ain't all gone yet."

"Let them bring it on," he says, savagely. The sky was brightening. Over all those states it brightened. Then clouds

came. There was no rain. There was wind and it smelled sometimes like the desert.

Rope of Gold

Midsummer Night's Dream: Vineland, New Jersey, 1935

*It's raining. Bring them mules in. Don't let no man fall on
them mules. Men, get shovels and dig trenches. Can't work in
the row on a rainy day but keep yourselves busy. No standing
around here, you lazy hunks. Get shovels, keep moving.*

*The lean long boy sticks in the shovel. In she go, out she
come, in she go, out she come, shubbel, shubbel, keep movin.
Now they're cutting a trench around the mule sheds. Don't let
no water drop on me, boys, I a first rate mule, got to keep my
feet dry. Shubbel, shubbel, keep movin. There's the dump.
Can't set fire to no dump today. All them good things throwed
away. Them peaches ain't half rotted. We could make us a fine
mess out of them string beans. That there asparagus, yum, yum.*

Shubbel, shubbel, keep movin.

*Look at that peach. See that tomato. Ain't more than
specked. Market was low, food must go. Shubbel, shubbel, keep
movin. Hey, don't tech that peach, you might eat the stone.
Member the kid who snitched the fruit off the dump. Thought
he was smart, thought he wouldn't have to heat no old beans in
no old tincan that day. Out he goes. Forward march. Down
that road. Don't want no thieves here. Hands off garbage.
Hands off food. Hands is to work with. Shubbel, shubbel, keep
movin.*

*Too tired to feel the rain. Too tired. Lay yourself down pore
boy 'fore the bugs begin their pickin. 'Fore the mosquitoes get
to itchin. Lay your bones down. Night's for you. Sweet dreams
for you. The rain leaks through. Tat, tat, on skin, a warm soft*

*spot, then a cold spot, turning, twisting, can't get rid of that
there spot, it's a burnin. Don't you light no lamp, pet, the dark
is kinder. Member old man Beaseley that cooked in his hut.
Smoked hisself a cigarette layin on the straw. Went a snorin
and straw was burnin. Up goes Beaseley in a bright red
flame.*

Boy, ain't you heard the boys call your name?

*Oh, oh, that smell, that man smell burnin. Shubbel, shubbel,
dig a big grave.*

But not for the boys that's a diggin in the rain.

Boy, don't you hear the boys say it again?

*Sleep, sleep, the cradle rocks, soon it's five and you'll have to
get up. Beans, peas, asparagus, and cucumbers. The garden
spot. The wondermaking garden. Shubbel, shubbel, keep
movin.*

7. The Grapes of Wrath

JOHN STEINBECK

*Only those who were on the scene at the time can fully under-
stand the impact that this book made upon a public hungering for good news about the oppressed and the exploited. For
hundreds of thousands of Americans,* The Grapes of Wrath,
*with its rough and coarse but essentially kindly and courageous
migrants, descendants of the men and women who built America, and themselves the last pioneers, seemed to sum up the
tragic but enriching experience of the entire decade. In its*

From *The Grapes of Wrath* (New York: The Viking Press, 1939),
Chap. V, pp. 26–33. Copyright 1939 by John Steinbeck. Reprinted by
permission of The Viking Press, Inc.

*monumentality (the vicissitudes of the Joad family are inter-
rupted from time to time with chapters, like the one that follows, on the social implications of the collapse of midwest agri-
culture) and its "scientific" veneer (the author had studied
marine biology at Stanford after growing up around Salinas),
it accorded with the American desire for an account of their
experience that would be both rational and optimistic, both
radical and affirmative. It is easy for us now to see that, despite
his Nobel Prize, the art of John Steinbeck (1902–   ) has
been irremediably flawed by sentimentality and oversimplifica-
tion of character. But it is important for us to understand the
magnetic power of the writer who could exclaim, in his grand-
est book:*

The decay spreads over the State, and the sweet smell is a great
sorrow on the land. Men who can graft the trees and make the seed
fertile and big can find no way to let the hungry people eat their
produce. Men who have created new fruits in the world cannot
create a system whereby their fruits may be eaten. And the failure
hangs over the State like a great sorrow. . . .

The people come with nets to fish for potatoes in the river, and
the guards hold them back; they come in rattling cars to get the
dumped oranges, but the kerosene is sprayed. And they stand still
and watch the potatoes float by, listen to the screaming pigs being
killed in a ditch and covered with quicklime, watch the mountains
of oranges slop down to a putrefying ooze; and in the eyes of the
people there is the failure; and in the eyes of the hungry there is a
growing wrath. In the souls of the people the grapes of wrath are
filling and growing heavy, growing heavy for the vintage.

The owners of the land came onto the land, or more often a
spokesman for the owners came. They came in closed cars, and
they felt the dry earth with their fingers, and sometimes they
drove big earth augers into the ground for soil tests. The
tenants, from their sun-beaten dooryards, watched uneasily
when the closed cars drove along the fields. And at last the
owner men drove into the dooryards and sat in their cars to

talk out of the windows. The tenant men stood beside the cars for a while, and then squatted on their hams and found sticks with which to mark the dust.

In the open doors the women stood looking out, and behind them the children—corn-headed children, with wide eyes, one bare foot on top of the other bare foot, and the toes working. The women and children watched their men talking to the owner men. They were silent.

Some of the owner men were kind because they hated what they had to do, and some of them were angry because they hated to be cruel, and some of them were cold because they had long ago found that one could not be an owner unless one were cold. And all of them were caught in something larger than themselves. Some of them hated the mathematics that drove them, and some were afraid, and some worshiped the mathematics because it provided a refuge from thought and from feeling. If a bank or a finance company owned the land, the owner man said, The Bank—or the Company—needs—wants—insists—must have—as though the Bank or the Company were a monster, with thought and feeling, which had ensnared them. These last would take no responsibility for the banks or the companies because they were men and slaves, while the banks were machines and masters all at the same time. Some of the owner men were a little proud to be slaves to such cold and powerful masters. The owner men sat in the cars and explained. You know the land is poor. You've scrabbled at it long enough, God knows.

The squatting tenant men nodded and wondered and drew figures in the dust, and yes, they knew, God knows. If the dust only wouldn't fly. If the top would only stay on the soil, it might not be so bad.

The owner men went on leading to their point: You know the land's getting poorer. You know what cotton does to the land; robs it, sucks all the blood out of it.

The squatters nodded—they knew, God knew. If they could only rotate the crops they might pump blood back into the land.

Well, it's too late. And the owner men explained the workings and the thinkings of the monster that was stronger than they were. A man can hold land if he can just eat and pay taxes; he can do that.

Yes, he can do that until his crops fail one day and he has to borrow money from the bank.

But—you see, a bank or a company can't do that, because those creatures don't breathe air, don't eat side-meat. They breathe profits; they eat the interest on money. If they don't get it, they die the way you die without air, without side-meat. It is a sad thing, but it is so. It is just so.

The squatting men raised their eyes to understand. Can't we just hang on? Maybe the next year will be a good year. God knows how much cotton next year. And with all the wars—God knows what price cotton will bring. Don't they make explosives out of cotton? And uniforms? Get enough wars and cotton'll hit the ceiling. Next year, maybe. They looked up questioningly.

We can't depend on it. The bank—the monster has to have profits all the time. It can't wait. It'll die. No, taxes go on. When the monster stops growing, it dies. It can't stay one size.

Soft fingers began to tap the sill of the car window, and hard fingers tightened on the restless drawing sticks. In the doorways of the sun-beaten tenant houses, women sighed and then shifted feet so that the one that had been down was now on top, and the toes working. Dogs came sniffing near the owner cars and wetted on all four tires one after another. And chickens lay in the sunny dust and fluffed their feathers to get the cleansing dust down to the skin. In the little sties the pigs grunted inquiringly over the muddy remnants of the slops.

The squatting men looked down again. What do you want us to do? We can't take less share of the crop—we're half starved now. The kids are hungry all the time. We got no clothes, torn an' ragged. If all the neighbors weren't the same, we'd be ashamed to go to meeting.

And at last the owner men came to the point. The tenant system won't work any more. One man on a tractor can take the place of twelve or fourteen families. Pay him a wage and take all the crop. We have to do it. We don't like to do it. But the monster's sick. Something's happened to the monster.

But you'll kill the land with cotton.

We know. We've got to take cotton quick before the land dies. Then we'll sell the land. Lots of families in the East would like to own a piece of land.

The tenant men looked up alarmed. But what'll happen to us? How'll we eat?

You'll have to get off the land. The plows'll go through the dooryard.

And now the squatting men stood up angrily. Grampa took up the land, and he had to kill the Indians and drive them away. And Pa was born here, and he killed weeds and snakes. Then a bad year came and he had to borrow a little money. An' we was born here. There in the door—our children born here. And Pa had to borrow money. The bank owned the land then, but we stayed and we got a little bit of what we raised.

We know that—all that. It's not us, it's the bank. A bank isn't like a man. Or an owner with fifty thousand acres, he isn't like a man either. That's the monster.

Sure, cried the tenant men, but it's our land. We measured it and broke it up. We were born on it, and we got killed on it, died on it. Even if it's no good, it's still ours. That's what makes it ours—being born on it, working it, dying on it. That makes ownership, not a paper with numbers on it.

We're sorry. It's not us. It's the monster. The bank isn't like a man.

Yes, but the bank is only made of men.

No, you're wrong there—quite wrong there. The bank is

something else than men. It happens that every man in a bank hates what the bank does, and yet the bank does it. The bank is something more than men, I tell you. It's the monster. Men made it, but they can't control it.

The tenants cried, Grampa killed Indians, Pa killed snakes for the land. Maybe we can kill banks—they're worse than Indians and snakes. Maybe we got to fight to keep our land, like Pa and Grampa did.

And now the owner men grew angry. You'll have to go.

But it's ours, the tenant men cried. We——

No. The bank, the monster owns it. You'll have to go.

We'll get our guns, like Grampa when the Indians came. What then?

Well—first the sheriff, and then the troops. You'll be stealing if you try to stay, you'll be murderers if you kill to stay. The monster isn't men, but it can make men do what it wants.

But if we go, where'll we go? How'll we go? We got no money.

We're sorry, said the owner men. The bank, the fifty-thousand-acre owner can't be responsible. You're on land that isn't yours. Once over the line maybe you can pick cotton in the fall. Maybe you can go on relief. Why don't you go on west to California? There's work there, and it never gets cold. Why, you can reach out anywhere and pick an orange. Why, there's always some kind of crop to work in. Why don't you go there? And the owner men started their cars and rolled away.

The tenant men squatted down on their hams again to mark the dust with a stick, to figure, to wonder. Their sunburned faces were dark, and their sun-whipped eyes were light. The women moved cautiously out of the doorways toward their men, and the children crept behind the women, cautiously, ready to run. The bigger boys squatted beside their fathers, because that made them men. After a time the women asked, What did he want?

And the men looked up for a second, and the smolder of pain

was in their eyes. We got to get off. A tractor and a superintendent. Like factories.

Where'll we go? the women asked.

We don't know. We don't know.

And the women went quickly, quietly back into the houses and herded the children ahead of them. They knew that a man so hurt and so perplexed may turn in anger, even on people he loves. They left the men alone to figure and to wonder in the dust.

After a time perhaps the tenant man looked about—at the pump put in ten years ago, with a goose-neck handle and iron flowers on the spout, at the chopping block where a thousand chickens had been killed, at the hand plow lying in the shed, and the patent crib hanging in the rafters over it.

The children crowded about the women in the houses. What are we going to do, Ma? Where we going to go?

The women said, We don't know, yet. Go out and play. But don't go near your father. He might whale you if you go near him. And the women went on with the work, but all the time they watched the men squatting in the dust—perplexed and figuring.

The tractors came over the roads and into the fields, great crawlers moving like insects, having the incredible strength of insects. They crawled over the ground, laying the track and rolling on it and picking it up. Diesel tractors, puttering while they stood idle; they thundered when they moved, and then settled down to a droning roar. Snubnosed monsters, raising the dust and sticking their snouts into it, straight down the country, across the country, through fences, through dooryards, in and out of gullies in straight lines. They did not run on the ground, but on their own roadbeds. They ignored hills and gulches, water courses, fences, houses.

The man sitting in the iron seat did not look like a man; gloved, goggled, rubber dust mask over nose and mouth, he

was a part of the monster, a robot in the seat. The thunder of
the cylinders sounded through the country, became one with
the air and the earth, so that earth and air muttered in sympathetic vibration. The driver could not control it—straight
across country it went, cutting through a dozen farms and
straight back. A twitch at the controls could swerve the cat',
but the driver's hands could not twitch because the monster
that built the tractors, the monster that sent the tractor out, had
somehow got into the driver's hands, into his brain and muscle,
had goggled him and muzzled him—goggled his mind, muzzled
his speech, goggled his perception, muzzled his protest. He
could not see the land as it was, he could not smell the land as
it smelled; his feet did not stamp the clods or feel the warmth
and power of the earth. He sat in an iron seat and stepped on
iron pedals. He could not cheer or beat or curse or encourage
the extension of his power, and because of this he could not
cheer or whip or curse or encourage himself. He did not know
or own or trust or beseech the land. If a seed dropped did not
germinate, it was nothing. If the young thrusting plant withered
in drought or drowned in a flood of rain, it was no more to the
driver than to the tractor.

He loved the land no more than the bank loved the land.
He could admire the tractor—its machined surfaces, its surge
of power, the roar of its detonating cylinders; but it was not his
tractor. Behind the tractor rolled the shining disks, cutting the
earth with blades—not plowing but surgery, pushing the cut
earth to the right where the second row of disks cut it and
pushed it to the left; slicing blades shining, polished by the cut
earth. And pulled behind the disks, the harrows combing with
iron teeth so that the little clods broke up and the earth lay
smooth. Behind the harrows, the long seeders—twelve curved
iron penes erected in the foundry, orgasms set by gears, raping
methodically, raping without passion. The driver sat in his iron
seat and he was proud of the straight lines he did not will,
proud of the tractor he did not own or love, proud of the

power he could not control. And when that crop grew, and was harvested, no man had crumbled a hot clod in his fingers and let the earth sift past his fingertips. No man had touched the seed, or lusted for the growth. Men ate what they had not raised, had no connection with the bread. The land bore under iron, and under iron gradually died; for it was not loved or hated, it had no prayers or curses.

At noon the tractor driver stopped sometimes near a tenant house and opened his lunch: sandwiches wrapped in waxed paper, white bread, pickle, cheese, Spam, a piece of pie branded like an engine part. He ate without relish. And tenants not yet moved away came out to see him, looked curiously while the goggles were taken off, and the rubber dust mask, leaving white circles around the eyes and a large white circle around nose and mouth. The exhaust of the tractor puttered on, for fuel is so cheap it is more efficient to leave the engine running than to heat the Diesel nose for a new start. Curious children crowded close, ragged children who ate their fried dough as they watched. They watched hungrily the unwrapping of the sandwiches, and their hunger-sharpened noses smelled the pickle, cheese, and Spam. They didn't speak to the driver. They watched his hand as it carried food to his mouth. They did not watch him chewing; their eyes followed the hand that held the sandwich. After a while the tenant who could not leave the place came out and squatted in the shade beside the tractor.

"Why, you're Joe Davis's boy!"

"Sure," the driver said.

"Well, what you doing this kind of work for—against your own people?"

"Three dollars a day. I got damn sick of creeping for my dinner—and not getting it. I got a wife and kids. We got to eat. Three dollars a day, and it comes every day."

"That's right," the tenant said. "But for your three dollars a day fifteen or twenty families can't eat at all. Nearly a hundred people have to go out and wander on the roads for your three dollars a day. Is that right?"

And the driver said, "Can't think of that. Got to think of my own kids. Three dollars a day, and it comes every day. Times are changing, mister, don't you know? Can't make a living on the land unless you've got two, five, ten thousand acres and a tractor. Crop land isn't for little guys like us any more. You don't kick up a howl because you can't make Fords, or because you're not the telephone company. Well, crops are like that now. Nothing to do about it. You try to get three dollars a day someplace. That's the only way."

The tenant pondered. "Funny thing how it is. If a man owns a little property, that property is him, it's part of him, and it's like him. If he owns property only so he can walk on it and handle it and be sad when it isn't doing well, and feel fine when the rain falls on it, that property is him, and some way he's bigger because he owns it. Even if he isn't successful he's big with his property. That is so."

And the tenant pondered more. "But let a man get property he doesn't see, or can't take time to get his fingers in, or can't be there to walk on it—why, then the property is the man. He can't do what he wants, he can't think what he wants. The property is the man, stronger than he is. And he is small, not big. Only his possessions are big—and he's the servant of his property. That is so, too."

The driver munched the branded pie and threw the crust away. "Times are changed, don't you know? Thinking about stuff like that don't feed the kids. Get your three dollars a day, feed your kids. You got no call to worry about anybody's kids but your own. You get a reputation for talking like that, and you'll never get three dollars a day. Big shots won't give you three dollars a day if you worry about anything but your three dollars a day."

"Nearly a hundred people on the road for your three dollars. Where will we go?"

"And that reminds me," the driver said, "you better get out soon. I'm going through the dooryard after dinner."

"You filled in the well this morning."

"I know. Had to keep the line straight. But I'm going through the dooryard after dinner. Got to keep the lines straight. And—well, you know Joe Davis, my old man, so I'll tell you this. I got orders wherever there's a family not moved out—if I have an accident—you know, get too close and cave the house in a little—well, I might get a couple of dollars. And my youngest kid never had no shoes yet."

"I built it with my hands. Straightened old nails to put the sheating on. Rafters are wired to the stringers with baling wire. It's mine. I built it. You bump it down—I'll be in the window with a rifle. You even come too close and I'll pot you like a rabbit."

"It's not me. There's nothing I can do. I'll lose my job if I don't do it. And look—suppose you kill me? They'll just hang you, but long before you're hung there'll be another guy on the tractor, and he'll bump the house down. You're not killing the right guy."

"That's so," the tenant said. "Who gave you orders? I'll go after him. He's the one to kill."

"You're wrong. He got his orders from the bank. The bank told him, 'Clear those people out or it's your job.'"

"Well, there's a president of the bank. There's a board of directors. I'll fill up the magazine of the rifle and go into the bank."

The driver said, "Fellow was telling me the bank gets orders from the East. The orders were, 'Make the land show profit or we'll close you up.'"

"But where does it stop? Who can we shoot? I don't aim to starve to death before I kill the man that's starving me."

"I don't know. Maybe there's nobody to shoot. Maybe the thing isn't men at all. Maybe like you said, the property's doing it. Anyway I told you my orders."

"I got to figure," the tenant said. "We all got to figure. There's some way to stop this. It's not like lightning or earthquakes. We've got a bad thing made by men, and by God that's something we can change." The tenant sat in his doorway, and the driver thundered his engine and started off, tracks falling and curving, harrows combing, and the phalli of the seeder slipping into the ground. Across the dooryard the tractor cut, and the hard, foot-beaten ground was seeded field, and the tractor cut through again; the uncut space was ten feet wide. And back he came. The iron guard bit into the housecorner, crumbled the wall, and wrenched the little house from its foundation so that it fell sideways, crushed like a bug. And the driver was goggled and a rubber mask covered his nose and mouth. The tractor cut a straight line on, and the air and the ground vibrated with its thunder. The tenant man stared after it, his rifle in his hand. His wife was beside him, and the quiet children behind. And all of them stared after the tractor.

8. Some American People

ERSKINE CALDWELL

Erskine Caldwell (1903–   ) has written so much, and sold so well, that it is difficult for some to remember that in the 1930's he was not only a very radical writer, but a very daring and powerful one. The boy from Coweta County, Georgia (born miles from the nearest landmark) went on to become the biggest-selling author in the world (twenty million copies of

God's Little Acre alone had been sold in various languages and editions by 1949). Caldwell was a dedicated and highly gifted young storyteller; if his stories were grotesque and weirdly comical, it was because no other response seemed appropriate to the scenes of horror which greeted his eyes wherever he turned. If his reactions were extreme, it was because no milder ones seemed reasonable, given the extremities to which human beings had been pushed in his native countryside. A number of Caldwell's finest stories were concerned with the exploitation and savage treatment of Negroes; in their humanity and rage at brutality they rank with the stories of Richard Wright and William Faulkner. Some of his short stories of that period are classic in their simplicity and terrifying in their credibility; it is likely that they will last long after many of his other works have been forgotten. The excerpts that follow are from one of the many travel volumes of a restless and searching man. They were written at a time when Caldwell was doing some of his best fiction, and they may help to explain why he wrote as he did—and why the American conscience was aroused by the plight of the descendants of revolutionary pioneers who had been reduced to an animal level and were quietly starving to death.

Tenant Farmers

For four years economic conditions in the South have been as acute as any in the United States, but in the fifth year of the depression conditions have never been so bad. In parts of the South human existence has reached its lowest depths. Children are seen deformed by nature and malnutrition, women in rags beg for pennies, and men are so hungry that many of them eat snakes, cow dung, and clay.

The State of Georgia, one of the largest cotton-producing

states, provides no direct relief. Governor Eugene Talmadge, the self-styled "wild-man," the dictator of three million people, who exercises more power than Huey Long, passes along to the Federal government the responsibility the citizens placed upon him—and without coöperation. Talmadge, when prodded, shouts that the state is no relief agency. While he is shouting himself red in the face, he holds one hand behind his back to receive money sent down from Washington to keep alive the men who voted him into power.

Talmadge is riding to greater power on his program of clearing the state of debt. By refusing to furnish food, clothing, or work to one-third of the population he intends to close his present term of office with a surplus in the treasury.

In some sections of the state, particularly in South Georgia and East Georgia, men who are unable to qualify for the meager relief provided by the Government offer their labor— eight, ten, twelve, fourteen hours a day of it—for what they can get. What they can get, one or two days a week, if they are lucky enough to find employment at all, is sometimes twenty-five cents a day. Thirty cents is the average, in this agricultural empire. Exceptional pay is fifty cents a day.

The wage-working tenant farmer, white or black, at the present time may work one day a week, he may even work ten days a month; or he may, as hundreds do, search fruitlessly day after day, week after week, for half a day's employment. On the other hand, if he happens to be one out of five, he may qualify for relief work and earn five or six dollars a week. Many, however, are forced to live on the minimum, which is three dollars and sixty cents a week. These relief workers are the aristocrats of Southern tenant labor. They earn enough to provide some food for their families.

The real sufferer in the cotton state is the former sharecropper. Sharecropping, once the backbone of the South's agricultural empire, is rapidly giving way to an even more vicious system of labor extraction. The new style is driving the sharecropper away from the fertile land, away from schools for his children, away from contact with civilization. The sharecropper of yesterday is the wage worker of today, the man who peddles his brawn and muscle for twenty-five and thirty cents a day, and who is lucky if he works one day a week during the winter months, and still luckier if he can collect it in cash instead of in cornmeal or old clothes. The sharecropper's place has been taken by the renter, who pays for the rent of the land whether there is anything left for himself or not.

This once-flourishing farming country is now a desolate land. Crop control has reduced the quantity of products without raising the quality. Fewer tenants can find employment. White men are being replaced by cheaper, more tractable Negroes. Land is concentrated in the hands of corporations, banks, and plantation owners, thereby forcing whole sections of the South into domains of absentee landlordism.

There are hundreds of sections in the South where the land has been bled of all fertility and now lies unproductive. It is in many of these sections that tenant farmers have been left stranded with neither mule, plow, food, nor land. In East Georgia is a section starting near the Savannah River with Columbia County and continuing in a southerly direction through McDuffie, Glascock, Jefferson, Richmond, and Burke counties for a hundred and fifty miles to the Atlantic Ocean. This territory is experiencing the decay that spreads westward through Alabama, Mississippi, and Arkansas. Railroads that contributed to the once healthy growth of the cotton empire are being scrapped, and in their places weeds are growing. Tenant houses, rotted and roofless, are the homes of families hoping that this year, next year, some year soon, will provide food, clothing, and shelter. When the house falls in, the family starts out with their belongings strapped to their backs in search of another home where hope may be continued.

These American people of the cotton country, robbed of their means of livelihood by the downfall of the old systems of farming, are being forced into the swamps, the stony acres, the steep hills, the waste land. The ground they are forced upon will not yield crops. Some of it is soil that will not even grow a good stand of broom sedge.

These hundreds of communities in Georgia, Alabama, Mississippi, and Arkansas exist without roads, and travel is done across creeks without bridges, fields without so much as a cow path.

These are the unknown people of today, the tenant farmer of the South. These are the people who hide their nakedness behind trees when a stranger wanders off the main-traveled roads. Here are the deformed, starved, and diseased children born since 1929. Here are the men who strip leaves off trees, dig roots out of the earth, and snare whatever wild animals they can. These are the people who were forced off the fertile land when sharecropping came to an end. These are the men, women, and children that many urban residents deny exist.

There is hunger in their eyes as well as in their bellies. They grasp for a word of hope. They plead for a word of advice. They have no friend or leader to help them.

The Government relief agencies in many Southern counties are inadequate to help them. Sometimes neither has ever heard of the other.

None of them wishes to kill and steal. He wishes to work, to secure food for his children, medicine for his wife, a shelter over his head. Some have covered the county in search of even a rumor of a job, and there is no means to travel any further. The mule has died of old age or starvation; or the mule was sold by the sheriff of the county to satisfy a judgment. There is no mule on which to ride or with which to work. There is nothing left except the roofless shack and a few pots and pans, and a corn-shuck mattress.

The Federal Government says that nobody starves, but the Federal Government does not know what its left hand does. The relief in these states is administered by local citizens, and in many cases a local citizen is an urban resident who knows the city street but who would be hopelessly lost ten miles from home where there are no highway signs along the creeks and cow paths.

In Georgia Governor Talmadge takes off his coat, snaps his red suspenders, and shouts from every crossroad that the "wild-man" is everybody's friend. If the tenant farmers who are made to suffer because of their Governor's refusal to allow the state to appropriate relief could have their way, it is not unlikely that they would petition the Federal Government to nationalize the State of Georgia.

Under present conditions that is the wisest step that could be taken. Laying aside the possibilities of political upheaval, it would at least give some tenant farmers and their families the opportunity to vary their diet of snakes and cow dung.

God-Forsaken—Man-Forsaken

A tenant farmer in the cotton states pays rent for tillable land either in cash or in bales of cotton. If he fails to make enough to do either, the contract with the landowner is broken, and the tenant and his family are likely to be evicted.

In 1934 tenant farmers were unable to purchase the necessary amount of fertilizer, and consequently their cotton crop was far below average. Those with short crops in many cases failed to produce enough cotton to pay their rent.

Their hope now is to secure Government-rented farm land which will enable them to become sharecroppers or renters. That failing, they will be forced into the wage-working class, the most insecure group of agricultural workers in the entire South.

In 1934 a tenant farmer in Jefferson County, Georgia, was unable, because of old age and illness, to work out his crop. A physician prescribed for his ailment, but the man could not buy the medicine, and no relief agency would supply it. A four-year-old girl in the family died at the end of the year of malnutrition and anemia. The tenant moved several miles away to another farm, but after several weeks the landowner decided that he was too old and ill to work a crop on a rental basis, or on any other basis, and he was evicted.

The household goods were carried to the land-limits and deposited by the side of the road. Another tenant took the goods under shelter, and the landowner gave notice that if they were not removed from his land he would come and burn them.

In the meantime the old man had gone into the swamp, without ax, saw, or hammer, with the intention of felling trees and building a log house for himself and family. After several days he was found in another county.

This tenant farmer had lost his health, and nobody would allow him to work, either on shares, for rental, or for wages. There was no house to shelter his family, there was no food to feed them. The four-year-old daughter had died with her body twisted and knotted by rickets and anemia.

This section in East Georgia is the scene of cases of human want that no relief agency, government, county, state, or private, has touched. More than that, it has been publicly denied that the section exists. And yet it is only five miles from U. S. Highway No. 1, and twenty-five miles from the county-seat.

Hundreds of families in the tenant-farmer class live in this strip of America twenty miles wide and a hundred miles long. In other parts of Georgia, and in Alabama, Mississippi and Arkansas there are hundreds of other families in similar communities. There is starvation, deformity, even death, for want of a loaf of bread.

Like the slums of a city, it contains the backwash of America; but unlike the slums of a city, it is unknown and unseen. Officially, on the rolls of the relief offices and on the mind of the Governor of Georgia, it does not exist.

Here is another Jefferson County tenant farmer. He begs to know how he can get a small acreage to farm. He is a young man, not over thirty-five. He is married and has three children. He has been to the county-seat, but each time he has visited the official in charge of government homesteads, he has been told nothing can be done for him for a while. He has worn out his shoes walking there and back.

His children have not enough clothing to wear to school. He will not talk about what they have to eat. Several miles away is a Government adult school, which provides a job for one teacher. The grown men and women who attend the school, learning to read and write, have to leave their children at home because they have no clothes to wear to the district school. The young tenant farmer cannot understand why an adult school is provided when his three children are unable to attend the district school. He thinks it must be the Governor's fault. Governor Talmadge will not coöperate with the Federal Government in supplying the necessities of life, because the Governor has some political ambition up his sleeve. He would like to become President of the United States. He may have to share the White House with Huey Long, but since they are on friendly terms, he is willing to do that if he can only get there.

Across the field is another tenant farmer. He has moved into a cabin recently occupied by a Negro sharecropper who was forced out by the landowner, and the white man had to have shelter for his family. It was the only available dwelling within ten miles and the landowner had promised full coöperation because the new tenant owned a pair of strong mules. No one knew what had become of the Negro family, but it was believed they had moved into an abandoned barn several miles away. The roof had fallen in, but otherwise the building was inhabitable.

Only half a mile in the other direction is a tenant farmer who has set his family up in an abandoned schoolhouse. None of the six persons in the family can read or write. The man sits on the schoolhouse steps wondering where he can find a plow to break the ground for his cotton crop. He has got to pay rent whether or no, and plowing time will soon be at hand.

Up the creek is another tenant farmer. In January and February there is little that can be done in the way of farming, but it is already spring, and the man sits on the ground splitting "splinters," small slabs of fat-pine used for the kindling of fire. There are eleven children helping him, their ages running from one year to seventeen. His wife is in bed, whitefaced with pellagra.

Somebody had heard of an organization of some sort that tried to help sharecroppers, renters, and wage-workers, but nobody had been able to find out where the organization was or what could be done about it. The rumor was that sharecroppers, renters, and wage-workers could join it and force the landowners into paying living wages. The organization, presumed to be the Sharecropper's Union, was like a rainbow after a storm, but nobody knew in which direction it could be found.

The man splitting the pine continued to tie the splinters into small bundles, each weighing two or three pounds. Sometimes he was able to get a cent a bundle for them in Augusta—sometimes he could not even give them away. He had sold a load for four dollars several weeks before, but out of that he had spent two dollars for gasoline and oil to run the broken-down truck. He had earned two dollars in two months, and it had kept his family alive. There were six or seven months ahead of him before he could harvest a crop. He did not know how long he would be able to keep his family alive at that rate. He was a tenant farmer without the benefits of a landlord to supply the necessities of life on credit.

The tenant wore an old sweater pinned across his chest, a pair of patched overalls, and some broken shoes. His wife had not been out of bed in eight months. One of his children, a girl of seventeen, had a growth closing over one eye that could be removed by a surgeon. The growth had been there for eight or nine years, and each year it became larger. Soon the girl will lose the sight of one eye when the growth closes over it.

The owner of the land on which the tenant lives is a well-known figure in public life. He comes to the farm occasionally, always once to see that the crop is planted on time, and always once to see that it is harvested on time. Rent is collected at the gin when the cotton is baled.

Hungry People

Working for a few cents a day, the wage-worker in the cotton country cannot afford to rent a house for the exclusive occupancy of his family. When the rate of pay is twenty-five cents a day, and when half a day's work is common, there is nothing to be done except double up with another family.

For anyone familiar with conditions among Southern tenant farmers, it is not difficult to cite cases that are representative of conditions in tenant-farmer communities from Georgia to Arkansas. These conditions are not typical of the South, but represent thousands of families that have been forced into isolated communities in these states.

One such case was found in a two-room house occupied by three families of tenant farmers, each family consisting of man and wife and from one to four children each.

While two eighteen-year-old girls from the house were chopping wood from a stump across the road with a plowshare tied to a hickory pole, one of the men came home in the middle of the day. He had finished half a day's work at noon, the first in two weeks' time, and with the pay he bought a pound of salted hogside, and two pounds of corn meal.

The third family refused to share in it, because the wife insisted that her husband would be home with something to eat before night.

In one of the two rooms a six-year-old boy licked the paper bag the meat had been brought in. His legs were scarcely any larger than a medium sized dog's leg, and his belly was as large as that of a 130-pound woman's. Suffering from rickets and anemia, his legs were unable to carry him for more than a dozen steps at a time; suffering from malnutrition, his belly was swollen several times its normal size. His face was bony and white. He was starving to death.

In the other room of the house, without chairs, beds, or tables, a woman lay rolled up in some quilts trying to sleep. On the floor before an open fire lay two babies, neither a year old, sucking the dry teats of a mongrel bitch. A young girl, somewhere between fifteen and twenty, squatted on the corner of the hearth trying to keep warm.

The dog got up and crawled to the hearth. She sat on her haunches before the blazing pine-knots, shivering and whining. After a while the girl spoke to the dog and the animal slunk away from the warmth of the fire and lay again beside the two babies. The infants cuddled against the warmth of the dog's flanks, searching tearfully for the dry teats.

The two girls who had been hacking at the pine stump across the road with a rusty plowshare dragged two sacks of wood across the yard and into the house. Pieces of fat-pine were thrown into the fire and the quick blaze warmed the whole room. The woman in the quilts stopped shivering and began to snore lightly. The girl squatting on the hearth moved back from the intense heat. The dog got up and shook herself and lay down several feet away. The babies crawled crying after her.

In the other room the meat and meal were being baked in a skillet over the open-hearth fire. Five persons crowded around the blaze watching the hoe-cake brown. The boy with rickets ducked under his father's arms and tried to snatch the hoe-cake from the pan. He burned his fingers and his mother rubbed some of the grease from the salted hog-side on them. He stopped crying while he was eating his portion, but as soon as that was gone he began crying again, and he did not stop after that. He said his head hurt him, too.

There was a laborer across the field who earned twenty-five cents a day. This he received from the landowner in the round sum of eight dollars a month. The only trouble was that the landowner more often than not brought him meat and meal instead of cash.

Formerly this eight-dollars-a-month wage-worker had a job on relief, and he received from seven to eight dollars a week. But the FERA told him one day that he was fired, because he had only one arm and could not do a man's full share of work. Cut off from relief and listed as an unemployable, he was forced into the wage-worker class of tenant, and every one of his neighbors said he was lucky to get a full-time job, at twenty-five cents a day. His nine children had to take turns of three in going to school, because there were only enough clothes for three of them to dress at a time.

Back in the room with the two babies there was no food. The husband should have been back the day before, but it was doubtful if he would return before another two or three days.

The girl squatting on the hearth wore a jumper made from flour sacks, and over that a piece of matting for a shawl. A corn sack had been split open at the bottom, and this she wore for a skirt. She was without underwear, stockings, and shoes.

The two girls who were the wood-gatherers sat down on the floor, one on each side of the dog and babies, and warmed themselves before the fire. It kept them busy most of the time getting wood, because the fat-pine stumps burned as if kerosene had been poured over them. They wiped the babies' faces and scolded the dog for moving so often.

There was nothing in that side of the house to eat, and there had been nothing for three days. The dog began to whine again, and tried to get up to go outside and hunt for some food, but the girls would not let her leave the babies. The dog had to keep them until the mother had finished her nap.

The girl on the hearth, raising her corn-sack skirt to let the warmth of the fire fall upon her body, said it ought to be easy to find something to eat if you only knew where to look for it. Her sisters looked at her but said nothing. The girl then asked herself a question. What wouldn't I do for a heaping dish of hog sausage?

When the condition of these families was brought to the attention of county officials, newspaper editors, and leading citizens of the community, the circumstances were indignantly denied. Later, after several investigations had been made and the conditions admitted, the only plan discussed was a sterilization program. Thus it was made plain that the citizenship of the areas will take no steps to remedy the cause of the conditions. Sterilization should be applied to certain individual mental and physical cases, but the thousands of Southern tenant farmers are in an economic condition that demands much more than superficial thought.

Freedom for the Tenant Farmer

Georgia, like most states, has been so busy telling the world about its natural assets and tricky golf courses that it has neglected to look into the mirror occasionally. Many of its up-and-coming citizens wish the world to know that Georgia is the Empire State of the South; quite a few of its common herd would prefer to have the state pay some attention to its home-folks. Georgia's common herd is its thousands of tenant farmers.

Central Georgia is a fertile land whose center is Macon. Extending in all directions lies land that produces abundantly and yields a handsome profit. If one were able to buy a farm in that section, even a few acres, he should be comfortable for life.

But this is not all of Georgia. This is only half of the state. There is a circular rim beginning in the west, passing through the north, and terminating in the east that holds thousands of tenant farmers who cannot find much to brag about. The land is poor and hilly.

Just why the white tenant farmer should be pushed back from the fertile lowlands and be forced to struggle on the clay hills for less than a living is a matter no one has given much attention to yet. As conditions are now, Negroes are welcome wherever the land is fertile, but white tenants are not welcome. A white tenant cannot be so easily defrauded of the fruit of his labor, and consequently he has been pushed back into the gully-washed hills to get along the best he can.

Back on the hillsides the tenant families fell prey to various forms of religious excitement which served to take the place of normal entertainment. Physically, they became abject specimens of humanity. They ate what they could get, usually cornmeal and molasses. As a change many of them began eating the earth, and now communities of clay-eaters exist almost wholly on meal, molasses, and clay. Clay-eaters may be identified by the color and texture of their skin, which looks and feels like putty.

In many such Georgia communities syphilis is as common as dandruff. Incest is as prevalent as marriage in these tenant regions where normal access to the outside is shut off because of the inability to travel. They are unable to travel except on foot, because there are few horses and mules, and almost no automobiles.

The machine of error whirs throughout Georgia, making the same sound there as it does in all the cotton states. The plantation system is still a barbaric method of making money. Some of the government relief agencies are in incapable, or rather, in ineffectual hands. Nearly all the organs of public opinion are in reactionary hands. And the victim of this machine of error is the tenant farmer. He is too poor, generally, to pay a poll tax, and hence cannot vote. He cannot read or write, and the newspapers never receive his political or economic protest. His charges against the local administration of relief are thrown out the window. He is a pretty helpless person, this Georgia tenant farmer of 1935.

There is nothing strange about the appearance on the scene as such men as Huey Long and Eugene Talmadge. By appealing to this majority any man with the necessary instincts can sway the vote of states by promising something, anything. The greater the promise, the larger the vote. Sinking men from the Carolinas to Texas grasp at any straw.

The desire of the landowning class is to keep the tenant in his place. The dominating voice in the matter is that of the local county official who holds office by means of a political machine. He may be the county health officer who refuses to furnish medical aid; he may be the county school superintendent who refuses to establish a school in a tenant community. Their reasons for not providing what elsewhere amount to public necessities are dictated solely by the landowning class. There is nothing that can be done about it until the strangle-hold of the landowner on the tenant farmer has been broken. To break the hold, a union of tenants is necessary.

It is astonishing to find in this Jim Crow state that the economic condition of this class of white tenant is lower than that of the Negro. His standard of living is lower, his education is more limited, and his health is worse. The Negro can be threatened into submission; the white farmer still thinks he should have what he earns, and as a result he is discriminated against.

The local administrators of the FERA and PWA have in many cases been reluctant to recognize these tenant families.

Where their eligibility for relief has been forcibly proved to the administrators, the result has been a disgraceful, misguided rule. In many cases rather than lend or give money to a tenant farmer for the rental of land or the purchase of seed or a work animal, the relief has taken the form of mattresses, which can neither be eaten nor made to pull a plow. In other cases a ditch will be dug at the expense of several hundred dollars, draining the earth dry of any chance moisture in this semi-arid state, and which eventually lowers the water-level until wells go dry. Tenant farmers without wells or other water supply can be counted by the hundreds in many Georgia counties. Instead of drilling wells with relief funds, and in spite of this devastation of the land, the program for the year is deeper and longer drain ditches.

The landowner-tenant system should not be permitted to exist. No act of its own is motivated by any desire save that of profit at the expense of the physical and moral and economic welfare of the worker. No other system has yet appeared on the scene to take its place, and until it does, the demoralizing spectacle of seeing thousands of men, women, and children, both black and white, being cheated and squeezed and crucified by a profit system that should have no foothold in modern civilization—until a better system arrives, the present one should make the American people hang their heads in shame.

The system of agricultural labor that will take its place in the cotton states is still problematical. And yet it is difficult to visualize any humane method of cotton production that will embody the present-day landowner and his plantation system. A unionized wage-scale would be ideal in theory, for a capitalistic nation, but in practice it is difficult to imagine any relationship succeeding between the present-day landowner and the worker. A far greater step would be the discarding of the landowner, and the cultivation of the large farm on a collective basis, or else the breaking up of large fertile units of land into small parcels for intensive cultivation by one or two persons.

9. Let Us Now Praise Famous Men

JAMES AGEE

Judging only from the facts of his biography, one would not be able to guess that James Agee (1909–1956)—middle-class native of Knoxville, Harvard '32, staff writer for Henry Luce (first Fortune, *then* Time), *movie reviewer for* The Nation, *screen writer, and would-be novelist—was capable of producing an extraordinarily haunting evocation of the life flow of the American tenant farmer. It took a long time, but it is now recognized almost universally that* Let Us Now Praise Famous Men *is a great work of reportage which, in its sensibility, its painstaking accuracy, its humility, its noble orchestration, its indissoluble marriage of words and unforgettable photographs (by Walker Evans), is also an American classic. The reason for it is quite simply that James Agee was—in addition to the other listable items of his tragically brief biography—a poet. And this not just because he had published a book of verse (Permit Me Voyage, 1934) but because he was driven as are all true poets to find the exact word, the exact phrase, and to hunt unflinchingly for the truth. Working during school vacations as a harvest stiff in the Kansas and Nebraska wheat fields, he had developed a deep love of the land. When, in the summer of 1936, he and Walker Evans went South on assignment from* Fortune *magazine to write up the sharecroppers, he was so overcome by the overwhelming reality of what he encountered that he gave up his job to devote himself to living with these people as one of them and to writing of what he had*

From *Let Us Now Praise Famous Men* (Boston: Houghton Mifflin, 1940), pp. 115–121, 319–348, and unpaged title poem. Copyright 1939 and 1940 by James Agee. Reprinted with the permission of the publisher.

seen. By the time the book was published, five years later,
America's passions and energies had turned from suffering at
home to the struggle against nazism. Despite Dwight Mac-
donald's efforts to promote the book just after the war through
his magazine, Politics, *it was not until the posthumous publi-*
cation of Agee's unfinished novel, A Death in the Family
(1957), that America was ready at last to take the measure of
this subtle, strong, beautiful writer. Three representative ex-
cerpts are extracted here: "Money," with its meticulous ac-
counting of the tenants' pathetic finances; "Work," which rises
to the lyrical in its detailed description of their daily lives; and
the poem which gives the book its title.

Money

You are farmers; I am a farmer myself.

FRANKLIN DELANO ROOSEVELT

Woods and Ricketts work for Michael and T. Hudson Margraves, two brothers, in partnership, who live in Cookstown.
Gudger worked for the Margraves for three years; he now
(1936) works for Chester Boles, who lives two miles south of
Cookstown.

On their business arrangements, and working histories, and
on their money, I wrote a chapter too long for inclusion in this
volume without sacrifice of too much else. I will put in its
place here as extreme a précis as I can manage.

Gudger has no home, no land, no mule; none of the more
important farming implements. He must get all these of his
landlord. Boles, for his share of the corn and cotton, also advances him rations money during four months of the year,
March through June, and his fertilizer.

Gudger pays him back with his labor and with the labor of
his family.

At the end of the season he pays him back further: with half his corn; with half his cotton; with half his cottonseed. Out of his own half of these crops he also pays him back the rations money, plus interest, and his share of the fertilizer, plus interest, and such other debts, plus interest, as he may have incurred.

What is left, once doctors' bills and other debts have been deducted, is his year's earnings.

Gudger is a straight half-cropper, or sharecropper.

Woods and Ricketts own no home and no land, but Woods owns one mule and Ricketts owns two, and they own their farming implements. Since they do not have to rent these tools and animals, they work under a slightly different arrangement. They give over to the landlord only a third of their cotton and a fourth of their corn. Out of their own parts of the crop, however, they owe him the price of two thirds of their cotton fertilizer and three fourths of their corn fertilizer, plus interest; and, plus interest, the same debts on rations money.

Woods and Ricketts are tenants: they work on third and fourth.

A very few tenants pay cash rent: but these two types of arrangement, with local variants (company stores; food instead of rations money; slightly different divisions of the crops) are basic to cotton tenantry all over the South.

From March through June, while the cotton is being cultivated, they live on the rations money.

From July through to late August, while the cotton is making, they live however they can.

From late August through October or into November, during the picking and ginning season, they live on the money from their share of the cottonseed.

From then on until March, they live on whatever they have earned in the year; or however they can.

During six to seven months of each year, then—that is, during exactly such time as their labor with the cotton is of absolute necessity to the landlord—they can be sure of whatever living is possible in rations advances and in cottonseed money.

During five to six months of the year, of which three are the hardest months of any year, with the worst of weather, the least adequacy of shelter, the worst and least of food, the worst of health, quite normal and inevitable, they can count on nothing except that they may hope least of all for any help from their landlords.

Gudger—a family of six—lives on ten dollars a month rations money during four months of the year. He has lived on eight, and on six. Woods—a family of six—until this year was unable to get better than eight a month during the same period; this year he managed to get it up to ten. Ricketts—a family of nine —lives on ten dollars a month during this spring and early summer period.

This debt is paid back in the fall at eight per cent interest. Eight per cent is charged also on the fertilizer and on all other debts which tenants incur in this vicinity.

At the normal price, a half-sharing tenant gets about six dollars a bale from his share of the cottonseed. A one-mule, half-sharing tenant makes on the average three bales. This half-cropper, then, Gudger, can count on eighteen dollars, more or less, to live on during the picking and ginning: though he gets nothing until his first bale is ginned.

Working on third and fourth, a tenant gets the money from two thirds of the cottonseed of each bale: nine dollars to the bale. Woods, with one mule, makes three bales, and gets twenty-seven dollars. Ricketts, with two mules, makes and gets twice that, to live on during the late summer and fall.

What is earned at the end of a given year is never to be depended on and, even late in a season, is never predictable.

It can be enough to tide through the dead months of the winter, sometimes even better: it can be enough, spread very thin, to take through two months, and a sickness, or six weeks, or a month: it can be little enough to be completely meaning-less: it can be nothing: it can be enough less than nothing to insure a tenant only of an equally hopeless lack of money at the end of his next year's work: and whatever one year may bring in the way of good luck, there is never any reason to hope that that luck will be repeated in the next year or the year after that.

The best that Woods has ever cleared was $1300 during a war year. During the teens and twenties he fairly often cleared as much as $300; he fairly often cleared $50 and less; two or three times he ended the year in debt. During the depression years he has more often cleared $50 and less; last year he cleared $150, but serious illness during the winter ate it up rapidly.

The best that Gudger has ever cleared is $125. That was in the plow-under year. He felt exceedingly hopeful and bought a mule: but when his landlord warned him of how he was com-ing out the next year, he sold it. Most years he has not made more than $25 to $30; and about one year in three he has ended in debt. Year before last he wound up $80 in debt; last year, $12; of Boles, his new landlord, the first thing he had to do was borrow $15 to get through the winter until rations advances should begin.

Years ago the Ricketts were, relatively speaking, almost prosperous. Besides their cotton farming they had ten cows and sold the milk, and they lived near a good stream and had all the fish they wanted. Ricketts went $400 into debt on a fine young pair of mules. One of the mules died before it had made its first crop; the other died the year after; against his fear, amounting to full horror, of sinking to the half-crop level where nothing is owned, Ricketts went into debt for other, in-ferior mules; his cows went one by one into debts and desperate exchanges and by sickness; he got congestive chills; his wife got pellagra; a number of his children died; he got appendicitis and lay for days on end under the ice cap; his wife's pellagra got into her brain; for ten consecutive years now, though they have lived on so little rations money, and have turned nearly all their cottonseed money toward their debts, they have not cleared or had any hope of clearing a cent at the end of the year.

It is not often, then, at the end of the season, that a tenant clears enough money to tide him through the winter, or even an appreciable part of it. More generally he can count on it that, during most of the four months between settlement time in the fall and the beginning of work and resumption of rations advances in the early spring, he will have no money and can expect none, nor any help, from his landlord: and of having no money during the six midsummer weeks of laying by, he can be still more sure. Four to six months of each year, in other words, he is much more likely than not to have nothing whatever, and during these months he must take care for himself: he is no responsibility of the landlord's. All he can hope to do is find work. This is hard, because there are a good many chronically unemployed in the towns, and they are more convenient to most openings for work and can at all times be counted on if they are needed; also there is no increase, during these two dead farming seasons, of other kinds of work to do. And so, with no more jobs open than at any other time of year, and with plenty of men already convenient to take them, the whole tenant population, hundreds and thousands in any locality, are desperately in need of work.

A landlord saves up certain odd jobs for these times of year: they go, at less than he would have to pay others, to those of his tenants who happen to live nearest or to those he thinks best of; and even at best they don't amount to much.

When there is wooded land on the farm, a landlord ordinarily permits a tenant to cut and sell firewood for what he can get. About the best a tenant gets of this is a dollar a load, but more often (for the market is glutted, so many are trying to sell wood) he can get no better than half that and less, and often enough, at the end of a hard day's peddling, miles from home, he will let it go for a quarter or fifteen cents rather than haul it all the way home again: so it doesn't amount to much. Then, too, by no means everyone has wood to cut and sell: in the whole southern half of the county we were working mainly in, there was so little wood that the negroes, during the hard winter of 1935–36, were burning parts of their fences, out-buildings, furniture and houses, and were dying off in great and not seriously counted numbers, of pneumonia and other afflictions of the lungs.

WPA work is available to very few tenants: they are, tech-nically, employed, and thus have no right to it: and if by chance they manage to get it, landlords are more likely than not to in-tervene. They feel it spoils a tenant to be paid wages, even for a little while. A tenant who so much as tries to get such work is under disapproval.

There is not enough direct relief even for the widows and the old of the county.

Gudger and Ricketts, during this year, were exceedingly lucky. After they, and Woods, had been turned away from gov-ernment work, they found work in a sawmill. They were given the work on condition that they stay with it until the mill was moved, and subject strictly to their landlords' permission: and their employer wouldn't so much as hint how long the work might last. Their landlords quite grudgingly gave them permis-sion, on condition that they pay for whatever help was needed in their absence during the picking season. Gudger hired a hand, at eight dollars a month and board. Ricketts did not need to: his family is large enough. They got a dollar and a quarter a day five days a week and seventy-five cents on Saturday, seven dollars a week, ten hours' work a day. Woods did not even try for this work: he was too old and too sick.

Work

To come devotedly into the depths of a subject, your respect for it increasing in every step and your whole heart weakening apart with shame upon yourself in your dealing with it: To know at length better and better and at length into the bottom of your soul your unworthiness of it: Let me hope in any case that it is something to have begun to learn. Let this all stand however it may: since I cannot make it the image it should be, let it stand as the image it is: I am speaking of my verbal part of this book as a whole. By what kind of foreword I can make clear some essential coherence in it, which I know is there, balanced of its chaos, I do not yet know. But the time is come when it is necessary for me to say at least this much: and now, having said it, to go on, and to try to make an entrance into this chapter, which should be an image of the very essence of their lives: that is, of the work they do.

It is for the clothing, and for the food, and for the shelter, by these to sustain their lives, that they work. Into this work and need, their minds, their spirits, and their strength are so steadily and intensely drawn that during such time as they are not at work, life exists for them scarcely more clearly or in more variance and seizure and appetite than it does for the more simply organized among the animals, and for the plants. This arduous physical work, to which a consciousness beyond that of the simplest child would be only a useless and painful encumbrance, is undertaken without choice or the thought of chance of choice, taught forward from father to son and from mother to daughter; and its essential and few returns you have seen: the houses they live in; the clothes they wear: and have still to see, and for the present to imagine, what it brings them to eat; what it has done to their bodies, and to their consciousness; and what it makes of their leisure, the pleasures which are made available to them. I say here only: work as a means to other ends might have some favor in it, even which was of itself dull and heartless work, in which one's strength was used for another man's benefit: but the ends of this work are absorbed all but entirely into the work itself, and in what little remains, nearly all is obliterated; nearly nothing is obtainable; nearly all is cruelly stained, in the tensions of physical need, and in the desperate tensions of the need of work which is not available.

I have said this now three times. If I were capable, as I wish I were, I could say it once in such a way that it would be there in its complete awefulness. Yet knowing, too, how it is repeated upon each of them, in every day of their lives, so powerfully, so entirely, that it is simply the natural air they breathe, I wonder whether it could ever be said enough times.

The plainness and iterativeness of work must be one of the things which make it so extraordinarily difficult to write of. The plain details of a task once represented, a stern enough effort in itself, how is it possibly to be made clear enough that this same set of leverages has been undertaken by this woman in nearly every day of the eleven or the twenty-five years since her marriage, and will be persisted in in nearly every day to come in all the rest of her life; and that it is only one among the many processes of wearying effort which make the shape of each one of her living days; how is it to be calculated, the number of times she has done these things, the number of times she is still to do them; how conceivably in words is it to be given as it is in actuality, the accumulated weight of these actions upon her; and what this cumulation has made of her body; and what it has made of her mind and of her heart and of her being. And how is this to be made so real to you who read of it, that it will stand and stay in you as the deepest and most iron anguish and guilt of your existence that you are what you are, and that she is what she is, and that you cannot for one moment exchange places with her, nor by any such hope make expiation for what she has suffered at your hands, and for what you have gained at hers: but only by consuming all that is in you into the never relaxed determination that this shall be made different and shall be made right, and that of what is 'right' some, enough to die for, is clear already, and the vast darkness of the rest has still, and far more passionately and more skeptically than ever before, to be questioned into, defended, and learned toward. There is no way of taking the heart and the intelligence by the hair and of wresting it to its feet, and of making it look this terrific thing in the eyes: which are such gentle eyes: you may meet them, with all the summoning of heart you have, in the photograph in this volume of the young woman with black hair: and they are to be multiplied, not losing the knowledge that each is a single, unrepeatable, holy individual, by the two billion human creatures who are alive upon the planet today; of whom a few hundred thousands are drawn into complications of specialized anguish, but of whom the huge swarm and majority are made and acted upon as she is: and of all these individuals, contemplate, try to encompass, the one annihilating chord.

But I must make a new beginning:

(Selection from Part I:

The family exists for work. It exists to keep itself alive. It is a cooperative economic unit. The father does one set of tasks; the mother another; the children still a third, with the sons and daughters serving apprenticeship to their father and mother respectively. A family is called a force, without irony; and children come into the world chiefly that they may help with the work and that through their help the family may increase itself. Their early years are leisurely; a child's life work begins as play. Among his first imitative gestures are gestures of work; and the whole imitative course of his maturing and biologic envy is a stepladder of the learning of physical tasks and skills.

This work solidifies, and becomes steadily more and more, in greater and greater quantity and variety, an integral part of his life.

Besides imitation, he works if he is a man under three compulsions, in three stages. First for his parents. Next for himself, single and wandering in the independence of his early manhood: 'for himself,' in the sense that he wants to stay alive, or better, and has no one dependent on him. Third, for himself and his wife and his family, under an employer. A woman works just for her parents; next, without a transition phase, for her husband and family.

Work for your parents is one thing: work 'for yourself' is another. They are both hard enough, yet light, relative to what is to come. On the day you are married, at about sixteen if you are a girl, at about twenty if you are a man, a key is turned, with a sound not easily audible, and you are locked between the stale earth and the sky; the key turns in the lock behind you, and your full life's work begins, and there is nothing conceivable for which it can afford to stop short of your death, which is a long way off. It is perhaps at its best during the first two years or so, when you are young and perhaps are still enjoying one another or have not yet lost all hope, and when there are not yet so many children as to weigh on you. It is perhaps at its worst during the next ten to twelve years, when there are more and more children, but none of them old enough, yet, to be much help. One could hardly describe it as slackening off after that, for in proportion with the size of the family, it has been necessary to take on more land and more work, and, too, a son or daughter gets just old enough to be any full good to you, and marries or strikes out for himself: yet it is true, anyhow, that from then on there are a number of strong and fairly responsible people in the household besides the man and his wife. In really old age, with one of the two dead, and the children all married, and the widowed one making his home among them in the slow rotations of a floated twig, waiting to die, it does ease off some, depending more then on the individual: one may choose to try to work hard and seem still capable, out of duty and the wish to help, or out of 'egoism,' or out of the dread of dropping out of life; or one may relax, and live unnoticed, never spoken to, dead already; or again, life may have acted on you in such a way that you have no choice in it: or still again, with a wife dead, and children gone, and a long hard lifetime behind you, you may choose to marry again and begin the whole cycle over, lifting onto your back the great weight a young man carries, as Woods has done.

That is the general pattern, its motions within itself lithe-unfolded, slow, gradual, grand, tremendously and quietly weighted, as a heroic dance: and the bodies in this dance, and the spirits, undergoing their slow, miraculous, and dreadful changes: such a thing indeed should be constructed of just these persons: the great, somber, blooddroned, beansprout helmed fetus unfurling within Woods' wife; the infants of three families, staggering happily, their hats held full of freshly picked cotton; the Ricketts children like delirious fawns and panthers; and secret Pearl with her wicked skin; Louise, lifting herself to rest her back, the heavy sack trailing, her eyes on you; Junior, jealous and lazy, malingering, his fingers sore; the Ricketts daughters, the younger stepping beautifully as a young mare, the elder at the stove with her mouth twisted; Annie Mae at twenty-seven, in her angular sweeping, every motion a wonder to watch; George, in his sunday clothes with his cuffs short on his blocked wrists, looking at you, his head slightly to one side, his earnest eyes a little squinted as if he

were looking into a light; Mrs. Ricketts, in that time of morning
when from the corn she reels into the green roaring glooms of
her home, falls into a chair with gaspings which are almost
groaning sobs, and dries in her lifted skirt her delicate and
reeking head; Miss-Molly, chopping wood as if in each blow of
the axe she held captured in focus the vengeance of all time;
Woods, slowed in his picking, forced to stop and rest much too
often, whose death is hastened against a doctor's warnings in
that he is picking at all: I see these among others on the clay
in the grave mutations of a dance whose business is the genius
of a moving camera, and which it is not my hope ever to record: yet here, perhaps, if not of these archaic circulations of
the rude clay altar, yet of their shapes of work, I can make a
few crude sketches:

A man: George Gudger, Thomas Woods, Fred Ricketts: his
work is with the land, in the seasons of the year, in the sustain-
ment and ordering of his family, the training of his sons:

A woman: Annie Mae Gudger, Ivy Woods, Sadie Ricketts:
her work is in the keeping of the home, the preparation of food
against each day and against the dead season, the bearing and
care of her children, the training of her daughters:

Children: all these children: their work is as it is told to them
and taught to them until such time as they shall strengthen and
escape, and, escaped of one imprisonment, are submitted into
another.

There are times of year when all these three are overlapped
and collaborated, all in the field in the demand, chiefly, of cotton; but more largely, the woman is the servant of the day, and
of immediate life, and the man is the servant of the year, and of
the basis and boundaries of life, and is their ruler; and the children are the servants of their parents: and the center of all
their existence, the central work, that by which they have their
land, their shelter, their living, that which they must work for
no reward more than this, because they do not own themselves,
and without hope or interest, that which they cannot eat and

get no money of but which is at the center of their duty and greatest expense of strength and spirit, the cultivation and harvesting of cotton: and all this effort takes place between a sterile earth and an uncontrollable sky in whose propitiation is centered their chief reverence and fear, and the deepest earnestness of their prayers, who read in these machinations of their heaven all signs of a fate which the hardest work cannot much help, and, not otherwise than as the most ancient peoples of the earth, make their plantations in the unpitying pieties of the moon.

WORK 2: COTTON

Cotton is only one among several crops and among many labors: and all these other crops and labors mean life itself. Cotton means nothing of the sort. It demands more work of a tenant family and yields less reward than all the rest. It is the reason the tenant has the means to do the rest, and to have the rest, and to live, as a tenant, at all. Aside from a few negligibilities of minor sale and barter and of out-of-season work, it is his one possible source of money, and through this fact, though his living depends far less on money than on the manipulations of immediate nature, it has a certain royalty. It is also that by which he has all else besides money. But it is also his chief contracted obligation, for which he must neglect all else as need be; and is the central leverage and symbol of his privation and of his wasted life. It is the one crop and labor which is in no possible way useful as it stands to the tenant's living; it is among all these the one which must and can be turned into money; it is among all these the one in which the landowner is most interested; and it is among all these the one of which the tenant can hope for least, and can be surest that he is being cheated, and is always to be cheated. All other tasks are incidental to it; it is constantly on everyone's mind; yet of all of them it is the work in which the tenant has least hope and least interest, and to which he must devote the most energy. Any less involved and self-contradictory attempt to understand what cotton and cotton work 'means' to a tenant would, it seems to me, be false to it. It has the doubleness that all jobs have by which one stays alive and in which one's life is made a cheated ruin, and the same sprained and twilight effect on those who must work at it: but because it is only one among the many jobs by which a tenant family must stay alive, and deflects all these others, and receives still other light from their more personal need, reward, and value, its meanings are much more complex than those of most jobs: it is a strong stale magnet among many others more weak and more yielding of life and hope. In the mind of one in whom all these magnetisms are daily and habituated from his birth, these meanings are one somber mull: yet all their several forces are pulling at once, and by them the brain is quietly drawn and quartered. It seems to me it is only through such a complex of meanings that a tenant can feel, toward that crop, toward each plant in it, toward all that work, what he and all grown women too appear to feel, a particular automatism, a quiet, apathetic, and inarticulate yet deeply vindictive hatred, and at the same time utter hopelessness, and the deepest of their anxieties and of their hopes: as if the plant stood enormous in the unsteady sky fastened above them in all they do like the eyes of an overseer. To do all of the hardest work of your life in service of these drawings-apart of ambiguities; and to have all other tasks and all one's consciousness stained and drawn apart in it: I can conceive of little else which could be so inevitably destructive of the appetite for living, of the spirit, of the being, or by whatever name the centers of individuals are to be called: and this very literally: for just as there are deep chemical or electric changes in all the body under anger, or love, or fear, so there must certainly be at the center of these meanings and their directed emotions; perhaps most essentially, an incalculably somber and heavy weight and dark knotted iron of subnausea at the peak of the diaphragm, darkening and weakening the whole body and being, the literal feeling by which the words a broken heart are no longer poetic, but are merely the most accurate possible description.

Yet these things as themselves are withdrawn almost beyond visibility, and the true focus and right telling of it would be in the exact textures of each immediate task.

Of cotton farming I know almost nothing with my own eyes; the rest I have of Bud Woods. I asked enough of other people to realize that every tenant differs a little in his methods, so nothing of this can be set down as 'standard' or 'correct'; but the dissonances are of small detail rather than of the frame and series in the year. I respect dialects too deeply, when they are used by those who have a right to them, not to be hesitant in using them, but I have decided to use some of Woods' language here. I have decided, too, to try to use my imagination a little, as carefully as I can. I must warn you that the result is sure to be somewhat inaccurate: but it is accurate anyhow to my ignorance, which I would not wish to disguise.

From the end of the season and on through the winter the cotton and the corn stand stripped and destroyed, the cotton black and brown, the corn gray and brown and rotted gold, much more shattered, the banks of woodland bare, drenched and black, the clay dirt sombered wet or hard with a shine of iron, peaceful and exhausted; the look of trees in a once full-blown country where such a burning of war has gone there is no food left even for birds and insects, all now brought utterly quiet, and the bare homes dark with dampness, under the soft and mourning midwinter suns of autumnal days, when all glows gold yet lifeless, and under constrictions of those bitter freezings when the clay is shafted and sprilled with ice, and the aching thinly drifted snows which give the land its shape, and, above all, the long, cold, silent, inexhaustible, and dark winter rains:

In the late fall or middle February this tenant, which of the three or of the millions I do not care—a man, dressed against the wet coldness, may be seen small and dark in his prostrated fields, taking down these sometimes brittle, sometimes rotted forests of last year's crops with a club or with a cutter, putting death to bed, cleaning the land: and late in February, in fulfillment of an obligation to his landlord, he borrows a second mule and, with a two-horse plow, runs up the levees,[1] that is, the terraces, which shall preserve his land; this in a softening mild brightness and odoriferousness of presaging spring, and a rustling shearing apart of the heavy land, his mules moving in slow scarce-wakened method as of work before dawn, knowing the real year's work to be not started yet, only made ready for. It is when this is done, at about the first of March, that the actual work begins, with what is planted where, and with what grade and amount of fertilizer, determined by the landlord, who will also, if he wishes, criticize, advise, and govern at all stages of planting and cultivation. But the physical work, and for that matter the knowledge by which he works, is the tenant's, and this is his tenth or his fortieth year's beginning of it, and it is of the tenant I want to tell.

How you break the land in the first place depends on whether you have one or two mules or can double up with another tenant for two mules. It is much better to broadcast if you can. With two mules you can count on doing it all in that most thorough way. But if you have only one mule you break what you have time for, more shallowly, and, for the rest, you bed, that is, start the land.

---

[1] These farms are the width of a state and still more from the river. Is levee originally a land or a river word? It must be a river word, for terracing against erosion is recent in America. So the Mississippi has such power that men who have never seen it use its language in their work.

To broadcast, to break the land broadcast: take a twister, which is about the same as a turning plow, and, heading the mule in concentrics the shape of the field, lay open as broad and deep a ribbon of the stiff dirt as the strength of the mule and of your own guidance can manage: eight wide by six deep with a single-horse plow, and twice that with a double, is doing well: the operation has the staggering and reeling yet steady quality of a small sailboat clambering a storm.

Where you have broadcast the land, you then lay out the furrows three and a half feet apart with a shovel plow; and put down fertilizer; and by four furrows with a turning plow, twist the dirt back over the fertilized furrow. But if, lacking mule power, you have still land which is not broken, and it is near time to plant, you bed the rest. There are two beddings. The first is hard bedding: breaking the hard pan between the rows.

Hard bedding: set the plow parallel to the line of (last year's) stalks and along their right, follow each row to its end and up the far side. The dirt lays open always to the right. Then set the plow close in against the stalks and go around again. The stubble is cleaned out this second time round and between each two rows is a bed of soft dirt: that is to say, the hard pan is all broken. That is the first bedding.

Then drop guano along the line where the stalks were, by machine or by horn. Few tenants use the machine; most of them either buy a horn, or make it, as Woods does. It is a long tin cone, small and low, with a wood handle, and a hole in the low end. It is held in the left hand, pointed low to the furrow, and is fed in fistfuls, in a steady rhythm, from the fertilizer sack, the incipient frock, slung heavy along the right side.

After you have strowed the gyewanner you turn the dirt back over with two plowings just as before: and that is the second bedding. Pitch the bed shallow, or you won't be able to work it right.

If you have done all this right you haven't got a blemish in all your land that is not broke: and you are ready to plant.

But just roughly, only as a matter of suggestion, compute the work that has been done so far, in ten acres of land, remembering that this is not counting in ten more acres of corn and a few minor crops: how many times has this land been retraced in the rolling-gaited guidance and tensions and whippings and orderings of plowing, and with the steadily held horn, the steady arc of the right arm and right hand fisting and opening like a heart, the heavy weight of the sack at the right side?

Broadcasting, the whole unbroken plaque slivered open in rectilinear concenters, eight inches apart and six deep if with one mule, sixteen apart and twelve deep if with two: remember how much length of line is coiled in one reel or within one phonograph record: and then each furrow, each three and a half feet, scooped open with a shovel plow: and in each row the fertilizer laid: and each row folded cleanly back in four transits of its complete length: or bedding, the first bedding in four transits of each length; and then the fertilizer: and four more transits of each length: every one of the many rows of the whole of the field gone eight times over with a plow and a ninth by hand; and only now is it ready for planting.

Planting

There are three harrs you might use but the spring-toothed harr is best. The long-toothed section harrow tears your bed to pieces; the short-toothed is better, but catches on snags and is more likely to pack the bed than to loosen it. The springtooth moves lightly but incisively with a sort of knee-action sensitiveness to the modulations of the ground, and it jumps snags. You harrow just one row at a time and right behind the harrow comes the planter. The planter is rather like a tennis-court marker: a séed bin set between light wheels, with a little plow protruded from beneath it like a foot from under a hoopskirt. The little beak of the plow slits open the dirt; just at its lifted heel the seed thrills out in a spindling stream; a flat wheel flats the dirt over: a light-traveling, tender, iron sexual act entirely worthy of setting beside the die-log and the swept broad-handed arm.[2]

Depending on the moisture and the soil, it will be five days to two weeks before the cotton will show.

Cultivating begins as soon as it shows an inch.

Cultivation:

Barring off: the sweepings: chopping: laying by:

The first job is barring off.

Set a five- to six-inch twister, the smallest one you have, as close in against the stalks as you can get it and not damage them, as close as the breadth of a finger if you are good at it, and throw the dirt to the middle. Alongside this plow is a wide tin defender, which doesn't allow a blemish to fall on the young plants.

Then comes the first of the four sweepings. The sweeps are blunt stocks shaped a good deal like stingrays. Over their dull foreheads and broad shoulders they neither twist nor roll the dirt, but shake it from the middle to the beds on either side. For the first sweeping you still use the defender. Use a little stock, but the biggest you dare to; probably the eighteen-inch.

Next after that comes the chopping, and with this the whole family helps down through the children of eight or seven, and by helps, I mean that the family works full time at it. Chopping

---

[2] I am unsure of this planting machine; I did not see one there; but what Woods described to me seemed to tally with something I had seen, and not remembered with perfect clearness, from my childhood. The die-log is still used, Woods says, by some of the older-fashioned farmers and by some negroes. I'm not very clear about it either, but I am interested because according to Woods its use goes a *way* on back. My 'impression' is that it's simple enough: a hollow homemade cylinder of wood with a hole in it to regulate and direct the falling stream of seed as would be more difficult by hand.

is a simple and hard job, and a hot one, for by now the sun, though still damp, is very strong, hot with a kind of itchy intensity that is seldom known in northern springs. The work is, simply, thinning the cotton to a stand; hills a foot to sixteen inches apart, two to four stalks to the hill. It is done with an eight to ten-inch hoeblade. You cut the cotton flush off at the ground, bent just a little above it, with a short sharp blow of the blade of which each stroke is light enough work; but multiplied into the many hundreds in each continuously added hour, it aches first the forearms, which so harden they seem to become one bone, and in time the whole spine.

The second sweeping is done with the twenty to twenty-two-inch stock you will use from now on; then comes hoeing, another job for the whole family; then you run the middles; that is, you put down soda by hand or horn or machine; soda makes the weed, guano puts on the fruit; then comes the third sweeping; and then another hoeing. The first and second sweepings you have gone pretty deep. The stuff is small and you want to give loose ground to your feed roots. The third sweeping is shallow, for the feed roots have extended themselves within danger of injury.

The fourth sweeping is so light a scraping that it is scarcely more than a ritual, like a barber's last delicate moments with his muse before he holds the mirror up to the dark side of your skull. The cotton has to be treated very carefully. By this last sweeping it is making. Break roots, or lack rain, and it is stopped dead as a hammer.

This fourth sweeping is the operation more properly known as laying by. From now on until picking time, there is nothing more a farmer can do. Everything is up to the sky, the dirt, and the cotton itself; and in six weeks now, and while the farmer is fending off such of its enemies as he can touch, and, lacking rations money to live on, is desperately seeking and conceivably finding work, or with his family is hung as if on a hook on his front porch in the terrible leisure, the cotton is making, and his year's fate is being quietly fought out between agencies over which he has no control. And in this white midsummer, while he is thus waiting however he can, and defending what little he can, these are his enemies, and this is what the cotton is doing with its time:

Each square points up. That is to say: on twig-ends, certain of the fringed leaves point themselves into the sharp form of an infant prepuce; each square points up: and opens a flat white flower which turns pink next day, purple the next, and on the next day shrivels and falls, forced off by the growth, at the base of the bloom, of the boll. The development from square to boll consumes three weeks in the early summer, ten days in the later, longer and more intense heat. The plants are well fringed with pointed squares, and young cold bolls, by the time the crop is laid by; and the blooming keeps on all summer. The development of each boll from the size of a pea to that point where, at the size of a big walnut, it darkens and dries and its white contents silently explode it, takes five to eight weeks and is by no means ended when the picking season has begun.

And meanwhile the enemies: bitterweed, ragweed, Johnson grass, the weevil, the army worm; the slippery chances of the sky. Bitterweed is easily killed out and won't come up again. Ragweed will, with another prong every time. That weed can suck your crop to death. Johnson grass, it takes hell and scissors to control. You can't control it in the drill with your plowing. If you just cut it off with the hoe, it is high as your thumb by the next morning. The best you can do is dig up the root with the corner of your hoe, and that doesn't hold it back any too well.

There is a lot less trouble from the weevils[3] than there used

---

[3] If I remember rightly, people never learned any successful method against him, and it is some insect, whose name and kind I forget, who holds him in check.

to be, but not the army worms. Army worms are devils. The biggest of them get to be the size of your little finger. They eat leaves and squares and young bolls. You get only a light crop of them at first. They web up in the leaves and turn into flies, the flies lay eggs, the eggs turn into army worms by the millions and if they have got this good a start of you you can hear the sound of them eating in the whole field and it sounds like a brushfire. They are a bad menace but they are not as hard to control as the weevil. You mix arsenic poison with a sorry grade of flour and dust the plants late of an evening (afternoon) or soon of a morning (pre-morning); and the dew makes a paste of it that won't blow off.

It is only in a very unusual year that you do well with both of the most important crops, the two life mainly depends on, because they need rain and sun in such different amounts. Cotton needs a great deal less rain than corn; it is really a sun flower. If it is going to get a superflux of rain, that will best come before it is blooming; and if it has got to rain during that part of the summer when a fairsized field is blooming a bale a day, it had best rain late in the evening when the blooms are shutting or at night, not in the morning or the mid day: for then the bloom is blared out flat; rain gets in it easy and hangs on it; it shuts wet, sours, and sticks to the boll; next morning it turns red and falls. Often the boll comes off with it. But the boll that stays on is sour and rotted and good for nothing. Or to put it the other way around, it can take just one rain at the wrong time of day at the wrong time of summer to wreck you out of a whole bale.

It is therefore not surprising that they are constant readers of the sky; that it holds not an ounce of 'beauty' to them (though I know of no more magnificent skies than those of Alabama); that it is the lodestone of their deepest pieties; and that they have, also, the deep stormfear which is apparently common to all primitive peoples. Wind is as terrifying to them as cloud and lightning and thunder: and I remember how, sitting with the Woods, in an afternoon when George was away at work, and a storm was building, Mrs. Gudger and her children came hurrying three quarters of a mile beneath the blackening air to shelter among company. Gudger says: 'You never can tell what's in a cloud.'

Picking season

Late in August the fields begin to whiten more rarely with late bloom and more frequently with cotton and then still thicker with cotton, a sparkling ground starlight of it, steadily bursting into more and more millions of points, all the leaves seeming shrunken smaller; quite as at night the whole frontage of the universe is more and more thoroughly printed in the increasing darkness; and the wide cloudless and tremendous light holds the earth clamped and trained as beneath a vacuum bell and burningglass; in such a brillance that half and two thirds of the sky is painful to look into; and in this white maturing oven the enlarged bolls are streaked a rusty green, then bronze, and are split and splayed open each in a loose vomit of cotton. These split bolls are now *burrs*, hard and edged as chiseled wood, pointed nearly as thorns, spread open in three and four and five gores or cells. It is slow at first, just a few dozen scattered here and there and then a few tens of dozens, and then there is a space of two or three days in which a whole field seems to be crackling open at once, and at this time it seems natural that it must be gone into and picked, but all the more temperate and experienced tenants wait a few days longer until it will be fully worth the effort: and during this bursting of bolls and this waiting, there is a kind of quickening, as if deep under the ground, of all existence, toward a climax which cannot be delayed much longer, but which is held in the tensions of this reluctance, tightening, and delay: and this can be seen equally in long, sweeping drivings of a car between these spangling fields, and in any one of the small towns or the county seats, and in the changed eyes of any one family, a kind of tightening as of an undertow, the whole world and year lifted nearly upon its crest, and soon beginning the long chute down to winter: children, and once in a while a very young or a very old woman or man, whose work is scarcely entered upon or whose last task and climax this may be, are deeply taken with an excitement and a restlessness to begin picking, and in the towns, where it is going to mean money, the towns whose existence is for it and depends on it, and which in most times of year are sunken in sleep as at the bottom of a sea: these towns are sharpening awake; even the white hot streets of a large city are subtly changed in this season: but Gudger and his wife and Ricketts and Woods, and most of the heads of the million and a quarter families who have made this and are to do the working of taking it for their own harm and another's use, they are only a little more quiet than usual, as they might be if they were waiting for a train to come in, and keep looking at the fields, and judging them; and at length one morning (the Ricketts women are already three days advanced in ragged work), Gudger says, Well:

Well; I reckin tomorrow we'd better start to picking:

And the next morning very early, with their broad hats and great sacks and the hickory baskets, they are out, silent, their bodies all slanted, on the hill: and in every field in hundreds of miles, black and white, it is the same: and such as it is, it is a joy which scarcely touches any tenant; and is worn thin and through in half a morning, and is gone for a year.

It is simple and terrible work. Skill will help you; all the endurance you can draw up against it from the roots of your existence will be thoroughly used as fuel to it: but neither skill nor endurance can make it any easier.

Over the right shoulder you have slung a long white sack whose half length trails the ground behind. You work with both hands as fast and steadily as you can. The trick is to get the cotton between your fingertips at its very roots in the burr

in all three or four or five gores at once so that it is brought
out clean in one pluck. It is easy enough with one burr in perhaps ten, where the cotton is ready to fall; with the rest, the
fibers are more tight and tricky. So another trick is, to learn
these several different shapes of burr and resistance as nearly
as possible by instinct, so there will be no second trying and
delay, and none left wasted in the burr; and, too, as quickly
to judge what may be too rotted and dirtied to use, and what is
not yet quite ready to take: there are a lot suspended between
these small uncertainties, and there should be no delay, no
need to use the mind's judgment, and few mistakes. Still another trick is, between these strong pulls of efficiency, proper
judgment, and maximum speed, not to hurt your fingers on the
burrs any worse than you can help. You would have to try
hard, to break your flesh on any one burr, whether on its sharp
points or its edges; and a single raindrop is only scarcely in-
strumental in ironing a mountain flat; but in each plucking of
the hand the fingers are searched deep in along these several
sharp, hard edges. In two hours' picking the hands are just well
limbered up. At the end of a week you are favoring your
fingers, still in the obligation of speed. The later of the three
to five times over the field, the last long weeks of the season,
you might be happy if it were possible to exchange them for
boils. With each of these hundreds of thousands of insertions
of the hands, moreover, the fingers are brought to a small point,
in an action upon every joint and tendon in the hand. I suggest
that if you will try, three hundred times in succession, the following exercise: touch all five fingertips as closely as possible
into one point, trying meanwhile to hold loose cotton in the
palm of the hand: you will see that this can very quickly tire,
cramp and deteriorate the whole instrument, and will understand how easily rheumatism can take up its strictures in just
this place.

Meanwhile, too, you are working in a land of sunlight and
heat which are special to just such country at just that time of

year: sunlight that stands and stacks itself upon you with the serene weight of deep sea water, and heat that makes the jointed and muscled and fine-structured body glow like one indiscriminate oil; and this brilliant weight of heat is piled upon you more and more heavily in hour after hour so that it can seem you are a diving bell whose strained seams must at any moment burst, and the eyes are marked in stinging sweat, and the head, if your health is a little unstable, is gently roaring, like a private blowtorch, and less gently beating with aching blood: also the bag, which can hold a hundred pounds, is filling as it is dragged from plant to plant, four to nine burrs to a plant to be rifled swiftly, and the load shrugged along another foot or two and the white row stretched ahead to a blur and innumerably manifolded in other white rows which have not yet been touched, and younger bolls in the cleaned row behind already breaking like slow popcorn in the heat, and the sack still heavier and heavier, so that it pulls you back as a beast might rather than a mere dead weight: but it is not only this: cotton plants are low, so that in this heat and burden of the immanent sun and of the heavying sack you are dragging, you are continuously somewhat stooped over even if you are a child, and are bent very deep if you are a man or a woman. A strong back is a godsend, but not even the strongest back was built for that treatment, and there combine at the kidneys, and rill down the thighs and up the spine and athwart the shoulders the ticklish weakness of gruel or water, and an aching that is increased in geometric progressions, and at length, in the small of the spine, a literal and persistent sensation of yielding, buckling, splintering, and breakage: and all of this, even though the mercy of nature has hardened your flesh and has anesthetized your nerves and your powers of reflection and of imagination, yet reaches in time the brain and the more mirror-like nerves, and thereby is redoubled upon itself much more powerfully than before: and this is all compounded upon you during each successive hour of the day and during each successive day in a force which rest and food and sleep only partly and superficially refresh: and though, later in the season, you are relieved of the worst of the heat, it is in exchange at the last for a coolness which many pickers like even less well, since it so slows and chills the lubricant garment of sweat they work in, and seriously slows and stiffens the fingers which by then at best afford an excruciation in every touch.

The tenants' idiom has been used ad nauseam by the more unspeakable of the northern journalists but it happens to be accurate: that picking goes on each day from can to can't: sometimes, if there is a feeling of rush, the Ricketts continue it by moonlight. In the blasting heat of the first of the season, unless there is a rush to beat a rain or to make up an almost completed wagonload, it is customary to quit work an hour and a half or even two hours in the worst part of the day and to sit or lie in the shade and possible draft of the hallway or porch asleep or dozing after dinner. This time narrows off as the weeks go by and a sense of rush and of the wish to be done with it grows on the pickers and is tightened through from the landlord. I have heard of tenants and pickers who have no rest-period and no midday meal,[4] but those I am acquainted with have it. It is of course no parallel in heartiness and variety to the proud and enormous meals which farm wives of the wheat country prepare for harvest hands, and which are so very zestfully regarded by some belated virgilians as common to what they like to call the American Scene. It is in fact the ordinary

---

[4] On the big plantations, where a good deal of the picking is done by day labor and is watched over by riding bosses, all the equations of speed and unresting steadiness are of course intensified; the whole nature of the work, in the men and women and their children, is somewhat altered. Yet not so much as might at first seem. A man and his family working alone are drawn narrowly together in these weeds even within themselves, and know they are being watched: from the very first, in town, their landlords are observant of which tenants bring their cotton first to gin and of who is slow and late; also, there is nearly always, in the tenant's family, the exceedingly sharp need of cottonseed money.

every day food, with perhaps a little less variety than in the earlier summer, hastily thrown together and heated by a woman who has hurried in exhausted from the field as few jumps as possible ahead of her family, and served in the dishes she hurriedly rinsed before she hurried out on the early morning as few jumps as possible behind them. When they are all done, she hurries through the dish washing and puts on her straw hat or her sunbonnet and goes on back into the field, and they are all at it in a strung-out little bunch, the sun a bitter white on their deeply bent backs, and the sacks trailing, a slow breeze idling in the tops of the pines and hickories along the far side but the leaves of the low cotton scarcely touched in it, and the whole land, under hours of heat still to go, yet listed subtly forward toward the late end of the day. They seem very small in the field and very lonely, and the motions of their industry are so small, in range, their bodies so slowly moving, that it seems less that they are so hard at work than that they are bowed over so deeply into some fascination or grief, or are as those pilgrims of Quebec who take the great flights of stairs upon their knees, slowly, a prayer spoken in each step. Ellen lies in the white load of the cotton-basket in the shade asleep; Squinchy picks the front of his dress full and takes it to his mother; Clair Bell fills a hat time after time in great speed and with an expression of delight rushes up behind her mother and dumps the cotton on all of her she can reach and goes crazy with laughter, and her mother and the girls stop a minute and she is hugged, but they talk more among themselves than the other families, they are much more quiet than is usual to them, and Mrs. Ricketts only pauses a minute, cleaning the cotton from her skirts and her hair and putting it in her sack, and then she is bowed over deeply at work again. Woods is badly slowed by weakness and by the pain in his shoulder; he welcomes any possible excuse to stop and sometimes has to pause whether there is any excuse or not, but his wife and her mother are both strong and good pickers, so he is able to get by without a hired hand. Thomas is not old enough yet to be any use. Burt too is very young for it and works only by fits and starts; little is expected of children so small, but it is no harm what little they do; you can't learn them too young. Junior is not very quick with it at best. He will work for a while furiously hard, in jealousy of Louise, and then slacken up with sore hands and begin to bully Burt. Katy is very quick. Last summer, when she was only eight, she picked a hundred and ten pounds in a day in a race with Flora Merry Lee. This summer she has had runarounds and is losing two fingernails but she is picking steadily. Pearl Woods is big for her age and is very steadily useful. Louise is an extraordinarily steady and quick worker for her age; she can pick a hundred and fifty pounds in a day. The two Ricketts boys are all right when their papa is on hand to keep them at their work; as it is, with Ricketts at the sawmills they clown a good deal, and tease their sisters. Mrs. Gudger picks about the average for a woman, a hundred and fifty to two hundred pounds a day. She is fast with her fingers until the work exhausts her; 'last half of the day I just don't see how I can keep on with it.' George Gudger is a very poor picker. When he was a child he fell in the fireplace and burnt the flesh off the flat of both hands to the bone, so that his fingers are stiff and slow and the best he has ever done in a day is a hundred and fifty pounds. The average for a man is nearer two hundred and fifty. His back hurts him badly too, so he usually picks on his knees, the way the others pick only when they are resting. Mrs. Ricketts used to pick three hundred and three hundred and fifty pounds in a day but sickness has slowed her to less than two hundred now. Mrs. Ricketts is more often than not a fantast, quite without realizing, and in all these figures they gave me there may be inaccuracy—according to general talk surrounding the Rust machine a hundred pounds a day is good picking—but these are their own estimates of their own abilities, on a matter in which tenants have some pride, and that seems to me more to the point than their accuracy. There are sometimes shifts into gayety in the picking, or a brief excitement, a race between two of the children, or a snake killed; or two who sit a few moments in their sweat in the shaded clay when they have taken some water, but they say very little to each other, for there is little to say, and are soon back to it, and mainly, in hour upon hour, it is speechless, silent, serious, ceaseless and lonely work along the great silence of the unshaded land, ending each day in a vast blaze of dust on the west, every leaf sharpened in long knives of shadow, the clay drawn down through red to purple, and the leaves losing color, and the wild blind eyes of the cotton staring in twilight, in those odors of work done and of nature lost once more to night whose sweetness is a torture, and in the slow, loaded walking home, whose stiff and gentle motions are those of creatures just awakened.

The cotton is ordinarily stored in a small structure out in the land, the cotton house; but none of these three families has one. The Gudgers store it in one of the chambers of their barn, the Woods on their front porch, raising planks around it, the Ricketts in their spare room. The Ricketts children love to play in it, tumbling and diving and burying each other; sometimes, it is a sort of treat, they are allowed to sleep in it. Rats like it too, to make nest-es[5] in, and that draws ratsnakes. It is not around, though, for very long at a time. Each family has a set of archaic iron beam scales, and when these scales have weighed out fourteen hundred pounds of cotton it is loaded, if possible during the first of the morning, onto the narrow and high-boarded wagon, and is taken into Cookstown to gin.

---

[5] Mrs. Gudger's word. Her saying of it was, 'rats likes it to make nest-es in.' It is a common pluralization in the south. There is no Cuteness in it, of speaking by diminutives, and I wonder whether this is not Scottish dialect, and whether they, too, are not innocent of the 'itsybitsying' which the middle-class literacy assumes of them. *Later*. On the proof-sheets is the following note, which I use with thanks: 'Isn't it the Middle-English plural? Chaucer used it for this same word and as a usual plural ending.'

It is a long tall deep narrow load shored in with weathered wagonsides and bulged up in a high puff above these sides, and the mule, held far over to the right of the highway to let the cars go by, steps more steadily and even more slowly than ordinary, with a look almost of pomp, dragging the hearse-shaped wagon: its iron wheels on the left grince in the slags of the highway, those on the right in clay: and high upon the load, the father at the reins, the whole of the family is sitting, if it is a small family, or if it is a large, those children whose turn it is, and perhaps the mother too. The husband is dressed in the better of his work clothes; the wife, and the children, in such as they might wear to town on Saturday, or even, some of them, to church, and the children are happy and excited, high on the soft load, and even a woman is taken with it a little, much more soberly, and even the man who is driving, has in the tightness of his jaws, and in his eyes, which meet those of any stranger with the curious challenging and protective, fearful and fierce pride a poor mother shows when her child, dressed in its best, is being curiously looked at; even he who knows best of any of them, is taken with something of the same: and there is in fact about the whole of it some raw, festal quality, some air also of solemn grandeur, this member in the inconceivably huge and slow parade of mule-drawn, crawling wagons, creaking under the weight of the year's blood-sweated and prayed-over work, on all the roads drawn in, from the utmost runners and ramifications of the slender red roads of all the south and into the southern highways, a wagon every few hundred yards, crested this with a white and this with a black family, all drawn toward those little trembling lodes which are the gins, and all and in each private and silent heart toward that climax of one more year's work which yields so little at best, and nothing so often, and worse to so many hundreds of thousands:

The gin itself, too, the wagons drawn up in line, the people waiting on each wagon, the suspendered white-shirted men on

the platform, the emblematic sweep of the grand-shouldered
iron beam scales cradling gently on the dark doorway their
design of justice, the landlords in their shirt-sleeves at the gin
or relaxed in swivels beside the decorated safes in their little
offices, the heavy-muscled and bloodfaced young men in baseball caps who tumble the bales with short sharp hooks, the
loafers drawn into this place to have their batteries recharged
in the violence that is in process here in the bare and weedy
outskirts of this bare and brutal town; all this also in its hard,
slack, nearly speechless, sullen-eyed way, is dancelike and tri-
umphal: the big blank surfaces of corrugated metal, bright
and sick as gas in the sunlight, square their darkness round a
shuddering racket that subsumes all easy speaking: the tenant
gets his ticket and his bale number, and waits his turn in the
long quiet line; the wagon ahead is emptied and moves forward lightly as the mule is cut; he cuts his own load heavily
under as the gin head is hoisted; he reaches up for the suction
pipe and they let it down to him; he swings and cradles its
voracity down through the crest of and round and round his
stack of cotton, until the last lint has leapt up from the wagon
bed; and all the while the gin is working in the deafening
appetites of its metals, only it is his work the gin is digesting
now, and standing so close in next its flank, he is intimate with
this noise of great energy, cost and mystery; and out at the
rear, the tin and ghostly interior of the seed shed, against
whose roof and rafters a pipe extends a steady sleet of seed and
upon all whose interior surfaces and all the air a dry nightmare
fleece like the false snows of Christmas movies hangs shuddering as it might in horror of its just accomplished parturition:
and out in front, the last of the cotton snowlike relaxing in
pulses down a slide of dark iron into the compress its pure
whiteness; and a few moments merely of pressure under the
floor level, the air of an off-stage strangling; and the bale is
lifted like a theater organ, the presses unlatched, the numbered
brass tag attached, the metal ties made fast: it hangs in the

light breathing of the scales, his bale, the one he has made, and a little is slivered from it, and its weight and staple length are recorded on his ginning slip, and it is caught with the hooks and tumbled out of the way, his bale of cotton, depersonalized forever now, identical with all others, which shall be melted indistinguishably into an oblivion of fabrics, wounds, bleedings, and wars; he takes his ginning slip to his landlord, and gets his cottonseed money, and does a little buying; and gathers his family together; and leaves town. The exodus from town is even more formal than the parade in was. It has taken almost exactly eighteen minutes to gin each bale, once the waiting was over, and each tenant has done almost exactly the same amount of business afterward, and the empty, light grinding wagons are distributed along the roads in a likewise exact collaboration of time and space apart, that is, the time consumed by ginning plus business, and the space apart which, in that time, a mule traverses at his classic noctambular pace. It is as if those who were drawn in full by the sun and their own effort and sucked dry at a metal heart were restored, were sown once more at large upon the slow breadths of their country, in the precisions of some mechanic and superhuman hand.

That is repeated as many times as you have picked a bale. Your field is combed over three, four or five times. The height of the ginning season in that part of the country is early October, and in that time the loaded wagons are on the road before the least crack of daylight, the waiting is endless hours, and the gin is still pulsing and beating after dark. After that comes hog-killing, and the gristing of the corn and milling of the sorghum that were planted late to come ready late; and more urgent and specific meditation of whether or not to move to another man, and of whether you are to be kept; and settlement time; and the sky descends, the air becomes like dark glass, the ground stiffens, the clay honeycombs with frost, the corn and the cotton stand stripped to the naked bone and the trees are black, the odors of pork and woodsmoke sharpen all over the country, the long dark silent sleeping rains stream down in such grieving as nothing shall ever stop, and the houses are cold, fragile drums, and the animals tremble, and the clay is one shapeless sea, and winter has shut.

Let us now praise famous men, and our fathers that begat us.

The Lord hath wrought great glory by them through his great power from the beginning.

Such as did bear rule in their kingdoms, men renowned for their power, giving counsel by their understanding, and declaring prophecies:

Leaders of the people by their counsels, and by their knowledge of learning meet for the people, wise and eloquent in their instructions:

Such as found out musical tunes, and recited verses in writing:

Rich men furnished with ability, living peaceably in their habitations:

All these were honoured in their generations, and were the glory of their times.

There be of them, that have left a name behind them, that their praises might be reported.

And some there be which have no memorial; who perished, as though they had never been; and are become as though they had never been born; and their children after them.

But these were merciful men, whose righteousness hath not been forgotten.

With their seed shall continually remain a good inheritance, and their children are within the covenant.

Their seed standeth fast, and their children for their sakes. Their seed shall remain for ever, and their glory shall not be blotted out.

Their bodies are buried in peace; but their name liveth for evermore.

PART THREE

Hungry Women and Faltering Homes:

MINNESOTA, COLORADO, NEW YORK

---

10. Women on the Breadlines

MERIDEL LESUEUR

At the time that Meridel LeSueur (1907?–   ) published this honest and unflinching account of human wretchedness, she was living with her two children in Minneapolis and contributing fiction to such magazines as the American Mercury *and* Scribner's. *"Women on the Breadlines" marked her first appearance in the* New Masses, *which took advantage of the occasion to lecture the young writer for the "defeatist" attitude of her contribution. (The magazine's editorial note is reproduced at the end of the article, the spelling and punctuation of which are also as they first appeared in print.) Unfortunately for the literary development of the writer, she took all too well to such tutoring, to judge by her subsequent writings; and although she did publish a volume of short stories (*Salute to Spring, *1940) and a regional history (*North Star Country, *1945), she never did fulfill her early promise. Her first publica-*

"Women on the Breadlines" (*New Masses*, January 1932), pp. 5–7. Reprinted with the permission of the author.

*tion in a Communist periodical is evidence of the attractive
pull of the New Masses on the eager young writers who were
growing out of the darkness of the depression years; in the
period of ferment after the Crash, few magazines were more
lively and more irreverent than this one, despite its domina-
tion by "the boys upstairs." It was only the Moscow Trials, a
far-off series of tragedies, that caused large numbers of radical
intellectuals to question seriously the legitimacy of the magazine's claim to succession to the old Masses and the Liberator.
But by that time the magazine was attracting other writers,
like the Hollywood hacks—less talented, less imaginative, and
above all more docile under front-office and party discipline.*

I am sitting in the city free employment bureau. It's the
woman's section. We have been sitting here now for four hours.
We sit here every day, waiting for a job. There are no jobs.
Most of us have had no breakfast. Some have had scant rations
for over a year. Hunger makes a human being lapse into a state
of lethargy, especially city hunger. Is there any place else in
the world where a human being is supposed to go hungry
amidst plenty without an outcry, without protest, where only
the boldest steal or kill for bread, and the timid crawl the
streets, hunger like the beak of a terrible bird at the vitals?

We sit looking at the floor. No one dares think of the coming winter. There are only a few more days of summer. Everyone is anxious to get work to lay up something for that long
siege of bitter cold. But there is no work. Sitting in the room
we all know it. That is why we don't talk much. We look at
the floor dreading to see that knowledge in each other's eyes.
There is a kind of humiliation in it. We look away from each
other. We look at the floor. It's too terrible to see this animal
terror in each other's eyes.

So we sit hour after hour, day after day, waiting for a job
to come in. There are many women for a single job. A thin

sharp woman sits inside the wire cage looking at a book. For four hours we have watched her looking at that book. She has a hard little eye. In the small bare room there are half a dozen women sitting on the benches waiting. Many come and go. Our faces are all familiar to each other, for we wait here everyday.

This is a domestic employment bureau. Most of the women who come here are middle-aged, some have families, some have raised their families and are now alone, some have men who are out of work. Hard times and the man leaves to hunt for work. He doesn't find it. He drifts on. The woman probably doesn't hear from him for a long time. She expects it. She isn't surprised. She struggles alone to feed the many mouths. Sometimes she gets help from the charities. If she's clever she can get herself a good living from the charities, if she's naturally a lick-spittle, naturally a little docile and cunning. If she's proud then she starves silently, leaving her children to find work, coming home after a day's searching to wrestle with her house, her children.

Some such story is written on the faces of all these women. There are young girls too, fresh from the country. Some are made brazen too soon by the city. There is a great exodus of girls from the farms into the city now. Thousands of farms have been vacated completely in Minnesota. The girls are trying to get work. The prettier ones can get jobs in the stores when there are any, or waiting on table, but these jobs are only for the attractive and the adroit, the others, the real peasants have a more difficult time.

Bernice sits next me. She is a large Polish woman of thirty-five. She has been working in peoples' kitchens for fifteen years or more. She is large, her great body in mounds, her face brightly scrubbed. She has a peasant mind and finds it hard even yet to understand the maze of the city where trickery is worth more than brawn. Her blue eyes are not clever but slow and trusting. She suffers from loneliness and lack of talk. When you speak to her her face lifts and brightens as if you had spoken through a great darkness and she talks magically of little things, as if the weather were magic or tells some crazy tale of her adventures on the city streets, embellishing them in bright colors until they hang heavy and thick like some peasant embroidery. She loves the city anyhow. It's exciting to her, like a bazaar. She loves to go shopping and get a bargain, hunting out the places where stale bread and cakes can be had for a few cents. She likes walking the streets looking for men to take her to a picture show. Sometimes she goes to five picture shows in one day, or she sits through one the entire day until she knows all the dialogue by heart.

She came to the city a young girl from a Wisconsin farm. The first thing that happened to her a charlatan dentist took out all her good shining teeth and the fifty dollars she had saved working in a canning factory. After that she met men in the park who told her how to look out for herself, corrupting her peasant mind, teaching her to mistrust everyone. Sometimes now she forgets to mistrust everyone and gets taken in. They taught her to get what she could for nothing, to count her change, to go back if she found herself cheated, to demand her rights.

She lives alone in little rooms. She bought seven dollars worth of second-hand furniture eight years ago. She rents a room for perhaps three dollars a month in an attic, sometimes in a cold house. Once the house where she stayed was condemned and everyone else moved out and she lived there all winter alone on the top floor. She spent only twenty-five dollars all winter.

She wants to get married but she sees what happens to her married friends, being left with children to support, worn out before their time. So she stays single. She is virtuous. She is slightly deaf from hanging out clothes in winter. She has done people's washings and cooking for fifteen years and in that time she saved thirty dollars. Now she hasn't worked steady for a year and she has spent the thirty dollars. She dreamed of having a little house or a houseboat perhaps with a spot of ground for a few chickens. This dream she will never realize.

She has lost all her furniture now along with the dream. A married friend whose husband is gone gives her a bed for which she pays by doing a great deal of work for the woman. She comes here every day now sitting bewildered, her pudgy hands folded in her lap. She is hungry. Her great flesh has begun to hang in folds. She has been living on crackers. Sometimes a box of crackers lasts a week. She has a friend who's a baker and he sometimes steals the stale loaves and brings them to her.

A girl we have seen every day all summer went crazy yesterday at the Y. W. She went into hysterics, stamping her feet and screaming.

She hadn't had work for eight months. "You've got to give me something," she kept saying. The woman in charge flew into a rage that probably came from days and days of suffering on her part, because she is unable to give jobs, having none. She flew into a rage at the girl and there they were facing each other in a rage both helpless, helpless. This woman told me once that she could hardly bear the suffering she saw, hardly hear it, that she couldn't eat sometimes and had nightmares at night.

So they stood there the two women in a rage, the girl weeping and the woman shouting at her. In the eight months of unemployment she had gotten ragged, and the woman was shouting that she would not send her out like that. "Why don't you shine your shoes," she kept scolding the girl, and the girl kept sobbing and sobbing because she was starving.

"We can't recommend you like that," the harressed Y.W.C.A. woman said, knowing she was starving, unable to do anything. And the girls and the women sat docilly their eyes on the ground, ashamed to look at each other, ashamed of something.

Sitting here waiting for a job, the women have been talking in low voices about the girl Ellen. They talk in low voices with not too much pity for her, unable to see through the mist of their own torment. "What happened to Ellen?" one of them asks. She knows the answer already. We all know it.

A young girl who went around with Ellen tells about seeing her last evening back of a cafe downtown outside the kitchen door, kicking, showing her legs so that the cook came out and gave her some food and some men gathered in the alley and threw small coin on the ground for a look at her legs. And the girl says enviously that Ellen had a swell breakfast and treated her to one too, that cost two dollars.

A scrub woman whose hips are bent forward from stooping with hands gnarled like water soaked branches clicks her tongue in disgust. No one saves their money, she says, a little money and these foolish young things buy a hat, a dollar for breakfast, a bright scarf. And they do. If you've ever been without money, or food, something very strange happens when you get a bit of money, a kind of madness. You don't care. You can't remember that you had no money before, that the money will be gone. You can remember nothing but that there is the money for which you have been suffering. Now here it is. A lust takes hold of you. You see food in the windows. In imagination you eat hugely; you taste a thousand meals. You look in windows. Colours are brighter; you buy something to dress up in. An excitement takes hold of you. You know it is suicide but you can't help it. You must have food, dainty, splendid food and a bright hat so once again you feel blithe, rid of that ratty gnawing shame.

"I guess she'll go on the street now," a thin woman says faintly and no one takes the trouble to comment further. Like every commodity now the body is difficult to sell and the girls say you're lucky if you get fifty cents.

It's very difficult and humiliating to sell one's body.

Perhaps it would make it clear if one were to imagine having to go out on the street to sell, say, one's overcoat. Suppose you have to sell your coat so you can have breakfast and a place to sleep, say, for fifty cents. You decide to sell your only coat. You take it off and put it on your arm. The street, that has before been just a street, now becomes a mart, something entirely different. You must approach someone now and admit you are destitute and are now selling your clothes, your most intimate possessions. Everyone will watch you talking to the stranger showing him your overcoat, what a good coat it is. People will stop and watch curiously. You will be quite naked on the street. It is even harder to try and sell one's self, more humiliating. It is even humiliating to try and sell one's labour. When there is no buyer.

The thin woman opens the wire cage. There's a job for a nursemaid, she says. The old gnarled women, like old horses, know that no one will have them walk the streets with the young so they don't move. Ellen's friend gets up and goes to the window. She is unbelievably jaunty. I know she hasn't had work since last January. But she has a flare of life in her that glows like a tiny red flame and some tenacious thing, perhaps only youth, keeps it burning bright. Her legs are thin but the runs in her old stockings are neatly mended clear down her flat shank. Two bright spots of rouge conceal her palor. A narrow belt is drawn tightly around her thin waist, her long shoulders stoop and the blades show. She runs wild as a colt hunting pleasure, hunting sustenance.

It's one of the great mysteries of the city where women go when they are out of work and hungry. There are not many women in the bread line. There are no flop houses for women as there are for men, where a bed can be had for a quarter or less. You don't see women lying on the floor at the mission in the free flops. They obviously don't sleep in the jungle or under newspapers in the park. There is no law I suppose against their being in these places but the fact is they rarely are.

Yet there must be as many women out of jobs in cities and suffering extreme poverty as there are men. What happens to them? Where do they go? Try to get into the Y.W. without any money or looking down at heel. Charities take care of very few and only those that are called "deserving." The lone girl is under suspicion by the virgin women who dispense charity.

I've lived in cities for many months broke, without help, too timid to get in bread lines. I've known many women to live like this until they simply faint on the street from privations, without saying a word to anyone. A woman will shut herself up in a room until it is taken away from her, and eat a cracker a day and be as quiet as a mouse so there are no social statistics concerning her.

I don't know why it is, but a woman will do this unless she has dependents, will go for weeks verging on starvation, crawling in some hole, going through the streets ashamed, sitting in libraries, parks, going for days without speaking to a living soul like some exiled beast, keeping the runs mended in her stockings, shut up in terror in her own misery, until she becomes too supersensitive and timid to even ask for a job.

Bernice says even strange men she has met in the park have sometimes, that is in better days, given her a loan to pay her room rent. She has always paid them back.

In the afternoon the young girls, to forget the hunger and the deathly torture and fear of being jobless, try and pick up a man to take them to a ten-cent show. They never go to more expensive ones, but they can always find a man willing to spend a dime to have the company of a girl for the afternoon.

Sometimes a girl facing the night without shelter will approach a man for lodging. A woman always asks a man for help. Rarely another woman. I have known girls to sleep in men's rooms for the night, on a pallet without molestation, and given breakfast in the morning.

It's no wonder these young girls refuse to marry, refuse to rear children. They are like certain savage tribes, who, when they have been conquered refuse to breed.

Not one of them but looks forward to starvation, for the coming winter. We are in a jungle and know it. We are beaten, entrapped. There is no way out. Even if there were a job, even if that thin acrid woman came and gave everyone in the room a job for a few days, a few hours, at thirty cents an hour, this would all be repeated tomorrow, the next day and the next.

Not one of these women but knows, that despite years of labour there is only starvation, humiliation in front of them.

Mrs. Grey, sitting across from me is a living spokesman for the futility of labour. She is a warning. Her hands are scarred with labour. Her body is a great puckered scar. She has given birth to six children, buried three, supported them all alive and dead, bearing them, burying them, feeding them. Bred in hunger they have been spare, susceptible to disease. For seven years she tried to save her boy's arm from amputation, diseased from tuberculosis of the bone. It is almost too suffocating to think of that long close horror of years of child bearing, child feeding, rearing, with the bare suffering of providing a meal and shelter.

Now she is fifty. Her children, economically insecure, are drifters. She never hears of them. She doesn't know if they are alive. She doesn't know if she is alive. Such subtleties of suffering are not for her. For her the brutality of hunger and cold, the bare bone of life. That is enough. These will occupy a life. Not until these are done away with can those subtle feelings that make a human being be indulged.

She is lucky to have five dollars ahead of her. That is her security. She has a tumour that she will die of. She is thin as a worn dime with her tumour sticking out of her side. She is brittle and bitter. Her face is not the face of a human being. She has born more than it is possible for a human being to bear. She is reduced to the least possible denominator of human feelings.

It is terrible to see her little bloodshot eyes like a beaten hound's, fearful in terror.

We cannot meet her eyes. When she looks at any of us we look away. She is like a woman drowning and we turn away. We must ignore those eyes that are surely the eyes of a person drowning, doomed. She doesn't cry out. She goes down decently. And we all look away.

The young ones know though. I don't want to marry. I don't want any children. So they all say. No children. No marriage. They arm themselves alone, keep up alone. The man is helpless now. He cannot provide. If he propagates he cannot take care of his young. The means are not in his hands. So they live alone. Get what fun they can. The life risk is too horrible now. Defeat is too clearly written on it.

So we sit in this room like cattle, waiting for a nonexistent job, willing to work to the farthest atom of energy, unable to work, unable to get food and lodging, unable to bear children; here we must sit in this shame looking at the floor, worse than beasts at a slaughter.

It is appalling to think that these women sitting so listless in the room may work as hard as it is possible for a human being to work, may labour night and day, like Mrs. Gray wash street cars from midnight to dawn and offices in the early evening, scrubbing for fourteen and fifteen hours a day, sleeping only five hours or so, doing this their whole lives, and never earn one day of security, having always before them the pit of the future. The endless labour, the bending back, the water soaked hands, earning never more than a week's wages, never having in their hands more life than that.

It's not the suffering, not birth, death, love that the young reject, but the suffering of endless labour without dream, eating the spare bread in bitterness, a slave without the security of a slave.

Editorial Note: This presentation of the plight of the unemployed woman, able as it is, and informative, is defeatest in attitude, lacking in revolutionary spirit and direction which characterize the usual contribution to *New Masses.* We feel it our duty to add, that there is a place for the unemployed woman, as well as man, in the ranks of the unemployed councils and in all branches of the organized revolutionary movement. Fight for your class, read *The Working Woman,* join the Communist Party. (*New Masses,* January 1932)

11. I Should Worry

WELDON KEES

*Weldon Kees (1914–1955?) was born in Beatrice, Nebraska,
and after graduating from the University of Nebraska, went to
work in Lincoln for the Federal Writers' Project. In 1937 he
moved to Denver, and was working in its Public Library when
"I Should Worry" appeared in the* New Directions *annual for
1939. During World War II he became a* Time *magazine staffer
in New York, where he also began to work seriously as a film-
maker and a painter (he had one-man shows at the Peridot
Gallery, and also showed with such fellow abstract-expres-
sionists as Hans Hofmann and Willem de Kooning). On the
West Coast (he had moved to San Francisco in 1951), he became deeply involved with jazz, both as pianist and composer,
made several movies, and collaborated with Dr. Jurgen Ruesch
on* Non-Verbal Communication, *illustrating the book with
photographs he had taken. On July 18, 1955, his car was found
abandoned on the approach to the Golden Gate Bridge and he
was never seen again; he had spoken of suicide and also of
going away to start a new life. Those readers familiar with his
work no doubt think of him primarily as a poet, which is as it
should be, even though he worked fruitfully in an extraordinary variety of fields. His three volumes of poetry, together
with some uncollected poems, were brought together by Donald Justice in 1962 in a volume entitled* The Collected Poems
of Weldon Kees. *His fellow poets have gauged him most
acutely: "Kees is one of the bitterest poets in history," writes
Mr. Justice, and then quotes Kenneth Rexroth: "Others have
called themselves Apocalyptics. Kees lived in a permanent and
hopeless apocalypse." The story that follows, published before*

"I Should Worry" (New Directions, 1939).

his poetry had begun to appear regularly, is not unrepresenta-
tive of his obsessions with the breakup of the family and with
suicide, obsessions that originated during the depression, long
before war and bomb.

Arch Boyle lounged in a broken wicker chair in front of his used auto parts place. A half-smoked cigarette was pasted in one corner of his mouth, and from the other corner a broken toothpick hung. Across the street, in front of the City Mission, an old man was sweeping the sidewalk with a worn broom. A bunch of kids were rollerskating, and each time they went by, the old man had to stop sweeping, leaning on his broom until they had passed. The wheels of their skates rasped on the concrete, and, whenever they rolled over divisions in the sidewalk, they made a clacking sound like a needle on a cracked victrola record. The old man would watch them and then return to his work, raising a thin sift of dust.

Arch deftly removed the toothpick without putting his hands to his face or disturbing the cigarette, and again he thought of his sister. Now, he thought, she would be standing in front of the mirror in the room above him, the room in which his parents had killed themselves, and she would be combing her hair with one hand, her eyes wandering from her distorted image to the pictures of movie actors on the wall that she had torn from magazines and pasted there. He could see her vividly, even the sling around her neck, and he wondered if she would be coming down before long.

He changed his position in the chair and crossed his legs. He was trying to keep his eyes out of the sunlight without going back into the store too far. It was an open-front place: all kinds of used auto parts were scattered over shelves and boxes and tables. He got into a comfortable position, and after he was settled, he crossed his legs and began to strike himself below the knee-cap with the side of his hand. He was testing his reflexes.

Satisfied that they were all right, same as they'd been yesterday, he began thinking of how much he wanted a drink of gin.
He wanted a drink in the worst way but that morning he had
paid O. B. Daniels the rent on the building, and now he was
flat. He didn't have a cent, and there hadn't been any business
all day. It was getting close to five o'clock, and he was broke
and needed a shot of gin. Better yet, two shots. He wished he
had held out a little on O. B.

Next door, at Womack's American Radio Repair Shop, a
loudspeaker blared the final chorus of *The Love Bug Will Bite
You If You Don't Watch Out.* Arch tapped his foot in time to
the music, imagining a scene in which he talked O. B. into lowering the rent.

*You are listening to "The World Dances," a group of re-
corded numbers by Howard Griffin and his Californians. We
hear them next in an interrogative mood, as they ask the musical question, "Am I Wasting My Time?"*

Or better yet: say he had something on O. B. Listen, O. B., I
know all about this little graft you're working and maybe some
other people'd like to know about it too. Huh? O. B. looked
green around the gills. Well, what is it you want, Boyle? The
rent on the building. That's all. O. B. not liking it but agreeing.
He had to. Shaking his head, saying okay. A cinch.

Nuts.

He took a last drag from his cigarette and tossed it on the
sidewalk. It rolled along, scattering sparks, and then fell off the
curb into the gutter. He yawned, wondering why Womack had
to play that thing so loud all the time. Made so much noise you
couldn't hear yourself think.

People went by: an old man in his shirtsleeves carrying a
basket, a fat Negress in a violet dress who dragged along with
one hand a little colored kid, a boy on a red bicycle, two young
fellows in overalls carrying dinnerpails. As they passed, one of
them said, They ain't going to get me over there. Hell no. Two
dogs trotted by, their noses to the ground. They paused for a

moment in front of Arch to sniff at a red popbottle cap on the sidewalk, and then went on, their tails held stiff and erect.

Arch got up and stretched. His shirtsleeves were rolled up above his elbows, and the wicker chair had left a mottled red print on his fat arms, corrugating them like a washboard. He walked over to Womack's American Radio Repair Shop and looked inside.

Womack! he yelled.

The radio was playing so loudly that his voice could scarcely be heard. The funnel-shaped loudspeaker boomed from above the doorway. Tendrils of wires escaped from its base through little holes bored in the wood.

Womack! he called again.

Finally a man came up from the cellar. He was carrying a pair of pliers. He looked up, frowning slightly, and said, Whatdya want? He stood there, the trapdoor behind him, looking first at Arch and then at the pliers in his hand.

Turn that thing down, can you? Arch said. I bet you can hear it clear over in the next block.

What's the matter? Don't you like it?

Whatdyou think?

That's what I'm asking you. He put the pliers down on a workbench.

Jesus, you can hear it for blocks. Why don't you turn it down?

Because maybe I want it loud, that's why.

Holy God, Arch thought. What can you do with a guy like him?

Womack came over close to him and tapped him on the chest with a pudgy forefinger. Listen, he said slowly, I play it loud on account of a good reason, see? Music's something people like to hear. I give em music. Music plays. Gives me more business, get the point?

Okay, okay. Only turn it down. You don't know what a racket that thing makes. A guy has to sit out there and listen to it. You can hear it for blocks.

And maybe I like it that way.

You must, Arch said. Listen, Womack, look at it this way. It stands to reason that nobody wants their eardrums ruined. That ain't going to get you no business. Sure, give em music, but turn it down. Jesus, I bet you can hear it clear over on Christopher Street.

Womack scratched his head.

Hell, it just stands to reason nobody wants their eardrums ruined. That's just sense.

Maybe so, Womack said.

It's just sense, that's all.

Okay, I'll turn it down a little. I guess it won't hurt none.

A guy just can't hear himself think the way it's going now, Arch said. Say, Womack . . .

Yeh?

You couldn't loan a guy a dollar, could you. Until Monday?

No, I couldn't, said Womack.

I didn't think you could, Arch said. Okay. Forget it.

I wasn't even thinking about it none.

Okay. Okay. I just thought.

Well, think again, said Womack.

He left him regulating the volume on the radio. Arch's sister, Betty Lou, had come down from their rooms over the shop, and now she sat in the wicker chair, a green knit dress stretched tight over her body. She had broken her arm about a week before. It hung in a white sling that was tied around her neck.

Arch looked at her, wishing that he were over at Freddie's picking up a couple of straight gins. He didn't say anything. She stared up at him, her jaws working at a piece of gum she had just started on. He was close enough to her to get a whiff of the wintergreen odor. She was deaf and dumb.

He wondered again just how she had broken her arm. All he knew was that some guy in a green sedan had picked her up last Thursday late in the evening, and when she had come back, alone, three or four hours later, she had a broken arm. She was whimpering, and she held the arm out to him, shaking her head and sobbing soundlessly. He had set it himself—doctors were too expensive—working carefully with the splints to make sure it would be all right.

Later, he had tried to get it out of her, tried to find out how it had happened. Time after time he had poked the piece of paper in front of her, the piece of paper on which he had written: *How did it happen? You better tell me.* He had put the pencil between her fingers, commanding her to write, but she had repeatedly thrown it on the floor, shaking her head and stamping her foot. He hadn't been able to get a thing out of her since it had happened. And now she sat there in the wicker chair, her jaws moving regularly behind the slash of scarlet on her lips that broke the paleness of her face, her green dress pulled up just a little too high, watching the cars that were going by in the five o'clock rush.

If my mother and the old man had lived, he thought. All right: break your goddamn arm, go ahead. See if I care. He put a cigarette between his lips and struck a match on his beltbuckle. Break your arm, he thought.

Womack hadn't turned his radio down so that you could notice it. . . . . *presenting a group of recorded selections by Howard Griffin and his Californians. Here's an old favorite for you! It's Howard Griffin's interpretation of "Ida." A recording.*

Maybe some people have lives that make sense, he thought. Maybe some of them do things that make some difference, maybe for some of them it goes some place and has some meaning. More meaning than getting up in the hot or the cold morning, it doesn't make any difference, and putting on a pair of dirty socks and clothes that you wore yesterday and eating breakfast with a sister that can't hear you or speak to you. And all of the time you're wondering what's going on in her mind. And then you go down to the shop and wait on customers, if you're lucky enough to have any, and then by the time night comes around you toss a slug of gin inside of you and after you're good and drunk you fall into bed dog-tired and feel it spinning around beneath you and hear the streetcars rumbling by in the dark and your head feeling like a bomb about to explode.

He went towards the back of the shop and dug around in some rubbish to see if he could find a bottle that he might have overlooked. They were all empties, though. He stood for a moment by the dirty window. Some kids walked up the alley, kicking a tin can. You going to the movies tonight? Nah. And the can banging on the concrete. He tapped the ash from the cigarette. If I only had some dough, he thought. If I only had a little dough. An automobile pulled up in front of the place, and without turning he knew by the sound of the motor that it was a Chevy, probably a 1934 model. When he heard the door of the car click shut, he looked around and saw a man in a grey suit walking towards him.

You got any straps for license plates? the man asked.

Arch looked him over. He was wearing a grey felt hat and a grey suit and limped slightly. He was about forty or so, Arch guessed.

Yeh, Right over here.

Arch led him to a table and indicated the straps. But the man wasn't looking at the merchandise on the table; instead, he was standing in the aisle watching Betty Lou. She was looking at him, too, her eyes half closed and one leg crossed over the other, swinging it slowly up and down.

Here they are, Arch said.

Huh? the man said, glancing up. Oh yeh, the straps. He glanced back at the girl for a moment and then fastened his eyes on the straps. How much? I only need one. The one on the front plate just broke.

Well, here's one I'll sell you for a dime. It's used a little.

The man looked at it briefly, holding it in his hands, and said, That's all right. I'll take it. I'll take this one. He fished a dime from his pocket and dropped it in Arch's hand. There you are, he said. Then his eyes went back to Betty Lou. His tongue kept going over his lower lip, slowly moistening it.

I've done it before, Arch thought. But never when she's had

a broken arm. But I could use the dough, and she doesn't care. It's nothing to her. A thing like that.

Something else? Arch said.

The man started. No, huhuh, I guess not.

Interested in the girl?

The man laughed nervously.

Betty Lou was half turned in the wicker chair, staring at the man, smiling. Her crossed leg moved up and down regularly.

Two bucks, mister, said Arch.

The man raised an eyebrow. Two? he said. What's the matter with her arm?

It's sprained. Don't worry about that. It won't bother you none. You ain't worrying about that, are you?

The man slapped the strap softly against his leg. *For the past thirty minutes you have been listening to a group of dance selections played by Howard Griffin and his Californians.* The man looked at Arch and then at the girl. The wicker chair squeaked faintly as she rocked back and forth. The green dress was tight as a bathing suit.

You can go upstairs if you want to, Arch said. How about it?

Well . . .

Two bucks, said Arch. You can give the money to me. Arch stepped on the cigarette, two faint spirals of smoke escaping from his nostrils. Come on, he thought. For God's sake. Make up your mind. I'm not going to beg you.

The man smiled slightly. Make it a dollar and a half.

Two. Now, honest, aint it worth that?

Dollar and a half. What the hell. A sprained arm . . .

Okay, Arch said slowly. Make it a dollar seventy-five. That's fair enough. He stuck his hands in his pocket, feeling the large hole in the bottom of the one on the left side.

The man glanced quickly at the girl and said, All right. Dollar seventy-five. You get the money, you say?

That's right.

Arch took the crumpled dollar bill, holding it in his palm,

while the man placed the coins over the smooth engraved face of George Washington. Arch nodded to Betty Lou. He watched her get up and come to the man and smile at him, the red smear crawling up both sides of her cheeks, taking his arm and looking up into his face.

She's a dummy, Arch said.

What? the man said. I don't get it. The smile he had arranged on his face for the girl began to fade.

She's deaf and dumb, Arch said. That's all. Not that that makes any difference to you, I suppose.

The man shook his head. Deaf and dumb?

That's right, Arch said.

And then Betty Lou was pulling him towards the door that led to the rooms above. He could hear their footsteps on the stairs. It was beginning to get dark. People were coming home from work and the streetcars went by, one after another.

He went to the front of the store and began to pull the large folding doors together, getting ready to close up for the night. One dime taken in, he thought. One dime and a dollar seventy-five. I'll put the dollar in my shoe for groceries so we'll have enough to eat on until something turns up, and I'll get drunk on the eighty-five. I'll get drunk and come home from Freddie's with my head going around and around and then it won't make any difference. Nothing. It doesn't make any difference anyway. It made some difference a long time ago, maybe seven or eight years ago, but that was when I had a lot of different ideas than I have now. Goofy ideas. When I thought that maybe there was something to it.

I should worry about her. He took the padlock and snapped it shut over the opening between the two doors. I should worry about her, broken arm and all. . . . *the weather forecast for tonight is fair and warmer in the southern part of the State. For Tuesday . . .*

The closed doors shut out all light except for the faint blue blur that hung in a square in back: the barred window. He felt his way through the store's darkness and opened the rear door. Before he closed it, he felt in his pocket to make sure that he had the keys with him.

I should worry about her. Because that's all she knows. Because it's been that way ever since the two of them stuffed the doors of the living room with newspapers and turned on the gas and waited there, sitting in the chairs by the window, with that slow hissing sound all around them. And the smell getting stronger all the time. Because that's the way it's been ever since then with her. I tried to stop her too many times and then I gave up.

He felt for cigarettes, but there weren't any left. I'll get some when I get to Freddie's. In the alley, the telephone wires hummed above him. Some kid had drawn something on the side of one of the buildings, but he couldn't make out what it was. I gave it up a long time ago. He turned where the alley met the street and walked without haste to the corner, waiting for a moment for the lights to change from red to green before he crossed to the other side.

12. My America

LOUIS ADAMIC

Like other immigrant writers before him, Louis Adamic (1899–1951), who was born in Slovenia and came to the United States as a teen-age boy, was intrigued by the vastness and com-

From *My America* (New York: Harper & Bros., 1938), pp. 283–293. Copyright 1938 by Louis Adamic. Reprinted by permission of Harper & Row, Publishers, and of Hamish Hamilton Ltd.

*plexity of his adopted land and by how it was bound, in his
own spirit, to his native land. It was not surprising that his biggest popular success was* The Native's Return *(1934), a chronicle of his voyage back to Yugoslavia. But before this, Adamic
had written a colorful narrative of labor violence in America
entitled* Dynamite *(1931), and as the depression deepened he
was obsessed—again, like many other writers—with the desire
to get out and see what was happening to his adopted country.
"Since 1931," he wrote in the preface to* My America, *"I have
traveled perhaps 100,000 miles here in America, by train, by
automobile, by plane, as well as afoot, pausing here and there
to look and listen, to ask questions, to get 'the feel of things';
and I have developed, I think, a fairly steady feeling about the
vast place. . . ." As for the chapter from that book which follows, it was "an attempt to make use of a mass of notes" that
he had taken when he hired himself out for a month "to the
Home Relief as an assistant case worker, visiting the homes of
the jobless, studying the Depression's effects on family life. I
thought I might publish an article on the subject, but did not.
My experiences and observations during that month—February, 1932—had affected me so that I could not write of them
objectively at the time. . . ."*

Family Life and the Depression: 1930–32

The Depression's effects upon the home or family life in the
United States were as varied as they were profound; but they
can be put into two general categories: On the one hand,
thousands of families were broken up, some permanently,
others temporarily, or were seriously disorganized. On the
other hand, thousands of other families became more closely
integrated than they had been before the Depression.

The reason for these different effects due to the same cause was that the economic crisis, which came upon many families in all sections of the country with the force and suddenness of a cyclone, in most cases intensified the various antagonistic and affectional attitudes or reactions of one to the other among the individuals within the family groups. Sudden economic adversity made family life more dynamic. In some cases, the so-called "hostility reactions" among the members of the family became more explosive, more damaging to the stability and harmony of the group. In other cases, conversely, the bonds of mutual affection, coöperation, and sacrifice were greatly strengthened, or even brought into full play for the first time.

These general statements apply, in greater or lesser degree, to all classes of society, except, of course, the uppermost class, in which the Depression was not felt acutely, at least not so far as family life was concerned. They apply most of all to the classes hit by unemployment.

In many working-class or white-collar homes, the man—the father and husband—was, by virtue of the dynamics of his position as breadwinner and conventional head of the family, the first to feel the impact of the unemployment situation. It was he who lost the job; in most cases, suddenly and unexpectedly. In the preceding years, what with children, illness, high-pressure salesmanship, and keeping up with the neighbors, he had been unable to save any substantial sum of money from his pay. Morally and legally he was responsible for the support of his wife and children. As soon as he lost his employment the atmosphere in his home changed. He noticed that his wife and children looked at him "funny," or at least differently. Sometimes, of course, he merely imagined that their looks were "funny" or different, but the effect upon him was the same. He became self-conscious, uneasy, resentful. This was the first hostility reaction, which often led to other sharply discordant reactions.

At the same time he began to have serious doubts about his

own worth and abilities. Why had he lost his job while Bill Jones and Steve Komonski remained working? Why hadn't the boss kept him on at least upon a part-time basis? In many cases, to hide these doubts and feelings of inferiority, which usually were not new but merely intensified, he assumed a gruff, hard, or even violent manner toward everybody, including (or especially) his family. He grumbled, growled, barked back at his wife. He issued sharp commands to his children, while two or three weeks before he had never or seldom bothered them. Such behavior, of course, produced open hostility reactions on their part toward him.

This happened especially after he had come to realize that job-hunting, somehow, was a hopeless proposition and his bewilderment deepened and he was being seized by a sense of frustration. Consciously or unconsciously, he commenced to feel that forces utterly beyond his control were operating to take from him the important rôle of provider for the family. This was a serious thing in his life, as Dr. Thorndike points out in his book, *The Original Nature of Man,* "the truly original tendency of the human male" is "to offer a little child scraps of food and to see it eat." Also, in America, more than elsewhere, the father holds the head position in the family chiefly by virtue of "bringing home the bacon."

The father was the first to realize the seriousness of the growing unemployment situation in relation to himself and his home. To the rest of the family, at the beginning, unemployment was half a myth. In many cases, the mother and the children blamed the father for losing his job. In her ignorance of the conditions, the woman, half hysterical because income had stopped, nagged him. Why didn't he get busy and get a new job rightaway? Why was he staying home so much? Did he expect somebody would come and offer him a job? What did he think this was, anyhow? She knew that Mrs. So-and-so's husband still had a job. She had heard that someone else in the next block, after losing his job, picked up another position three weeks later. Why had her husband lost his? Why couldn't he get another one? Knowing many of his faults, she imagined all sorts of reasons. Now and then she dropped meaningful hints, infuriating him.

Something similar was true of the children's attitude toward the father, especially if they happened to be adolescent boys. Until lately they had more or less looked up to him. One of the reasons for this was that he had been passably successful in his line of work; at any rate, in one way or another he had managed to maintain an air of competence and superiority which had impressed them. He had been making enough money for all of them to live on in comparative decency and comfort. By virtue of his position as the sole or chief breadwinner, even if he was not a particularly inspiring specimen of manhood, he had been a vital factor in the development of his sons' ego ideals. Consciously or unconsciously, they had aspired to be like their father when they grew up: get a job, work, and earn money. They had boasted of their father to other boys. Now, of a sudden, he was out of work, while some of the other boys' fathers—early in the Depression—still had jobs and wages. Immediately, because economically inadequate, he became less of a hero in their eyes. Very often he was right when he thought that they were looking at him "funny." Naturally, he did not like this and often he could not control himself.

During the 1931-32 winter, when the schools and social agencies began to interest themselves in the material welfare of the children apart from their parents, there was a tendency among numerous depression-stricken youngsters to look to their teachers and to social workers and even to policemen—*i.e.*, to the community—for their necessities.

I talked to an American-born Italian boy who, I had been told, had asked a policeman to get him a pair of shoes. He had received the shoes, and I asked him where he supposed the policeman had gotten the shoes or the money to buy them.

The boy's first answer was that he did not know; then he said, "I guess at the police station or the City Hall or in the bank." It did not greatly interest him where.

But some of the most serious intra-family reactions developed in cases where one or more of the boys had little jobs after school, or shined shoes or sold newspapers. In such cases the sons soon commenced to assume superior attitudes, thus infringing on the father's position in the family; which, as a rule, simply burned him up. In some cases young boys earning money allied themselves with the mother against the father in the belief that, since he was jobless, he was inferior. Then there was trouble, of course; especially if the man was just beginning to develop his gruff or violent manner as a defense mechanism.

When the Depression was still young and unemployment was not yet so general as it became later, it often was months before the man succeeded in imparting to his family a sense of reality about the situation. In some cases he clipped out of the newspapers the items and articles dealing with the situation and left them on the kitchen table for his wife and children to read. In other cases, he asked employment agents and social workers to call on his wife and tell her, the poor, ignorant ninny, that there was no work to be had, for when he himself told her she did not believe him.

Nagging on the part of the mother, who was unaware of the general unemployment situation, or for some other reason could not look at the problem from the man's angle and sympathize with him, was one of the worst things that the suddenly disemployed *paterfamilias* had to contend with in the early stages of the Depression. In some cases, the children—girls more frequently than boys—on realizing that the jobless father was a victim of circumstances, allied themselves with him against the mother on the grounds that she was unreasonable and unfair. Such a development inevitably caused new hostility reactions of the most damaging and complex sort—damaging to the family as a group as well as to individuals as characters and personalities.

There were cases where the father, on losing employment in his line, took a job in a grade of work lower than that in which he had earned his living before the slump, and in consequence also lost considerable standing in the eyes of his children—to say nothing of his wife. This was natural enough. Indeed, it seems that the fear of losing their families' and friends' respect was one of the main reasons why a majority of jobless men—particularly in the early months of the Depression—refused to take or seek employment in lower grades of work than those in which they had earned their living before.

But no matter how much he resented his plight, in numerous cases, as the Depression went from bad to worse, the father was compelled in the end, in one way or another, to give up his position of authority and prestige in the family. He became a back number. The position of authority sometimes passed to the mother, who had become the provider. Sometimes he retained but vestiges of his old standing. In many instances authority and discipline entirely disappeared from the home.

Often the man was finally overwhelmed by the feeling of being rejected, not only by the social-economic system, which he had heard praised so much by great men like Arthur Brisbane and President Hoover, but even by his own family. His gruff or violent attitude toward his wife and family began to falter. His reactions toward them were still hostile, but gradually they were less deliberate, less a part of his defense mechanism. They became real, spontaneous. Now and then he was seized by blind punitive impulses. I came upon cases where, a few months after losing his job, the man—like Mary and Jimmie S——'s father, in the preceding chapter—had walked up and down the room all night, talked, shouted, wept, cursed, and finally beat his wife and children. One man I met almost beat his wife to death upon learning that she had accepted food from a neighbor. His explanation was, "I couldn't see straight."

If the wife, after realizing that the man could not get another job, went out and herself found employment in spite of the Depression, that fact frequently was the cause of an explosion in the home. In good times, largely to keep up his sense of adequacy, the man had forbidden her to seek outside employment. Now, all at once, she became the breadwinner and, consciously or unconsciously, began to usurp his natural position in the house. In his hurt pride he developed new hostile reactions. Time hung on his hands. In the morning before she left for work his wife told him to make the beds. The children, seeing him in this new rôle, sometimes laughed at him. I came upon a man who, making the beds one day, was so enraged by his son's laughter that he had nearly killed the child.

Gradually, with all this discordance and bickering in the home, the man began to seek "escapes" from the situation. If he had liked to drink before, he now took to alcoholism, drinking, of course, only the cheapest stuff, including "canned heat," which undermined his whole makeup. If he had the gambling instinct, he began to gamble. Sometimes he took to both drinking and gambling. Or, as Mary S——'s father, he deserted the family. Or, as suggested earlier in this book, he committed suicide or turned on the gas at night and wiped out the whole family.

In a good many cases, too, the woman, on becoming the sole or principal breadwinner, responded to the man's hostility attitude or "escape" tendencies by so conducting herself and manipulating the affairs of the home, or what was still left of it, that ultimately the man was compelled to leave. In some cases employed women took their children and literally deserted their husbands.

Of course, these latter cases, although numerous, were extreme. In most instances where hostility reactions were intense for months immediately after unemployment first hit the family, the relations of individuals within the home more or less adjusted themselves; very gradually and very painfully, of course; and the family stuck together in a loose, desperate way, fighting the battle against inimical economic forces.

So much, for the time being, of the first category of Depression-smitten families as they were affected by their economic misfortunes early in the crisis.

On the other hand, as I have suggested, almost the exact opposite was true of families in whose cases economic adversity operated to preserve the spiritual and economic unity of the home or even brought the individuals within the family closer together than they had been before the Depression. Indeed, some of the social workers with whom I discussed the matter inclined to the belief that this category was more numerous than the one I have just described, while others—apparently just as competent to express their views on the matter—maintained that the Depression had caused more destructive havoc than consolidation, integration, or reintegration in American family life. Which of the two opinions is correct will, perhaps, never be known.

At any rate, in no end of instances, as soon as unemployment struck a family, the individual members thereof immediately pooled their resources and were welded closer together by mutual sympathy and willingness to sacrifice and coöperate. In such cases, of course, harmony rather than discord and a sense of humor rather than bitterness and nagging had been the rule before the Depression, just as in the other category the opposite was true prior to the slump. In this category, when the crisis came, everybody became more appreciative of one another and of whatever comforts they jointly possessed. This inevitably deepened the spiritual quality of home life; it made the group more compact than it had been before, and helped individuals to bear their plight with more fortitude. The family discipline was preserved. There was much good-natured joking in the home. The father, although out of work, usually retained the headship of the family without any struggle.

Of course, in this category I found also a great many men and women who suppressed their various emotional difficulties when the panic came, and stayed together mainly or merely for economic reasons, figuring that apart they probably would be even worse off than they were together.

Also, the crisis suddenly brought out the fine characteristics of a great many people which in good times had not been apparent to other members of the family. There were cases, for instance, where husbands or wives who commanded some resources were seized by the spirit of sacrifice and helped their in-laws or their spouse's friends, although but a short while before the couple had been on the verge of separation or divorce; and later, when their own affairs were anything but looking up, the desire for breaking up the marital or family ties on the part of one or the other, or both, was less strong, with the result that they stuck it out.

The Depression also had some curious beneficial effects upon families not directly affected by it in an economic way through unemployment or otherwise. There were instances where the wife had been hostile to the husband before the crisis because she considered him economically inferior. His job was low-grade and his income was small in comparison with incomes of their friends, neighbors, and acquaintances. The family's social standing was low. They had no car, no radio, which made her unhappy. She nagged him. There were emotional storms. Then, when the Depression came and *he kept his job* at a time when everybody else seemed to be losing theirs, all this suddenly changed. The woman's opinion of the man, including his economic standing, immediately improved. Her disparagement of him diminished. She ceased to nag him. He was all right. He had a job. People who formerly used to look down upon them as economically inferior now envied them; the man had work while they had none. The family's social standing improved

immensely. Now the home that once was full of discord, thanks
to the Depression, became a happy one.

A great many families of "the better classes," of course, were
also affected almost as soon as the Depression began. They
were the business and professional people. They had played the
stock market and enjoyed annual incomes running into five
figures. In the fall of 1929 many of them, desperately trying to
save their stakes in the Wall Street débâcle, mortgaged their
homes and other properties to the limit, and in the course of
the next year or two were deprived of everything, anyhow.
During 1930 they lost their positions or failed in business, and
it was not long before many of them were not far above the
level of the unemployed men's families. Some of the formerly
opulent people who once had supported charity organizations
became charity cases themselves. I found a man whose fortune
in 1928 was figured in millions. In 1925 he had donated a million dollars to an Eastern college, his alma mater. In 1931, lest
he and his family starve, he was forced to appeal to the college
authorities to put him on the payroll.

This, of course, was an extreme case. But I became aware of
many families who had been compelled to give up their
suburban homes, motors, motor-boats, along with their several
servants. In these families the same sort of antagonistic and
affectional tendencies that I have described as true among the
working-people had been at work since 1929. Some of them
now were closer together than ever before. Women went back
to housekeeping in narrow quarters without servants. Some
joked about their plight from the start. Many of them, however,
had had no previous experience in managing a home; such
things had previously been left to their housekeepers. Not a
few women in such changed circumstances were anything but
happy. They were rather helpless and absurd. They could not
prepare a decent meal. This led to words with the husband,
and so on. There is no doubt that some of these women—to say

nothing of the men—suffered as much on account of economic reverses as most of the unemployed men's wives whose plight actually was much worse than theirs. They wept for days at a spell and suffered nervous breakdowns.

In times of prosperity, many marriages among the well-to-do were endurable only by virtue of the money. These couples had large houses or apartments, where they did not see one another for days. The woman could have a lover, the man a mistress. When they found it impossible to stay in the same town, one or the other took a trip. . . . Now, with not enough money left to pay for a divorce, life was simply hell. There were divorces or separations—more of the latter than the former, for the reason that divorces were more expensive than separations.

One of the biggest problems of those people who were no longer rich—in 1930 and through most of 1931—were their children. In good times the children had been raised by governesses and in private schools. Some of them had been spoiled or problem children, but wealth had worked to smooth things over. The parents actually had had little to do with them. In the summer they sent them to camps while they themselves went on a cruise around the world. Now governesses, private schools, and summer camps were out of the question. The children were more difficult than ever before and the parents did not know what to do with them.

Early in the Crisis, as I have suggested, the father and husband bore the brunt of the family difficulties. For a while— especially in the lower-class homes in which there was little harmony—the Depression was in many cases almost purely his personal problem. Later, however, when the Depression was recognized even by the Hoover administration as the paramount fact in America's national life, the difficulties were accepted by all members of the family. There followed a painful process of mutual readjustment. Hostility reactions drowned in common misery. Standards of living were consciously lowered—in millions of cases to rock bottom. There were evictions, foreclosures, actual starvation, crime, deep social agony.

A case history:

Jim F—— had worked as a truck-driver for the same concern for five years, making forty-five dollars a week. He and Mrs. F—— were a happy, respectable couple. They had four children, all of them fairly normal. In April, 1930, when he was thirty-six years old, Jim lost his job when the firm went bankrupt. For six months he had no work at all. In September he drove a truck for another concern for two weeks, making only twenty-three dollars a week. It was his last job. In December he lost all his savings—$350—in a bank failure. Then two of the children became ill. He had a hard time in borrowing money to pay the doctor and the druggist. They began to pawn things; finally, Mrs. F—— was forced to pawn her wedding ring. In September, 1931, the rent was three months in arrears. The landlord threatened eviction. Then Jim "got out of his mind," as Mrs. F—— put it to me, and joined two other men (also married men and fathers of children, living in the same apartment-house) in a robbery. They got thirty-three dollars and were arrested almost at once. The family situation was explained to the district attorney and reputable persons testified as to Jim's pre-Depression character, but in vain. Jim was sentenced to five years in Sing Sing. In October, when Jim was being tried, Mrs. F——, not knowing what else to do, appealed to organized charity for the first time and now, living in a single-room flat with her children, she managed to keep them and herself alive on the few dollars she received as relief. She felt disgraced. None of her relatives and former friends knew where she was. Jim himself was a hopeless man in Sing Sing. He felt that when he got out of prison, even should the conditions improve, his chances of employment would be slim because of his criminal record. Mrs. F—— visited him in prison just before Christmas (the fare was paid by the charity organization). His forehead, when she saw him, was scarred and blue, because every now and then he went "crazy" and banged his head against the walls of his cell. But the worst phase of the situation was that the children were being seriously affected. Unable to restrain herself, Mrs. F——

wept a great deal, and the children bawled with her. There were
nights when all five of them cried for hours. They all slept in the
same room, except the oldest boy, whose bed was the tub in the
windowless bathroom. All four children, two of them of school age,
were underweight, suffering with frequent ailments due to poor
resistance. When I visited the family one child was in bed with a
cold; two other children were in the same bed—the only one—"to
keep warm." There was no heat in the dwelling. Mrs. F—— said
to me, "We'd all be better off dead."

In some cases which came to my notice whole families had
developed antisocial, criminal tendencies. In extreme cases entire families whose heads formerly were respectable and successful workingmen now coöperated in making their living
expenses by thieving.

One of the worst problems in connection with family life during the Depression, especially on the lower economic levels,
was the problem of shelter. During 1931 there were nearly
200,000 evictions in New York City alone, a majority of them
during the second half of the year. In Chicago there were almost as many. New York had more than 60,000 eviction cases
in the first three weeks of January, 1932. Dr. John Lovejoy Elliott, headworker of the Hudson Guild, said in a public address
early in January: "I was told the other day of a judge who had
425 eviction cases in one day! The situation for the rent-
payer, as well as the landlord, is a terrible one."

Alone or in company with professional social workers, I
visited 107 depression-stricken families in Greater New York;
practically all of them were threatened with eviction. Four of
them had been evicted twice and eleven once before since
1930. In the Williamsburg-Greenpoint slum districts of Brooklyn I visited thirty-one families. In every case the rent had not
been paid for from two months to a year. In many cases the
landlords "hadn't the heart" to evict them. In one instance the
landlord was even paying the family's gas bill. Most landlords,
however, pressed eviction actions. With their buildings one-

third or half vacant, they themselves were desperate. If they let one family stay without paying, other families in the same house learned of it and stopped rent payments, too.

Things were little better in the "nice sections." Thousands of families which in 1930 still could afford eighty- and ninety-dollars-a-month apartments were evicted in 1931. These evictions continued at an increasing rate in 1932.

When families were evicted, they sometimes moved into one-room flats in the cellars, or into cheap furnished-room houses. I came upon families of seven, eight, and even ten living in one-room flats. They slept on chairs and on the floor, in bathtubs (if they had them) and over sinks.

Other evicted families "doubled up" with other families, sometimes in the same apartment-house. The families often were comparative strangers. The better-off people took pity on the evicted ones. In some cases the families were related, or of the same nationality or religious faith. I saw or heard of cases where two, three, and even four evicted families pooled their resources and moved into one flat or apartment. In one two-room flat I saw eleven persons; in another flat with the same number of rooms, twelve persons, eight of them children. In one three-room apartment I came upon four families, which included two deserted wives, two wives and their husbands, and thirteen children. Two of the latter were ill in bed. Most of the others were clearly undernourished.

In a basement flat of two rooms in Harlem I found three white families, which included nine children and four adults. One of the men was an unemployed carpenter—out of work since 1930—who had "picked up" some lumber somewhere and built about a dozen bunks along the walls, one above the other, three deep, like berths on a steerage steamer or in a trench dugout.

Most of these people were charity cases to begin with; others became charity cases later. In one way or another they "chiseled along." But, of course, there was a great deal of bickering and intriguing in such establishments. Mothers hid food from one another, in order to feed their children. Men came to blows. They got on each other's nerves. They stole from one another. Some dwellings sheltered two or three different nationalities, and the diverse temperaments clashed. But they stuck together because that was all they could do.

A great many young couples, married in the years just before the Depression, were forced to give up independent apartments, store their furnishings, and move in with the old folks, if the latter happened to live in the city where the young husband, perhaps, still had a part-time job. If the parents, who still had a home, lived elsewhere, the couple separated. The young wife and the baby went home to her people, while the young man remained in the city, to fight things out alone.

During 1930-31 numerous families lost their furniture because unable to continue payments on the instalment plan. Instalment-furniture houses were crammed with "junk," as they called furniture recovered from Depression-stricken families. The collector of a Bronx firm told me that many families, on moving to smaller and cheaper quarters, simply abandoned their partially paid-for furniture in the old, more expensive apartments.

In 1931 tens of thousands of families in New York and vicinity lost their homes through foreclosures, which was true also in other cities. Most of these luckless families, of course, were working-people, but a great many of them also were families who, not so very long ago, belonged among the "better classes"—business and professional people, some of whom considered themselves wealthy in 1929. One such case was brought to my attention:

In 1929 Mr. D—— was worth over $200,000. He was a retired business man, playing the market "a little." He had a fine home in a New York suburb. His oldest son was at Harvard. Two daughters were in private schools. Mr. and Mrs. D—— had just booked a 'round-the-world passage when the Crash came. Of a sudden the world tumbled down about their heads. Hoping to save at least a part of his fortune, Mr. D—— mortgaged his home, but he no sooner got the mortgage money than it was "swallowed up by Wall Street." He was too proud to appeal to people he knew who were still wealthy. For two years the whole family struggled to save the home. During 1931 they actually starved. They sold their expensive furniture, piece by piece. The girls had to be recalled from their schools. The son quit Harvard. But it was no use. Gradually the family broke up even before the foreclosure on the home, late in 1931. The children now were scattered all over the country. One of the girls sang in a night club in Chicago. The son was a Communist who swore he would never marry or have children under the "present system." After the foreclosure Mr. and Mrs. D—— moved into a furnished room in New York City. He could get nothing to do. His mind was being affected by his plight. Finally, Mrs. D—— appealed to the charity organization they had supported in a small way for years before the Crash.

The above, again, was an extreme case. In a great many cases, of course, Depression-stricken families still hung on to their homes, which, since they had to fight to keep them, were all the more precious to them.

The Depression was having several other general effects on the home or family life of the country, and on the individuals in the home.

The number of marriages fell off during 1930 and still more during 1931. It was hard for a young man to get or keep a job. Then, too, boys and girls saw the economic agony and frustration of their elders and they figured—girls more frequently than boys—that it would be sheer madness to marry. I heard boys and girls still in high school state their decision never to marry. They appeared to have an instinctive feeling that they were living in a period of uncertainty and insecurity which was apt to last a long time. They were developing so-called "balked dispositions."

There was this tendency among children of Depression-smitten parents, especially among adolescent girls: they saw the agony of their fathers and mothers, and responded to them with intense love, an overdevelopment of filial affection, which precluded normal interest in contemporaries of the opposite sex, laying the basis for various neuroses.

As a result of financial and related difficulties, men in their prime became victims of psychic and physiological disorders, which led to sexual impotence. Physicians, whom I met in Home Relief work, informed me that Depression-induced impotence was common in men under forty. This was true not only of jobless workers, but of business men whose fortunes had been affected by the slump. One doctor in close touch with the situation maintained that many separations and not a few suicides and wife-murders during 1930-31 had been due in part to the fact that economic frustration made men sexually inadequate. On the other hand, this was true, too—since the men were home so much, many more children were produced than there would have been normally.

The Depression tended to cramp social intercourse among families. Fewer invitations were extended, fewer parties given. Those most seriously affected by the crisis and most in need of a good meal did not accept invitations, if they received them, because they were unable to invite anyone in return.

The hard times cooled many friendships among families, especially on the lower levels. Groups and individuals kept more to themselves. Endless instances of homely pleasures and contentment were curtailed and forbidden by narrow means.

Many learned and elaborate studies of the great Depression will be written from various angles, for it had many angles. As I work on this book I learn that Charles and Mary Beard are preparing a history of it, which will surely be more than worthwhile. . . . But it was such facts, conditions, and tendencies as the above-mentioned that interested me most. For me they were a part of the essential picture, the human drama, the human truth, of the complex, painful, deep and far-reaching situation, for which, I inclined to think, no one and everyone was to blame. It was a product of America's basic incongruity.

13. The Reckoning

THEODORE ROETHKE

Educated at Michigan and Harvard, Theodore Roethke (1908–1963) was a poet who made his living as a college teacher—at Bennington, Lafayette, and the University of Washington, until his untimely death. But he was quite the opposite of the popular conception of the reclusive academic poet. A great bear of a man, six foot three, he was a tennis coach as well as a teacher, and he lived out his life with gusto. His reputation grew steadily with each volume that he published—Open House—The Lost Son (1941), Praise to the End! (1951), The Waking (1953)—until his death brought with it the realization of the extent of the loss American letters had suffered. He is not commonly thought of as a poet of the depression decade—and indeed, there is no particular reason, aside from dates, why he should be—but surely there is more of the anguish of those years compressed into "The Reckoning" than can be found in all the works of the now-forgotten bards who shouted of barricades, workers' blood, and the red dawn to come.

From *Open House* by Theodore Roethke (New York: Alfred A. Knopf, 1941), p. 61. Copyright 1941 by Alfred A. Knopf, Inc. Reprinted with the permission of Beatrice Roethke.

All profits disappear: the gain
Of ease, the hoarded, secret sum;
And now grim digits of old pain
Return to litter up our home.

We hunt the cause of ruin, add,
Subtract, and put ourselves in pawn;
For all our scratching on the pad,
We cannot trace the error down.

What we are seeking is a fare
One way, a chance to be secure:
The lack that keeps us what we are,
The penny that usurps the poor.

PART FOUR

Jobhunting:

EVERYWHERE

---

14. Puzzled America

SHERWOOD ANDERSON

In this vignette, Anderson displays precisely the qualities that, even while they baffle the critics, have endeared him to the countless readers who are always rediscovering him. He senses the drama in the life of an ordinary man who has been thrown out of work in a Southern industrial town ("It was an every-day, common enough story"), because he respects the intelligence and sensitivity of the American workingman, who is helpless in the face of the depression, advancing technology, and his own aging. Anderson ends by echoing, more in sorrow than in anger, what James Rorty had castigated as the "where-life-is-better daydream": the castoff workman's "undying so-American optimism."

From *Puzzled America* (New York: Charles Scribner's Sons, 1935), pp. 103–110. Copyright 1935 Charles Scribner's Sons; renewal copyright © 1963 Eleanor C. Anderson. Reprinted with the permission of Charles Scribner's Sons and Harold Ober Associates Inc.

"I Want to Work"

I went home with a workman from a meeting of unemployed. He had come in there, out of curiosity, as I had. We happened to come out of the meeting at the same time and stopped outside to talk.

The preliminary talk led to another and the next day we met. "Yes, I'm out of work. I'm fifty-two, you see." He was a sturdily-built, clear-eyed man. "I used to make big wages. I should have got fixed for this. I didn't. I was proud, sure of myself, I thought things would always go on as they were. When I did make good money I spent it."

He had been a machinist as a young man and later had become a machine-tender in a factory. He had been out of work for two years. I asked him to come with me to my hotel but he didn't like the idea.

"No," he said, "I'm not dressed for it. You come on home with me."

This was in the early afternoon of a cold day. He was in blue overalls and wore a shabby coat. His thick, stiff gray hair was only half concealed by his cap. He wore the cap tilted a bit to one side—as though to say—"O. K.—after all I'm as good as the next man."

We went on down to where he lived, stopping at a corner grocer's on the way. "I'll get a few bottles of beer," I said.

"All right. I wouldn't mind having a bottle with you."

I got his story, going down and as we sat in his house. It was an every-day, common enough story.

He had got married as a young man and had one daughter who married a young workman, a machine-fixer like himself. When he was forty his wife died and two years later he got a new wife. He got a young one, nearly twenty years younger than himself, but they had no children.

"They are all at work," he said, "my wife, my daughter, and her husband."

His daughter and her husband had no children. The three of them, his own wife, his daughter, and her husband, had bought a house—it was a small, neat frame house on a little hill beyond a district of huge factories in a Southern industrial town and when we got there we climbed a flight of stairs to a bedroom on the second floor. "You wait and I'll go stir up the furnace and get some glasses for the beer," he said, and when he returned he began to talk—"You see," he said, "I tend to the furnace. I do what I can around here."

He said something, speaking a little bitterly, about what he couldn't do, "I should have been born a woman. If I could cook for the others now. If I could do the family wash, it would save money for them."

You could see that he had been lifted, by circumstances, outside the life of the house in which he had once been the head man.

The point is the way he was taking it. It was obviously the old story of a man whose civilization had got through with him before he was through with it. He had got laid off, when the depression hit the town, and then, later, when his shop started up again, a younger man got his place. "I'm not as fast as I once was," he said, "but I'm a careful man, a good workman yet."

He said he didn't want to offer to work for less wages than the younger man, who has been taken back. "If you begin that," he said, "you cut the standard of a whole shop."

We sat in two chairs by a window that looked down on the factories while we drank our beer and talked. An old feeling, so common in American men, concerned with modern industry —pride in the very thing that has apparently thrown life out of gear.

I have talked to many manufacturers and factory superintendents, and rarely, I think never, have I gone into a shop without being shown some new machine.

Here, in a tin can factory, is a machine that makes can tops.

It is the superintendent of the shop showing me through. "When I first came to work here, when I first became a foreman, we had a machine that turned out forty can tops a minute. There was a man at work on every machine. Now you see this long battery of machines. The two men you see walking up and down take care of them all. They don't work so hard. There isn't any heavy work in any modern shop.

"When I was a young man here, a young foreman, I used to go home at night, having seen a new machine installed that would knock out forty can tops a minute. I used to think: 'Are there people enough in the world to use so many tin cans?'" He laughed. "Look at these machines," he said, with pride in his voice. "Every machine in this long row of machines is knocking out three hundred and sixty can tops a minute."

"And you have laid off many men who can never get back into this shop?"

"Yes."

"I do not see many older men."

"No. The younger ones have the call. They are quicker, you see, less likely to get hurt."

I asked him what I have asked many men in positions of control in industry. "When you are all doing it, laying off so many men who can never get back, aren't you laying off your own customers, users of the goods you make here?"

"Yes, we are, all right."

"Well, what are you fellows going to do?"

"I don't know."

That attitude on the part of most of the men in control of the shops. What about the workmen?

Those who say that American workmen, so often now thrown out of their place in our social and economic scheme by the modern machine, so often robbed of something peculiarly vital to their feeling of manhood—this I keep thinking the most important thing of all, the thing I keep hoping that

we may come more and more to understand and appreci-
ate————

The machines themselves apparently becoming always faster
and faster, more and more efficient—the man in the street can
see it with his own eyes in the increased beauty, speed, and
efficiency of the automobile————

As though there were actually a kind of devil sleeping down
in these so-gorgeously beautiful masses of steel in action————

Those who hold that American workmen do not want to
work with the machines, that they do not want to be in the
factories, simply do not know what they are talking about.

In the greater majority of American workmen, and now in
American workwomen, actual love of the machines and—yes,
I am sure of it—in spite of everything—love of the factories.
There are, to be sure, always the stupid ones, the dull ones,
but the numbers of the other constantly amazes.

The workman, past his prime, who knew what had happened
to him and with whom I drank the beer, had got into the
habit of going into the public library of the town. As I have
said, we were in a Southern town. "I was born a Yank," he
said.

"So was I," I said.

His father, a carriage blacksmith, had come South after the
war when he was a young boy.

"The kids here used to dog me a lot about being a Yank.

"So I thought, sometime, I thought, when I have time, I'm
going to read up on the war.

"I'd never been much to read."

He had got on to one of my own hobbies. "Well," I said.

"Now there was Grant," he said. "I've got to liking that man,
at least to liking what he was when he was just a general,
before he got to be President. He wasn't such a smart man,
but I figure he had the big idea all right."

"Yes? And how?"

"I've been figuring it out. I've got plenty of time to figure things out. A lot of the Northern generals during the war couldn't see the war as a whole. That's what made it last so long."

"You mean?"

"You see, I figure, they thought of a battle as a battle. I think he saw the war as a war."

"He and Lincoln, eh?"

"Yes," he said.

"I've been thinking," he said, "that some day, maybe———

"We may see it as a whole, what we are up against."

I left him sitting in the room and went down the stairs and into the street and on the next day I got into the factory where he had been employed. It was a good one, very modern, very big, light, and efficient.

On the day when I left him and got into the street I wasn't thinking of that.

"They are O. K. They can sure take it," was what I was thinking. And I was thinking that the most pathetic thing of all—in the workman who had been put to one side by his civilization—was his undying so-American optimism.

15. Studs Lonigan

JAMES T. FARRELL

James T. Farrell (1904–   ) was already writing as an under-graduate at the University of Chicago; he has not stopped writing since. He was a famous man of letters by the time he was

From *Studs Lonigan* (New York: The Vanguard Press, 1938), Volume III (*Judgment Day*), Chap. XVI, pp. 347–388. Copyright 1932, 1934, 1935, by James T. Farrell. Reprinted by permission of the Vanguard Press.

thirty years old; but since then he has withdrawn from the
world of literary and political combat. Questing and pugna-
cious, Farrell turned from Catholicism to Marxism, and was
one of that small but honorable band of intellectuals who did
not later simply exchange Marxism for reaction or conformity
when communism came to be seen as a false god. During the
decades that have followed the publication of the trilogy Studs
Lonigan, *book after book has issued from him, ranging from*
the Danny O'Neill tetralogy (on the molding of a young intel-
lectual) to novels of old age and dissolution. Most recently, as
if to demonstrate that his range is not restricted to the Chicago
Irish or the New York literati, Farrell has published a novel
dealing with the life of a Protestant family in the Indiana of
the twenties; but nothing that he has written seems likely to
rival Studs *in humanity and in the passion of its despair. It*
cannot be overemphasized that it was not Farrell's intention
to depict these Chicago Irish as bums, castoffs, or even
lumpenproletarians, as many have mistakenly supposed (per-
haps because of the sordidness and violence of many episodes).
Rather, he was insisting upon the desperation with which these
lower-middle-class people were attempting to cling to "re-
spectability"—a desperation which could only grow in in-
tensity as the depression closed in on'them. Nothing demon-
strates this more sharply than the following brilliant chapter,
which takes Studs on his hopeless hunt for respectable employ-
ment.

Where would he go to look for a job? And what would he
say? And on such a lousy day.

Studs glanced out the window of the moving Illinois Central
suburban train and saw the rain beating down on Seventy-first
Street. He turned over the pages of the newspaper, and his
eyes hit on the column of advice to the lovelorn. Should the
girl, who signed herself Terribly Puzzled, go out with a young
man to whom she had never been properly introduced? Jesus,

she had a tough problem on her mind, he thought ironically. If the gal asked him, he'd just tell her to find out how much dough the lad had.

In just two weeks now, he would be married. And who ever would have thought that Studs Lonigan would be up the creek the way he was when he was getting married? He had to get a job, too, because even if the old man could let him work every day, there were the doctor's orders. With his heart, he couldn't be climbing ladders, and he had to get different work. And where would he get it? All the dough he had was four hundred and sixty dollars out of the two thousand he'd sunken. The brain of Solomon Imbray had guaranteed the stock. Wait till he saw that rat, Ike Dugan. Wait! Lucky he'd been able to get six bucks a share, and if he had waited until Tuesday, instead of selling on Monday, he'd only have gotten five a share. But now where was he going to get a job?

With determination he looked to the classified advertisements.

> HAT   SALESMAN—STEADY   &
> SAT. XTRA. Expd. only. gd.
> refs. Abraham and Solomon.

Experienced. That let him out. Might, though, try bulling them. Experienced store workers. Nothing there. Commission salesman. On that he and Catherine could eat air.

Executives And Managers

Could he find something here?

> SHOE BUYER and manager for
> women's,   men's   and   children's
> shoes of quality. This position has
> great possibilities and we want
> the best man available. State age,
> nationality and full business his-
> tory. For large west side depart-
> ment store. Address Box Xk 49.

Nothing doing again.

Professions And Trades

Engineer. No soap. Engineer Mechanic. No soap again. Fur designer.

> MAINTENANCE MAN—MUST BE
> EXPERIENCED on starch mogul
> machine. American. Protestant.
> South Side candy factory.

That guy must be an A. P. A. Protestant only. He'd like to run a business and fix 'em. Put in ads Catholic only. Dirty A. P. A.'s. Masseur. Nope. Physician. No.

> POLICE DUTY
> TEN MEN FOR NEARBY TOWN.
> ONLY THOSE WITH CITY PO-
> LICE EXPERIENCE OR LEGION-
> AIRES NEED APPLY. MUST
> FURNISH REFERENCE. MEM-
> BERS OF UNIONS NOT WANT-
> ED. APPLY RM. 216. . . .

He couldn't do police duty. Had to be tough for that. And he belonged to the painters' union, but that was just to avoid any trouble, and all he did was pay his dues. Sign Painter. Could do that if his heart was good. Window trimmer.

> Clubs Hotels And Restaurants
> WAITER — ROADHSE., THURS.
> SAT. NTS. husky, sober.

Nothing there for him.

Salesmen And Solicitors

Might be something here. He knew, though, from the way he'd heard guys talk about looking for jobs, that most of the selling jobs advertised in the papers were sucker propositions. But maybe there might be a real steer in one of these. And he could sell without endangering his heart. Still, to sell, you had to have a line and he didn't have one. But what the hell, if other guys could develop a line, why couldn't he? Red Kelly had sold refrigerators for a while. And he had to do something. Anything he could. He would have to support a wife in two weeks, and a baby in seven or eight months.

> LIFE INSURANCE MEN—FULL
> OR PART TIME. Comm.

He marked the ad with a pencil, figuring that even if he got another job, he might try selling a little insurance on the side. Phil Rolfe might take some, and Carroll, Red, lots of his friends. He'd see about it.

> UNUSUAL SALES OPPORTUNI-
> TY FOR A 1 men calling on
> Funeral Directors, Metal vault
> with patented features, backed by
> live-wire merchandising plans.
> Good territory. Open and generous
> commissions that mean real money
> for man who can qualify. Write
> experience.

He would write a letter on this one when he got home. Might as well try everything. He imagined himself going around to undertaking parlors. Not the most pleasant sort of business.

> CONFIDENCE INCORPORATED
> has openings for neat appearing,
> courteous young men to sell ice
> cream confections; commission
> basis. Apply . . . .

He couldn't see himself standing outside the South Shore Country Club with a little wagon, selling ice cream cones.

> TO SALESMEN—SELL SOBER-
> UP CAPSULES taverns and road-
> houses.

He smiled, thinking of how there were so many goddamn funny jobs in the world.

> MAN—YOUNG (GENTILE) WHO
> COULD SING AND PLAY UKE-
> LELE EVENINGS. . . .

Employment agencies. He wondered if anything might be gotten that way, or would he just be handing his dough out. Jobs advertised by them for fifteen or twenty dollars a week and only college graduates need apply. Things must be tough if that's all college graduates could get after four years of education. And trade schools.

> LEARN SCIENTIFIC SWEDISH
> MASSAGE.

That would have been good work for Hink Weber.

> THE IMPORTANT THING IN
> LEARNING BARBERING IS
> THE JOB AFTER YOU
> COMPLETE IT
> Hollywell not only creates the un-
> usual jobs but the unusual gradu-
> ates by their distinctive individual
> short course.

He could see himself going to a barber college. Studs Lonigan the barber.

Help Wanted Female

More jobs for women than men. Not too promising. Hell, he didn't even know where to go. Through the train window he saw the lake, gray, sullen, and he thought that, Christ, he did not see why he instead of someone else had to get a break like the one he had gotten. It hadn't happened to Red Kelly, or Stan Simonsky. Stan at least had his health. But suppose his baby should be born crippled like Stan's? It couldn't. He couldn't have one additional jolt of tough luck. The world wasn't made that way. He turned back to the classified advertisements.

> BE A TRAFFIC MANAGER Learn
> newest growing profession. Rail-
> roads, industries, motor freight
> carriers need men trained in modern
> methods. Big pay and free emp.
> Help to qualify. Class forming. Call
> 9 A. M. to 9 P. M. . . . .

That was something it might be well to follow up. As soon as he and Catherine got really settled down, he'd take a course like this one, and see if he couldn't get himself lined up with a job as a traffic manager. He saw himself a business man wearing a classy suit, getting up from a glass-topped desk, turning to a pretty stenographer and saying with an air of authority, Lucy, I'll be back at two-thirty. And then, walking out of an office with WILLIAM LONIGAN painted large on the glass window. The train was crowded. Were all these people going to jobs? Was the dopey fellow beside him going to work or to look for it?

"Gee, kid, that association in our store is all a racket. I know it. They take a quarter out of our pay every week, and we don't ever get anything out of it," a girl in back of him was saying.

"Well, if you die, they'll bury you."

He wondered what the girls looked like, but he did not turn around to see. And damn it, he had to line up work right now. Suddenly, almost over night, his whole life had changed, and all this had come on him. So here he was with no future, nothing ahead of him, unless he could go out and get it for himself. The best thing, if it only could be done, would be to get into politics. Red Kelly had, but he'd run in luck, and was in now. How was he going to get in and get lined up? Yes, how? Oh, Christ, wouldn't his luck ever change?

"But, kid, there must be some good in the association. Mr. Goldensteiner says it's for us, and you know how much he thinks of all us girls who work for him."

"Well, before I believe it's not a racket to get something out of us, you got to show me."

He slouched in his seat, wondering what would come next, feeling that his life was going to be short, and that he'd thrown it away for nothing. He felt cramped, too, in the seat, damp. And the day was so damn gloomy. He had no spirit. He couldn't put his heart into trying to get a job today. And he had to. Now there was no let-up. All day and always now he would have to keep himself going, and all the boozing and things he had done in his life, they had sure backfired on him. And he had never really been happy. Always in the midst of forgetting or getting over one trouble, he had always walked into another. The image of Catherine semed to flash into his mind. It was for her now that he had to face things and keep going on. Anyway, she would stick things out.

"But, Hazel, even if Mr. Browne is hard to work for, still, isn't he handsome?"

The girls in back of him sounded like dumb clucks. But hell, in the old days, he never would have pictured Studs Lonigan having to have someone like Catherine, or anyone, stick by him. And he remembered that night when he had a scrap with the old man, and he'd left home with a gat in his pocket to become Lonewolf Lonigan. Swell Lonewolf now, he was, hemmed in on every side. And how was he going to get out?

He saw that the train was pulling into Roosevelt Road. He jumped up and elbowed to the door. He didn't understand why this sudden idea hadn't occurred to him sooner. He could try getting a job in a gas station, and the Nation Oil Company offices were nearby on Michigan. Swell idea, he thought, stepping onto the wet platform.

His indecision grew as he stood sheltered in the entrance to the Nation Oil Building, watching the rain ink the boulevard, seeing people hurry by. Automobiles and motor busses passed, their tires swishing.

Across the street Grant Park was desolate, and over it was the heavy, downward sky.

He wanted to forget everything. If it was only a decent day, he knew he would feel better and maybe be able to look for a job with more confidence. He began to grow nervous, and wondered if the elevator starter was noticing him and would suddenly tell him that loitering in the building was not allowed. Now, what the hell would he say when he got upstairs? Maybe it would be useless to try here.

He compressed his lips, turned, approached the middle-aged uniformed elevator starter whose face was forbidding.

"Where is the employment department for the service stations?" he asked.

"Personnel Department, eighth floor. Take the last elevator," the starter said coldly, pointing as he spoke.

Entering the elevator he felt ashamed, because the starter knew his purpose. Three young fellows followed him and he wondered were they also looking for a job.

"Late today," the runty elevator man said as a pretty girl, wearing a blue raincoat, stepped into the car.

"Who wouldn't be in this weather?"

He closed the gates and the elevator shot upward. "It's a bad day out, all right," the elevator man told the girl.

"Is it! Say, I could hang myself on the line today, I'm so wet."

The girl left the car at the third floor. Studs became more and more anxious as one of the other fellows walked out at the fifth floor. The other two followed Studs out at the eighth floor. He walked along the narrow, tiled corridor, hearing the clicking of typewriters from behind glazed glass doors. Finding the door to the Personnel Department, he entered, followed by the other two fellows.

It was a wide office with dark rubber flooring. A freckle-faced office boy sat behind a closed gate, within which there were two large, unused desks. A line of applicants sat waiting on the two benches panelling the walls outside the gate, and seeing them, Studs' hopes again sank, and he wished that he had tried some other place. He walked hesitantly toward the office boy, permitting the two fellows who had entered with him to speak first, and then he immediately cursed himself for having let them get ahead of him.

"Is the Personnel Manager in?" he asked when his turn came.

"Want a job?" the office boy asked. Studs nodded his head.

"There isn't much chance. We're not hiring," the office boy said officially, handing Studs a card. "Fill that out and return it to me."

After waiting for the fellows ahead of him to fill in cards, Studs sat at a small desk in the corner by a water cooler and wrote in his name, age and address. The blank space for the reason he wanted to work with the Nation Oil Company stumped him. He noticed that another applicant was behind him, also waiting to fill out a card, and, feeling a mounting pressure within him, he wrote down in semi-legible handwriting that he needed a job with the prospect of a future in it. He returned the card.

"Take a seat," the office boy said, and Studs frowned, resenting this punk's snotty manner.

He noticed that the applicants on the benches were nervous and anxious. A gray-haired man with a kindly, friendly face sat in the center of the bench by the right wall, and beside him a thin-faced chap. From his looks, Studs decided he was a wise-guy bastard. Studs sat at the end of the opposite bench, and noticing the bull-necked applicant on the left of the wiry-looking skinny fellow, he guessed he must be in his thirties. He was dark-haired, with big ears and thick brows, a straight, long nose, and wide, thin, irregularly slanting lips. He sat as if holding himself together, giving off the effect of persistent sneering. Suddenly, his expression seemed to alter from a sneer to a pout. Studs decided he was a big sack of mush, and shifted his eyes to the floor, uneasy because he had stared so long at the fellow. Beside him, a weak-shouldered little man sat, nervously folding and opening his fingers, his wrists narrow and powerless, his face blown with yellowish, unhealthy fat, a tb face. He wondered what about this fellow, and the bull-necked one, and the gray-haired man, and the others? They all must be hoping for a job, and maybe they needed one just as much as he did. If he got a job, it would mean some of them would be s. o. l. Well, the same would apply to him if they got jobs. It was just the breaks. A dark foreigner hurriedly emerged from an inner door on the right, crowded through the gate with eyes on the floor, probably to avoid meeting the questioning stares of the waiting applicants. He departed. No soap for that guy, Studs could see. The office boy barked out a name, and a little fellow in a loud shabby gray suit swung through the gate and disappeared inside the inner door on the right.

Studs felt let down because the fellow who had just come from his interview hadn't, it seemed, gotten anything. If these fellows ahead of him couldn't, how could he? Still, if he was to land something, most of these others would have to get the bums' rush, and each one who did meant one less rival. He tried to hope. And looking around, he could see the others must be thinking much the same as he was, because they all sat waiting, their faces hardening, their muscles tight, alert, scraping their feet, making all sorts of little motions and gestures because they were so nervous.

The freckle-faced office boy was checking over a stack of cards, and, watching him, Studs got the feeling that the punk was showing off, trying to tell them all that he had a job and they didn't. Just the kind of a face that Studs would like to have mashed in a little. He stared at the wall above the office boy. He wished the waiting could be shortened.

The small fellow in the loud shabby suit appeared through the gates, smiling artificially. Again Studs could feel how they became tense. The gray-haired man went in. Two tall fellows entered, spoke to the office boy, filled out cards, waited, standing to the left of Studs' bench and he enjoyed seeing how nervous and jumpy they were. He told himself that misery loved company. Well, if he failed here, he wouldn't be alone. If he made a fool out of himself, well, maybe others would, too.

The mush-faced, bull-necked fellow stretched out his legs and opened a copy of *The Chicago Questioner*. Studs pulled out his newspaper and looked at the front page. Police blamed Reds for recent eviction riots in the Black Belt. Reds must be nigger-lovers. Mayor says city finances in dangerous condition. That was bad, all right. Just what Barney McCormack had told his old man. Forced labor of women on Russian boats. Maybe every night the men lined up outside the women's cabins. How would the women like that? But there weren't enough details in the paper. He skipped the account of farmers rioting with guns and pitchforks, and avidly turned to one next to it. Sixteen-year-old girl found unconscious in forest preserve. Did a guy pulling such a stunt get anything worth the effort? He folded up his newspaper and noticed that the mushy-faced fellow had gone in, and that there were three more talking to the office boy. He looked at his watch. Ten o'clock already. Seemed he might waste the whole morning here and get out too late to look any place else until after lunch. Might as well get up and leave, because the way they kept coming out of that office, glum and hasty, there didn't seem to be much chance here. A nice smoke would go good, too, only for the doctor's orders. He'd stick it here, too, damn it if he wouldn't, and find out. Getting up and leaving now would just be showing that he had no guts. This might be just his chance. After all these guys getting the air, he might just walk in and get a job. But if he did, could he do the work well enough? He didn't want it long, just to carry him over and bring in regular dough until he could get started on that course in traffic managing and find a place in something that had a real future in it. Still, from the looks of it here, wasn't he wasting his time? But no, he ought to stick it out and see, since he'd waited this long. He slouched on the bench and noticed a roughly dressed Polack or Hunky whose face was deep with wrinkles, a coarse-skinned man of about forty-five or so with a dirty, tobacco-stained mustache. Reminded Studs of old Boushwah, the crabby old janitor he and the other guys had hated when he was a kid. And he'd be willing to bet that this Boushwah was as bad, and could hardly speak English. Such a guy had nerve looking for a job here. It perked up his own confidence. If such a guy thought he could get a job here, why shouldn't Studs Lonigan have more right to think the same thing? What could he say? Should he talk big? Walk in like he owned the office and this whole building and say, I'm the nuts, give me a job? He could just see himself getting a job that way. He imagined himself really getting a job, and he saw himself wearing overalls, working his ears off in a gas station on a hot Sunday. Anyway, he would just walk into the office inside and talk naturally to the Personnel Manager. Of course, though, he couldn't say that he only wanted a job for a short time. If business picked up for the old man, he could work with him, not painting, but just helping out. He knew enough about the business. But he was tired of it. What he really wanted to do was to be a high-class, well-paid traffic manager, , and if he got this job, he would use it as a stepping stone to that.

But these other fellows? Were they as nervous and afraid as he was? And did they need a job as much as he did? Another exit. Another entrance. His turn very soon now. And what the hell would he say?

Behind a glass-topped desk, set diagonally on a dull, green carpet, Studs saw a thick-browed, full-faced, coldly efficient-looking man whose broad shoulders were covered by the jacket of a black business suit. He seemed to have the appearance of being fraternity and ex-collegiate, and Studs felt ready to give up.

"Mr. Lonigan, how do you do? I'm Mr. Parker," the man said, arising and extending a large, hairy-backed hand.

"How do you do," Studs mumbled, trying to act like an equal.

"Won't you have a seat?" Mr. Parker said, pointing to the chair at the near side of his desk.

They sat down, and from the corner of his eye Studs glimpsed the wet, dreary panorama of Grant Park, the blackened driveways, the gray lake, half-smothered in thick mist.

"Now, what can I do for you, Mr. Lonigan?"

"Well, I thought I would come down to see you about a job," Studs said, and the man's disconcerting smile made Studs wish that he was anywhere else but sitting opposite this fellow.

"I don't know if you are aware of it or not, but hundreds come here for that purpose every week."

Studs smiled weakly, feeling that he was giving himself

away and showing by his smile that he had no guts, but still he was unable to check it. The man quietly studied him, his penetrating glance making Studs feel even more hopeless.

"How old are you, Mr. Lonigan?"

"I'll be thirty this coming fall," Studs answered, glad for the question because it would lead to talk and break that sitting in silence while that fellow looked through him.

"And how is it that you happen to come to Nation Oil Company? Did somebody send you, or do you know someone already employed here?"

"Well, I just thought that it would be a good company to work for," Studs said, hoping that his answer was satisfactory.

Studs felt as if he were a mouse in the hands of a cat while Mr. Parker looked down at his desk, toyed with his pencil. Then with a pointed glance he forced Studs to meet his gaze.

"When did you work last?"

"I've been working right along," Studs said, heeding a warning thought not to show his hand or reveal that he desperately needed a job.

"What sort of work have you been doing, Mr. Lonigan?"

"Painting," Studs answered, and the man seemed to raise his eyebrows.

"Artist, you mean?"

"No, house painting," Studs smiled, receiving a return smile which put him more at his ease.

"How does it happen that you want to come to work in a gasoline-filling station? Is it just a lull in your line, and a desire to tide over? Because, you should be informed, when we employ a man, we employ one whom we expect to stay with us and work his way up. Most of our salesmen and many of our executives here, you know, have worked their way up from the service stations. We consider our service stations as a training ground, and hence we cannot employ men just to tide over in dull seasons in their own occupation."

"Well, I'm giving up painting on account of my health, and

I got to get a steady job right away. I have to get some other kind of work," Studs said, and, perceiving the frown his remark occasioned, he immediately realized that he had pulled a boner.

"What's the matter with your health, Mr. Lonigan?"

"Well, you know, painting, that is, house-painting, isn't the most healthy occupation in the world. You can get lead poisoning, and then, too, my lungs, I've got to watch them and get different work. I'm not in any serious danger, you see, but I just have to change and get some different work. And in changing, I've got to get a good job at outside work, and still something with a future in it."

"Of course, Mr. Lonigan, I trust that you don't consider the Nation Oil Company a health resort," Mr. Parker said after a moment of deep reflection.

"Naturally not," Studs said, not liking the crack, but holding his temper. "I've got to find a job and I'm willing to work hard, as long as there is a chance to get ahead."

He wondered would he have done better by putting all his cards on the table and shooting square. He didn't trust this fellow, but still, if he told more of his story, well, the fellow would have to sympathize with him and give him a break, if there was any break to be given.

"Married?"

"I'm getting married in two weeks."

"How long have you been a painter?"

"Since 1919. I've been working with my father."

"Business bad now?"

"Well, it isn't good. But that's not the reason. I'm leaving because I want to get into something new, and because I got to change my work. You see, on my getting married now, well, I lost two thousand bucks, dollars, that is, on Imbray stock, and then I'm broke, and then, as I said, I got to change my job on account of my health." Studs noticed the immobile, cold face before him, and it seemed useless to go on. "Of course, things are not so hot, good, I mean, with my father, and well, under the circumstances, I think I ought to go out and work at something for myself. I've been a painter long enough, and now, I'm looking about for a change."

"I see now. At first I wasn't able to understand why you should want to go to a new work that pays less," Mr. Parker said, but still there was that lifelessness in his features.

"And, of course, I'm only asking for a start in a station," Studs said, spurred on to win interest and sympathy. "And I'm sure I can work my way up. I'm not lazy. I've always worked, and I can work."

"What education have you had?"

"Grammar school and some high school."

"Some high school—how much?" Mr. Parker asked querulously.

"Two years."

"In Chicago here?"

"Yes, Loyola on the north side," Studs said, and he waited in uncertainty while the man made some jottings on a scratch pad. Maybe he would get it.

"Well, Mr. Lonigan, there isn't really an opening at present. Times are, you know, not the best, and we have only a limited capacity for hiring people. We would like to hire as many as we could, but that, of course, is out of the question. If you and your father have a contract to paint a house, and you hire more men than you need, there isn't any profit. And you say you are how old?"

"I'll be thirty this fall."

"That, also, isn't so good. At thirty a man is still young. But we, you see, like to get our service-station men younger. Just out of college, especially, and train them in our own way. I can't hold out much hope for you, but I'll give you an application blank to fill out and mail to me, and if there is an opening, I shall get in touch with you."

"Well, thank you. And, oh, yes, I wanted to say, also, that I can give you good references."

"Of that I don't doubt. I can see that you are an experienced man in your own line, and that you have undoubtedly made good at it."

"Well, I can give references like Judge Dennis Gorman, and Mr. McCormack who's high up in the Democratic party."

"Of course, there is no connection between the Nation Oil Company and politics. But then, of course, such references are worthy ones, references of men in public offices, and they will count for you favorably when your application is considered. Now here is an application blank. It is self-explanatory. You fill it out tonight and mail it to me."

"Thanks, I'll do that," Studs said, accepting the blank.

"I'm very glad to have met you, Mr. Lonigan," Mr. Parker said, arising and offering a limp hand.

Studs hurried out past the waiting lineup on the benches. In the corridor, he looked at his watch, eleven-thirty, and pressed the button for an elevator.

From the entrance-way to the Nation Oil building he watched the rain sweep Michigan Boulevard like a broom. The damp atmosphere seemed to penetrate to his bones and he felt lousy enough as it was, without having to take any disappointments.

What now? He tried to make himself believe that he hadn't been dumb in the way he had talked upstairs, but he knew differently. Goddamn it, why did he have to go through this? Giving him the same kind of a go-by they would hand to a chump. It would just be a waste of time filling out the application and mailing it in. He wasn't a dummy, either, and if they'd only give him the chance, he'd show them. He saw himself getting the chance, working himself up, becoming a big shot in the Nation Oil Company. But things had gone too far for him to be kidding himself with such dreams.

That Parker was one cold and clammy bastard. A fake high-brow, lording it over every poor guy who came along looking for a job. What education? What the hell was college anyway? But still, he did wish he hadn't been such a mutton-head as to pass up the chance to get an education when he had had it. Just now, when he needed help most, an education would put him a long way ahead of many others.

Studs noticed a fellow who had been after him in the lineup waiting upstairs. He wanted the fellow to speak, but he passed out. He guessed the guy had gotten the same kind of crap that they'd given him.

A bum shambled by the building. A taxicab skidded on the wet street. Still, what next? He looked at the Help Wanted column of his newspaper, again figuring that he had time for one more attempt before lunch. Opportunity for a salesman. And the building was just over on Wabash Avenue. It didn't look any too hot, but a chance was a chance, and he couldn't afford to ignore anything if it looked at all likely. A green-slickered girl passed the doorway, and Studs thought how nice it would be to follow her, spend the day forgetting everything by fooling around with her. He wished to all holy hell that he didn't have to go through with all this, and he stood watching the splattering rain. He felt sorry for himself.

And maybe the ad for a salesman wasn't even worth trying. He stepped out onto the sidewalk and ran, hugging the building. He soaked his left foot and trouser cuff in a puddle, cursing as he hastened on. Turning a corner, breathless, he was forced to pause because of a stitch in his side and an aching heaviness in his back and arms. He jammed his hands into his raincoat pockets, gasped for breath, and began to worry over his wet feet. Rain beat off his hat and back, and a drop oozed inside his collar, slid coldly down his back.

On Wabash Avenue he found his number, a dirty, brown-stone building, and he entered the gloomy cavern of the tile-doored entrance-way. Reading the bulletin board, he was depressed by the general seediness of the building, and decided to follow up the ad only because it would keep him out of the rain. The iron-grilled elevator jerked and rattled upward, and Studs reflected that such a rickety elevator ought to fall, anyway, and smash itself at the base of the elevator shaft. Stepping out at the fifth floor, he shook his wet hat, and heard the elevator doors clanking shut and the creaking and straining of the car. He pulled a comb out of his pocket and quickly ran it through his dampened hair. Again he heard the slamming elevator doors as he searched for the right room number along a dim corridor with soiled, yellow calcimined walls.

He entered a small, dim office and found six others waiting on a bench to the left of the door. Same thing all over again with a line ahead of him, he thought spiritlessly. What time did one have to get out to be first in following a lead for a job? Was it necessary to bring a tent along and camp outside the building all night? There was certainly something wrong between seeing the lineups for jobs and listening to Carroll Dowson tell how times weren't so bad, the way he'd done last Sunday.

Studs timidly approached the flapper with thickly rouged lips, who sat before a typewriter at a desk in a corner. Shame came upon him, and his cheeks were hot. Coming here and going to this dame was admitting to her that he wanted a job, putting himself at a disadvantage because it was acknowledging a kind of failure.

"I saw your ad in this morning's paper," he began with attempted casualness.

"What's the name?" she interrupted.

"Lonigan," he answered, feeling as if the hostile eyes of those on the bench were boring into his back.

"Well, Mr. Lonergan, will you sit down and wait? Mr. Peters will see you just as soon as he gets through seeing those ahead of you."

"Thanks," he said, not bothering to correct her mispronunciation of his name.

He sat down at the edge of the stiff bench. He was wet and

chilled. His trouser legs were soggy, and the rain had soaked through his shoes. He watched the girl at the desk chew gum as she typed rapidly. Hard and tough-looking baby, all right, the kind who knew what it was all about, he guessed.

"Nasty day," the fellow beside him said.

"Damn rotten, and I'm soaked," Studs replied, surprised.

He watched the stranger squeeze slimy bubbles of ooze from his shoes by pressing continually on the balls of his feet. Noticing the rip on the instep of the right shoe, he guessed that here was a guy who was plenty hard up, and he seemed at least forty, his face thin, wrinkles under the eyes, the cheeks sunken.

"Hell to be looking for something to do on a day like this," the fellow said, revealing discolored teeth when he spoke.

"Damn right," Studs said, telling himself that the fellow's teeth gave him the willies, they looked so ugly.

"But then, these are hard times. I've been through other depressions, but none of them can match this one."

"Yeah, times are tough," Studs said, holding back the impulse to talk about his own troubles.

"Me, maybe I don't look it, but I once was up in the class. I'm a college graduate. Michigan, and I've been up in the class. Maybe I don't look it, but I was a ten-thousand-dollar-a-year man, and I had my money tucked neatly in the bank. And the bank failed. So here I am, holding the sack. But I'll come back."

Studs nodded agreement. The other went on, "Stranger, these are tough times. And don't I know it! It's quite a comedown from being a ten-thousand-dollar-a-year man to this, but I'll come back."

Studs saw clearly that this fellow was full of bull, but the guy had a good line anyway, ought to make a good salesman.

"You know it's these rich louses who ruined the country. They want to take everything for themselves and leave nothing for anybody else. So all of us, even those like myself, who've been in the class, we're just underdogs to them. But they can't keep a man like myself down. I'm a college graduate, Missouri University, and I'll get back in the class."

"Well, I was getting along. I studied to be a traffic manager, but things are bad and I had a set-back. I've got to get something for a little while to get back on my feet."

"You and I, well, just to take a look at us, anybody could tell we're not the underdog or working-stiff type. And when we got to go out looking for something to do, and the breaks have gone against us, well, it only goes to show how hard times are."

Studs nodded. He saw that the heavy fellow next to this guy was giving the two of them a fishy eye, and he wished this fellow would stop shovelling out so much crap.

"I'll tell you, stranger, it's a dirty shame when you and I and our type have to take it on the chin. Take myself now, I get pretty damn sore when I think of what I had. A swell apartment out on Wilson Avenue, gals, all the wine, woman, and song my little heart desired, and a nice wad socked away. Nothing in the world to disturb my peace of mind, or my night's rest. And then, the firm goes bust, the bank closes its doors, so here I am. But I ain't through, not by a damn sight. I was in the class once, and that's where I'll be again."

Studs turned away, not wanting to see any more of the fellow's teeth, hoping the others on the bench or the girl typing wouldn't take him to be the same type of crap artist.

The girl walked out of the office, wriggling with each step. The way they all gave her the once-over reminded Studs how the boys used to line up in front of the Fifty-eighth Street poolroom and undress every girl who passed. And this dame, he could see that she was a teasing bitch who liked to be looked at. Well, let her flaunt herself. He wasn't exactly hard up.

"Jesus Christ!" he heard a little fellow at the opposite end of the bench exclaim in an enthusiastic half-whisper.

"She's something that could make a man forget whether or

Courtesy of Dorothea Lange

Bindle stiff (itinerant farm laborer) searching work, California, 1937

WHAT HURTS BUSINESS
HURTS ME

NEW
RIC
100% PAR
RICH

Courtesy of Dorothea Lange

Signs of the times, 1938

Dorothea Lange (Farm Security Administration), Courtesy of The New York Public Library

The 'Okies' arrive at their goal, 1935

Jobless, Stockton, California, 1936

Courtesy of Dorothea Lange

Breadline: "Every Dollar Pays for 20 More Meals"

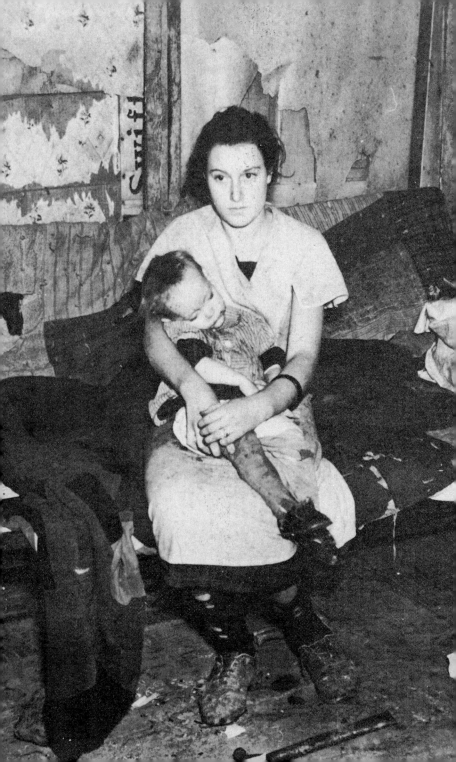

Refugee from rural poverty, 1937

Aliquippa, Pennsylvania, July 1938

Salvaging coal at Nanty Glo slag heap, 1937

Ben Shahn (Farm Security Administration), Courtesy of The New York Public Library

Arthur Rothstein (Farm Security Administration), Courtesy of The New York Public Library

Missouri sharecroppers, January 1939

Arthur Rothstein (Farm Security Administration), Courtesy of The New York Public Library

Failure, 1936

The Plow, 1936

Arthur Rothstein (Farm Security Administration), Courtesy of the Library of Congress

Breadline, San Francisco, 1933

Courtesy of Dorothea Lange

May Day, San Francisco, 1933

The Great Depression

White-collar workers sheltered in warehouse, 1933

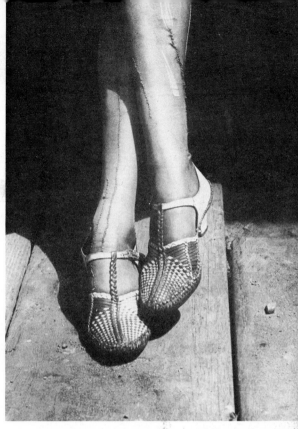

Waitress with silk stockings, 1933

Courtesy of Dorothea Lange

Unemployment compensation: the first day, June 1938

Courtesy of Dorothea Lange

Georgia, 1936

Independent gas station during migrant cotton pickers' strike, 1938

Courtesy of Dorothea Lange

Hooverville in a river bed, 1935

Dorothea Lange (Resettlement Administration), Courtesy of The New York Public Library

Chain Gang

Dorothea Lange (Farm Security Administration)
Courtesy of The New York Public Library

Hoe culture, Alabama, 1936

Let Us Now Praise Famous Men

Walker Evans (Farm Security Administration), Courtesy of the Library of Congress

Cleveland, Summer 1932: Veterans tie up railroad yards in Bonus March

not he had a job on a day like this," the crap artist beside him said insinuatingly, slyly poking Studs as he spoke.

A wiry, nervous, bald-headed man came from an adjoining office, followed by a barrel-like fellow who walked out of the office, carrying a folded newspaper under his arm.

"Who's next?"

A tall lad arose and walked into the adjoining office after the bald-headed man.

The girl returned.

"Sticks what's she's got right up into your face," the crap artist whispered.

Sitting down, the girl flashed an annoyed glance at them, and Studs flushed. But how could a guy help getting het up when a dame did everything she could to tantalize him? She was crossing her legs, showing one leg above the knee. Ought to be a law forbidding broads to tease that way. She pulled the gum from her mouth, stretched it several feet, pulled it back into her mouth, resumed chewing it, and began typing as if the lineup on the bench were non-existent.

He looked toward the unwashed windows at the opposite end of the office and, staring at the heavy pall of gray sky, he became aware of traffic noises from the street below. He was damp, wet, and what would he do if there was nothing decent here? And how long would he have to wait? He looked at his watch: a quarter to twelve.

Two shabby men entered and walked to the girl. The tall lad came out of the inner office. Didn't look like he'd gotten anything. Maybe, then, it might be a good job. And if he got it, his troubles might be ended. If not, a whole morning wasted.

Studs saw the wiry, bald-headed man sitting at the littered desk of the cramped adjoining office, and beside him there were stacks of paper cups.

"How do you do, ah, Mr. . . ."

"Lonigan," Studs volunteered, taking the chair opposite the man.

"Glad to meet you, I'm Mr. Peters. Now tell me, Mr. Lonigan, are you, or are you not, a live-wire?" the man said, giving Studs a penetrating look.

Too stunned to answer, Studs stared back, puzzled.

"I have here a proposition that is for live-wires, and for live-wires only. Slackers, slow-pokes, easy-going, unambitious fellows, I neither want nor can tolerate. I am not even interested in the kind of salesman who thinks that because he has made a few sales in the morning, his day's work is done and he can knock off. The reason I'm saying these things at the beginning of this interview is because if you are that type, we are both wasting our time in even discussing the proposition I have to offer you."

"Well, I'd like to hear what your proposition is," Studs said, not liking this oozy bastard, but trying to act up to him.

"I've got here the kind of proposition a genuine live-wire recognizes immediately for what it's worth when it is presented to him. He sees that it is a sure-fire proposition that he can make plenty of money out of. I can prove, too, that I've got a real money-maker here by showing you the reports of some of our salesmen." Mr. Peters dug through the papers on his desk and found a blocked-off, criss-crossed sheet. "Here's a report from one of our salesmen who earned sixty dollars commissions last week."

Studs' eyes opened widely, and his suspicion momentarily quieted. Sixty bucks in one week. If sixty, why not seventy or seventy-five? Leaning his elbows on the desk, his head bent forward.

"Here's another whose net was fifty-four dollars. And fifty-four dollars a week in these days is real money. It's big money for salesmen new at the game, who are selling a new product which is just being put successfully on the market. I can vouch for that. Our product is new, and anyone starting in with us at this stage of the game has boundless opportunities ahead. There's no telling where the limits are, and he can make, from his very first week, more money than thousands and thousands of men are earning today after years of work in one line. The opportunities are boundless."

Perspiring, Studs wished this goofy bald-headed bastard would come down to earth. But, gee, if this only was the genuine article and he could make sixty a week!

"We don't want coming to us the type of man who cries he's licked before he has even started, and who blames his failure on the business depression. A business depression is a smart man's opportunity. Too many people, today, are crying they're licked and not putting forth their best efforts. Well, that only means so much more opportunity for the live-wire. It's the time for him to plug, while others whine. It gives him less real competition in selling and if he throws his heart and soul into his efforts and his sales talks, he wins out, just because of the simple fact that so many of his rivals are beating themselves by whining. It is worth repeating that today is the smart man's opportunity. Today is the time for the real, high-class salesman to show his real mettle. And any man can sell if he has the courage and ambition to make a live-wire of himself. The stuff is there in every man. The question is, if you'll pardon my language, whether he's got the guts to bring it out."

Studs squirmed in his chair. Guts. Well, he had the guts. Studs Lonigan had guts, even if he had nothing else.

"Why, today so many people are whining, and whimpering, and prostrating themselves to Old Man Gloom, that the good salesman has an ocean of clear sailing ahead of him. Because this country is not licked and it won't be. And the service the good salesman can perform for this country today is to show it that it isn't licked. What we lack today is confidence. It is contagious. It peps up the sales prospect. Because people, even though they whine and whimper, sigh and decry and put faces on a yard long, cry out that times are bad and they're licked, people still don't want to believe it. They want to have faith. They want confidence. And remember this, they are going to pay the man who gives them confidence and faith. This is the one cardinal principle of salesmanship, the principle of the ir-radiation of confidence," Mr. Peters emphasized with a snapping gesture of his right fist.

"Yes, I think you're right. . . . But now, what is the proposition?" Studs asked, trying to make his tone of voice circumspect.

"I'm coming to that," the man said, knitting his brows.

Studs was sure it was all bull. But Jesus, if it only wasn't, if he could only knock off sixty a week. Then he wouldn't have to be marrying Catherine like a damned gigolo.

"Now, to continue, I have here the kind of proposition that only a real salesman wants. If you're not a real salesman, you don't want this proposition, and there is no need of prolonging our interview. Now, do you have faith enough in yourself to believe that you can bring out that something in you that is the makings, the basis of real salesmanship?"

Trying to conceal his surprise under the man's direct stare and pointing finger, Studs shook his head in affirmation.

"Well, speak up!" Mr. Peters said frettingly. "Speak up!" You know a real salesman has to be able to talk. Nodding your head, you know, that's not a positive answer. You got to speak out straight from the shoulder, crisp, straight, hard language. Even when you only say yes and no, you should say them with a punch."

"Well, I think so. I haven't ever sold, but I'd like to know what this business is, and then we could see."

"That's the idea. Now, if you want to handle our product, you got to be a real salesman. But if you are, there's big money waiting for you. . . . Are you married?"

"I'm getting married."

"And you want a job. Well, you've come to the right place. If you're the right person, you'll have no further worries. With

the money you'll earn on our product, you'll be able to furnish
that little love nest for yourself and the little girl. And you
know what you need for smooth sailing on the stormy seas of
matrimony? Money. As I have said, if you're the right kind, if
you can speak up, always dance on your toes, grasp your opportunities, be a character psychologist on sight, read a man's
mind, see the weak spots, the Achilles heel in his armor and
drive a telling wedge through it to carry the sales off, and
above all, always remember that cardinal principle of the ir-
radiation of confidence, well then, you and I can talk business."

Studs glanced aside to prevent himself from smiling. He was
sure that it was a sucker proposition, but then, there was one
born every minùte, and if there were enough chumps in the
world, well, maybe, fifty, sixty dollars a week.

"Our proposition is this. We have a new sanitary paper cup.
Now there are in Chicago hundreds and thousands of industrial
establishments, stores, offices and the like that are backward
and unsanitary, because they use the medieval method of letting employees drink from one drinking glass, or even a tin
cup. These are old-fashioned, backward, stone-age methods,
unmodern, unscientific, and they help to spread disease. Nobody likes to use another person's, a stranger's, drinking glass,
and particularly not some rusty old tin cup that scores drink
out of. Throughout this city there are people who spread
diseases through drinking cups and glasses. That's one of your
principal selling points. It constitutes an irrefutable argument,
and if you are clever it will gain you a high percentage of sales.
The man who refuses to listen to it, who refuses to substitute
our sanitary paper drinking cup for the old-fashioned, anti-
quated, disease-ridden drinking glass or tin cup, that man is
backward, and he is risking the health of countless people."
The man pointed his index finger at Studs and glared until
Studs felt like reminding him that he wasn't making anyone
drink out of a rusty tin cup. "A sanitary drinking cup, such as
ours, is first of all scientific, and this is the age of science, the

era of hygiene. Also, it is an aid to efficiency in a store, office, or factory. Why? Because it ministers to the better health of all concerned, and this makes for that increased efficiency. How does it achieve the purpose? Ha, proving that argument is like knocking over a straw man! If people are well, if they have less fear of disease, they work more efficiently because their psychology, their psychological attitude, is the right one. If there is a diseased employee in an office using an unsanitary medieval drinking glass or cup, the baneful, the dangerous, the mortal, results can be incalculable. That person can infect a valued member of the office force, and require him or her to remain out of work. A new person must be temporarily employed. The new person does not know the work, and must be broken in. There is resultant inefficiency. Inefficiency means demoralization and there is a contagious spread of inefficiency. The employer himself is not immune to disease, and probably, in some instances, uses the same backward drinking glass or cup that his employees use. He can become infected with a contagious disease, and can carry it home to his wife and children. They can become sick, even die. You see the point? In selling you stress it, only make it more concrete than I have done. Pick out someone working in an office, the secretary, concrete, you know, and speak of some specific disease like consumption." Studs nodded courteously, thinking that this guy was a new one to him. And he could see himself stringing out a line like this guy's. "Now as to our cups, we have an unusual offer of five hundred paper cups for a dollar, and with any order of twenty-five hundred or more cups, we will give as a premium an attractive glass container that is not only useful but also decorative in an office, store or factory. Now, isn't it worth a dollar to insure efficiency in your office and home? That's our argument to the buyer. Here is our proposition to the salesman. You buy the cups for fifty cents, and a cardboard carrier box goes with it, free. You sell them for a dollar and make your own delivery. We assign you a territory which is large enough, and has sufficient potential sales in it, to insure you a good living income, fifty, sixty, even a hundred dollars a week."

Studs tried to think of something to say that would permit him an easy exit.

"What do you think? How does it sound to you?"

"All right," Studs said to prevent the fellow from unwinding into another long breath-taking spiel.

"Well, would you like to try it?"

"I might."

"That's no way to be a salesman," Mr. Peters said, his expression pained as he emphatically shook his head from side to side. Rising half way from his chair, he surprised Studs by pounding his fist on the desk and gimleting Studs with a searching eye-to-eye gaze. "You got to be positive, direct, forthright. You'll never be able to sell with that wishy-washy kind of an attitude and manner."

"I think I might try it but I can't today because I haven't any money with me to buy the cups," Studs said apologetically, but determined not to be roped in.

"You know every day lost is so much money lost. So much time squandered. And time is the most valuable and precious possession of mankind."

"I didn't think to take money with me."

"Usually an initial order of our new salesman is five packages of cups for two-fifty, but you might start with a lower order, one or two packages. One package is only fifty cents. You could sell in the territory I assign you here in the Loop and earn the price of your lunch and carfare. Then you could come down early tomorrow prepared to dig right in, or even, you could buy one package, sell it, and come back for two more with your dollar from the same."

"I couldn't even do that. I've only got my I. C. ticket and the price of my lunch."

"That's too bad, and it may be your tough luck. By tomorrow many good territories will have already been given out. First come, first served. That has to be our motto. Each day you lose means you are sacrificing the prospects of so much good money. After we get our product on the market, we will change our methods, and employ regular salesmen. Then the opportunities will be less than they are now. If a man starts in with our organization now at the beginning, he is in line for advancement. Inside of a year, we'll need sales managers, and they will have positions that any man would envy. They'll go into the real money, over a hundred dollars a week, and they will have the guarantee of a future of useful and profitable work. If a man goes in with us now, and he shows he has the genuine goods, his worries, for the future, are over, depression or no depression."

"Well, I could come back tomorrow."

"Think it over, Mr. . . . ah . . ."

"Lonigan."

"Mr. Lonigan, yes. I interview so many people daily that I can't remember new names always. Now, Mr. Lonigan, if you are interested, I'll be glad to discuss this proposition of ours with you further in the morning, and start you off on the right foot. But don't forget, every day, every minute that you lose means that valuable territories and Loop buildings are going to others."

Studs arose.

"Think it over, Mr. Lonigan," the man said, lifelessly shaking Studs' hand.

"I will."

Studs walked from the office, tired, almost dizzy, from the man's talk. There was a lineup on the bench, but the girl was gone. He examined his watch: twelve twenty-five, and left. But, gee, if it had only been a real and genuine proposition that would have netted him his sixty a week.

He walked in the rain, north along Wabash Avenue, worn out, with his feet soaked, fighting the discouraging idea of giving up for the day, wondering where to go and what to do next. He dashed into a Thompson restaurant to get out of the rain. He noticed the clock to the right of the cashier's desk. Seven minutes to one. It probably wouldn't do much good to try any other place until at least one-thirty. He could sit here over a cup of coffee until then. Should have taken longer with his lunch. He carried his cup of coffee from the counter, put sugar into it at a service stand, and found a one-arm chair. He slouched, and stared around at the many people scattered over the place, noticing a shabby, graying man wolfing a sandwich. Two chairs away from this man, a bum snoozed half asleep over a cup of coffee. At a table, two young lads talked rapidly over plate dinners. Near them two bell-hops or doormen in braided uniforms drank coffee. Down to his right, an old man with shaking hands slobbered as he drank. All these people, some happy, some not, how many were worse off than he?

He drank coffee, and determined to force his mind on the problem of what to do this afternoon, and what to say when he went out looking again. He lifted the cup and noticed the manager, a sour-faced fellow in a clean white coat, move officiously around, seeming to give orders to the hustling busboys. The man took a position near the door and stood with folded arms as if he owned the joint. Studs thought of how he would hate to work for a nasty-looking bastard like that manager. In a far corner two girls talked at a table. What about them?

There was no urge in him now to do anything. He was too damned tired. His feet were wet, and they felt dirty. His suit seemed not to fit, hanging loosely and unpressed on his body, the trousers about the cuffs heavy from rain. He told himself that he was whipped. He told himself, that no, damn it, no, he wasn't whipped. He would just sit here a while, rest himself, get his bearings, figure out a clear line to use in getting a job, and then go out and look until he did get something.

He walked to the cashier's counter and bought a package of cigarettes. He knew he shouldn't smoke, but one now, in his present state, wouldn't hurt. Returning to his chair, he saw that his cup had been removed. He walked to the counter and came back with another cup. He lit a cigarette and inhaled deeply. He shook his head, thinking that Christ, the times sure must be hard, all right. At both places where he'd been this morning, fellows had kept streaming in. And there would be some chumps, so dumb, or so hard up, that they would fall for that bald-headed guy's paper-cup racket. Have a scientific drink of water in a scientific paper cup, he smiled to himself, drinking coffee. But Studs Lonigan had not been one of that boy's suckers. No, sir.

"Well, Joe, I got a job."

Studs turned to his left, and saw two young lads in blue suits a few chairs down from him.

"Anything good?"

"You can't tell. It's commission selling."

"That ain't a job, that's a question of reducing weight."

He had to get a job, because if he didn't he would be living on Catherine's dough, and on what she could earn until she would have to quit because of the kid she was having. Jesus, it was just dumb, tying themselves down with a kid in the first inning, refusing to take anything or have something done about it. His eye, wandering over the restaurant, caught a coal black and perspiring Negro, in an almost filthy white apron, who slung a mop rhythmically back and forth along the dirty tile floor.

"It's this way, Joe. Now, what gave us good times? The automobile industry. Why? Because it was something new to develop. Now, what do we need now to bring back better times? Something else that's new, to develop. Well, that's the idea, see. This outfit I'm with has got something new. An electric shaver. All right. If it can sell an electric shave to every man in the country who is working, well, think of what that means."

"Don't let anybody from the barber's union hear you say that."

"I'm serious."

If he could think of something new, or get in on something new that was really a good thing and not just a racket like that paper-cup dodge. If he could go back to painting.

From somewhere outside he heard fire-engine sirens, and he sat on the edge of his chair and saw that all over the restaurant people got excited. A man arose, hurried out of the restaurant. He felt like dashing out to see the fire. But he couldn't. Not in the rain. And anyway this afternoon he had ahead of him the serious business of getting a job. The Negro passed him, humming quietly as he mopped. Looked like a happy shine. Wished he was as naturally happy as all the shines were. Suppose he had been born a jigg. Christ! That, at least, was one thing to be thankful for.

"Joe, it's a chance. But it's worth taking. There's a whole new virgin field here, just as Mr. Cathaway, he's the man I just got the job from, just as he said."

"Sure, you wear out your shoes, feed yourself, and take the change. If you sell anything, he collects, and then you do."

"You're just cynical, Joe."

"Sure I am. I've worked at enough jobs and seen enough rackets to be cynical."

"Well, I'm not."

Studs was too nervous to keep sitting. He got up and paid his check. He walked along Wabash Avenue, rain pelting him, worried over getting wet and catching cold, not knowing what to do, a feeling of confusion spreading like a fog over his thoughts. He scarcely knew where he was. He heard an automobile horn and stepped back two feet on the sidewalk, standing in momentary paralysis. He had to laugh at himself. In the middle of the block, jumping back, afraid of being run over because he heard an automobile horn in the street! He had to, damn it, just pull himself together.

Oh, my Jesus Christ, if only something would happen! Again that confusion, like a fog, numbed his senses, and he became unaware even of the rain battering against his raincoat. Suppose he should just clear out on a freight, and go to-hell-and-gone, letting everything just go to pot. What then? Consumption, like Davey Cohen had gotten on the bum. Or maybe lose a leg or get killed under a train, or freeze to death riding the rods in winter, or just poop out with heart failure. He imagined himself a politician, with a fat cigar in his mouth, a bigger shot in the racket than Red Kelly, a boss sitting over a table with Barney McCormack, deciding on what to do with jobs and rake-offs.

"Buddy, can you spare a man the price of a cup of coffee?"

Studs turned to see an unshaven man in a soaked, torn coat. He walked on, turning east on Randolph Street. Women's dresses in a window. The same window that Catherine had looked at the night they became engaged. Maybe he should take in a show this afternoon and get started bright and early in the morning. He passed the public library, seeing hoboes cluttered around the entrance way, looking out at the rainy street. He turned north on Michigan Avenue. Well, he at least wasn't a bum. He asked himself where he was going. Well, maybe he might just stumble into a job somewheres along here. He entered a building near the bridge and read the bulletin board, his eyes stopping at the name, Royal Insurance Company.

On a hunch that it might be his ticket, he rode on the elevator to the tenth floor. He stood outside the entrance door to the insurance company offices, trying to pump courage into himself. What the hell, wouldn't be anything doing there. He walked back to the elevator, and riding down he told himself that he didn't want to go around begging his friends to buy insurance off him. And anyway, it might be a little too early to go looking for a job in the afternoon. Best maybe to wait until about two-thirty.

Walking back toward Randolph Street, Michigan Boulevard lost itself in mist, and the Art Institute down at Monroe Street was like some very distant building. People were hurry-

ing by, and the crawling, honking traffic beat a confusion into
him. He collided with a stout woman, hurried on without
an apology. Maybe he ought to go home. He was too wet and
mussed to look for a job. At Randolph, he dashed across the
street and up the steps of the public library building, winded
by the short run. He looked at the small crowd of people who
stood sheltered from the rain. The boes made him laugh. So
many of them looked like mopes. He watched a stream of people pour up from the Illinois Central subway exit. Train had
just pulled in. Lots of women. Some neat girls, too. If it was
only a hot sunny day, they wouldn't be wearing raincoats and
slickers, and he could get a better look at their figures. He
watched one girl in a yellow slicker, with blonde hair curling
out from a black hat, as she minced to a taxicab. Neat little
parcel of femininity, young and budding just like Lucy had
once been. Lucy again. If he could only see her, talk to her,
even if she was fat and used up and another man's woman.
Lucy, like she used to be. Even to see her would give him a
feeling of those other days, when he had never dreamed that he
would be in the kind of a hole he was now in. Or to see good
old Helen Shires, a girl he could talk to, tell her of his feelings
and troubles, and she would understand. Another cute dame,
her dainty steps, the shocked look on her face as she avoided a
puddle. He laughed. An old Jew with black whiskers getting
wet, maybe a rabbi smelling of gefillte fish. Boy, what wind
tormentors that old Abie had! They fell halfway down his
chest. He watched the automobiles curving onto and off
Randolph Street. Two students entering the *Cresar* Library
Building across the street caught his eye. Lucky boys getting
an education. And the cartoon coming up the library steps with
books under his arm. A nose that hooked and stuck out all over
his face, blue corduroy pants, leather jacket, no hat. Must be
one of those Bohemians or a pansy. Lots of goofs in the world.

"Got a cigarette, Mister?"

Studs turned to face a jerking little gray-haired man with

ill-fitting old clothes that hung over his body like a wet sack.

"Thanks," the man muttered, taking a cigarette from Studs' extended pack.

Studs nodded as if he had done the man a great favor.

"Got a match?"

Studs handed him a book of matches, looking on as the fellow unconfidently and excitedly wasted four matches before getting a light.

"Terrible weather," the man said.

Studs grunted agreement. The bum stood beside Studs as if expecting something. Studs watched a green-bellied surface car swerve onto Randolph Street and clang to Wabash Avenue surrounded by automobiles.

"Say, Mister, you couldn't spare a dime for a bite to eat? I've been carrying the banner all night, and I'm goddamn hungry." Studs did not hear, and his thoughts dragged up Lucy again. The bum walked off, muttering curses. Studs stood watching people pass in the rain, thinking of Lucy, and wondering, now what would he do?

Studs stepped out of another building. Four straight turn-downs, one right after the other. It was about a quarter to three, and disappointment was deep and like a worm inside of him. Walking again in the rain, he was afraid, afraid that he was no good, useless, that he would never be able to get any-where. If the old man lost everything, he would just be a pauper without a pot to take a leak in. He walked rapidly, half running until he was forced to slow down. He knew he shouldn't exert himself in this manner, tiring his heart, getting more and more soaked, his clothes hanging wet on him, his trouser legs and cuffs heavy and soggy, his shoes sopping out wetness with every step, his hat dripping. Again he hurled himself forth, with head lowered, street sounds beating in his ears while he kept telling himself, goddamn it, he had to have a stretch of luck. There was nothing he could do but paint, and that was out, and at anything else he'd be lucky to make a measly fifteen bucks a week.

He entered a building on North Wabash Avenue, read the bulletin board. Emmett Jewelry Company. He took the elevator, hoping again. A girl by a telephone board in an outer office looked at him impersonally.

"I want to see the man in charge."

"For what purpose?"

"I'd like to interview him about a position."

"I'm sorry, but we have no openings."

"Well, couldn't I just see him?"

"He isn't in."

"Is his assistant or secretary in?"

"She's busy."

He turned away, slammed the door behind him. Another defeat. He told himself that he didn't give a good goddamn. Let himself get sick. Let anything happen. He'd already had so much tough luck that what the hell difference did it make. He stepped carelessly into the rain, faintly aware of streets and people.

He had a picture in his mind of Studs Lonigan courageously telling life and the world to shove itself up it's old tomato, and let it stick there. He saw himself walking in the rain, wet and tired, with things crashing down on his head, being screwed at every turn, forced to do something. He saw himself walking south along State Street in the sloshing rain, past department stores, past attractive windows full of suits and ties and shirts and dresses and furniture and baseball bats and football suits and feminine lingerie and refrigerators. Walking past tall buildings full of people at work who didn't have the troubles Studs Lonigan had. He looked at people on the street, their faces indistinct, and an unquenchable hate rose up in him, and he wanted to punch and maim and claw them. He caught a close-up view of a fat male face, a sleeping contentment in the features. There went another sonofabitch, another sonofabitch who had a job and did not have to marry a girl he'd knocked up when he was sick and didn't have any dough, a sonofabitch who wasn't afraid of dying of heart failure. And there was a high-hat black-haired broad who probably thought that hers was gold, a broad who ought to be raped until she was exhausted and couldn't take another goddamn thing.

The sneer from the old days, the old Studs Lonigan sneer of confidence and a superior feeling came on his face, and he threw back his aching shoulders. He wanted to be noticed by these passing strangers, wanted them to see his surly expression telling them, he hoped, that here was a guy who did not give a good whooping goddamn and just walked along, taking his time and did not run to get out of the rain and hide from it in doorways, worried and afraid. A guy who had a perfect right to worry about plenty of things, plenty, and still did not worry. He stopped in a building entrance-way and drew out his package of cigarettes. Shouldn't smoke. Phrigg you Doctor O'Donnell! Phrigg you Catherine! Phrigg everybody! He made the act of lighting a cigarette into a gesture of defiance. He stood watching a street car crawl northward, its roof blackened by rain. Automobiles swished past it. Its gong clanged. A second surface car crawled behind it.

"Look at the rain, just like a silver stream from the heavens, Martha," a sallow fellow with a ruined panama hat said to a girl.

Studs glanced at them, sneered. But she was nice.

"It just looks wet to me," she said.

"But you don't see it with the poet's lyric eye."

Poet. He better watch himself before somebody slapped his wrist and kidnapped him.

"Now, as a poet, what does it mean, this silver rain, these puny crawling little packages of wet mortality?"

"Oh, Alvin, please."

Studs sneered at the nut, walked out of the entrance-way laughing to himself. Anyway, he wasn't like that pansy. He tried to forget the discomforts of wet feet, soaked clothing, the feeling of dirtiness he had. That pansy poet. Silver rain. B.S. A cold rain-drop spattered on his cheek. Some day, some day, goddamn it, if he wouldn't make the f——n world take back everything it was doing to him. Some day he would make the world, and plenty of damn bastards in it, too, eat what he was eating, and in bigger doses. Some day, he, Studs Lonigan, was going to bust loose like hell on wheels, and when he did, look out, you goddamn world!

He lit a fresh cigarette from his soggy butt. He sneezed. He had to laugh, and couldn't get over what that lily of a poet had been springing on the dame. Tell it to Martin tonight. He sneezed again, and the sneeze made him fear he was getting sick. He felt himself growing weak, and under the armpits he was sticky and clammy. He was afraid. He sensed himself beginning to feel dizzy. He was afraid of poverty, and the fight he would have to make. He was afraid that he would get sick, die, from being exposed in this rain. He wished, with a weak will, that many things that had been done could be undone. If he had never met Catherine. If they'd never had that scrap and made up just the way they had. If he had never gone to that New Year's Eve party in 1929. If he hadn't drunk as much as he had in the old days. If he had only let himself get an education. If he hadn't lost his dough in Imbray stock. He stepped into the crowded entrance-way of a music store near Van Buren Street and stood listening to radio music. He noticed the faces on the men about him, blank and dull and dreamy, hopeless-looking. They seemed half asleep on their feet. Mopes. Studs muttered to himself. Look out, boys, or you'll wake up.

He slouched near a window, mopped himself, and a sugary male voice sang.

> *Just a gigolo,*
> *Everywhere I go,*
> *People know the part I'm playing . . .*

The song filled him with a soft kind of sadness, and he listened, forgetting things, feeling as if the music was a sad thing running through him.

> *When the end comes,*
> *I know they'll say,*
> *Just a gigolo.*

And he looked like he would be something of that, marrying Catherine without a job when she'd have more dough than he had. Hot, ragging, snappy jazz music broke loose, and Studs sneered at the sight of a kid of seventeen or eighteen, with down on his upper lip, snapping his fingers, shaking his shoulders, gyrating his legs to the music. Disconcerting and shrill static cut into the music, and then it beat again in quick rhythms. Studs tapped with his foot, dreamily thinking of himself as just going along the same as he had in the old days, strong and tough and with nothing serious to cramp his style and his fun. Studs Lonigan, hard as nails, chased by broads who just begged to lay down for him.

His lips twisted in a sneer at himself, and he thought that he was just a goddamn washed-up has-been. Sneezing again. He was catching cold, and he ought to go home and get in bed. The music softened into a slow and sighing sentimental tune, and it struck at Studs, made him brood with pity for himself, worry, regret. Lucy, Catherine, the days when he was a punk kid. A crooner sobbed with the music. Felt low, walking in the moonlight of a summer night, because she had left him. He now, well, he had gotten something else again. He smiled ironically. If Catherine had left him, he might have felt the song, but he wouldn't feel like he did this minute.

Vacant-eyed, he looked over objects in the window, music rolls, violins, saxophones, sheet music, victrola records, piccolos, horns, tuning forks, mouth organs. He turned from the window. He clenched his fists and compressed his lips in explosive tenseness.

Goddamn it! he silently spit at himself.

What he needed was something to make him forget such things. A burlesque show. The hottest ones were south of Van Buren. He crossed under the elevated structure, and on toward the cheap shows on South State Street.

The urinal smell of the ten-cent burlesque show made Studs feel as if he would become diseased or contaminated just by sitting in it. Four beefy women in narrow strips of colored cloth slowly rolled and twisted their abdomens to the tune of catching, tinny music. The music beat more swiftly, and the belly movements of the dancers quickened. Studs clenched his hands, leaned forward in his seat located at about the center of the small theatre. He watched closely while the women stood, legs spread, orgiastically shaking their wobbly bellies. Washed out, painted whores. But they sure could shake that thing. His whole body seemed to narrow into one canal of desire.

"Take 'em off," a man cried.

With a final beat of the music, and a last lascivious twist, the girls trotted off the stage, their large breasts bouncing with each step.

A page-boy placed a sign at the right-hand corner of the stage.

SHIMMY CONTEST

A peroxide blonde, with purple tights and breast cloth, heavily skipped to the center of the stage. She began slowly, worked herself into rapid, shimmying twists, flung her head back in abandon, stood with her feet planted widely apart, her belly thrust forward. Sick with desire, wanting to see, and imagining the sight of the woman's hidden flesh, Studs watched the rippling of muscles beneath the purple tights. The woman let go completely, and with a final crescendo of jazz drew wild applause from the male audience.

"Take 'em off. Take 'em off," a man cried, and Studs joined others who took up the cry, stamped their feet, clapped.

The woman removed her breast cloth deftly, shielding her breasts almost with the same movement, robbing her audience of the desired sight. She coyly winked, turned about, projected her fat buttocks to her applauders, wriggled them, trotted off the stage.

Just enough to make a fellow want more. This one was stringy with legs like poles, black-haired, lousy-looking. And she shimmied in an annoying, jerky way. But there was hard bone and muscles behind those scarlet tights, flesh and muscles and bones, meat to be laid against a guy. Come on, sister, shake it, shake it. Her breasts bounced. He wanted to see the rest.

Faster, sister, faster, baby, oh, sister, shake yourself.

"Take 'em off. Take 'em off."

Tough luck. Too quick in covering to let them see her boobs. Another blonde, shaking the same way, oh, Jesus Christ, he wanted a woman. One of these would be the trick if he could put a towel over their faces. Come on, sister, let it go, come on, sister. Jesus Christ, this was too much, that flesh wriggling beneath pink tights, faster, head flung back just as if she was taking it standing up, and oh, sister, stop it, stop it, this was too much.

"Take 'em off. Take 'em off."

Studs relaxed in his seat. His hands unclenched. He sighed, wished he hadn't come in. Glancing to his right, he saw, two seats away, a man's hand running up the thigh of a young kid of eighteen or nineteen. Ugh!

He arose, crushed out to the aisle, walked to the exit. Dazed, sleepy, he walked back toward Van Buren Street, past barber shops, employment agencies, cheap and greasy restaurants, shows, shooting galleries, flop houses, without seeing them. Stray bums scurried past him. He was so disgusted with himself that he could almost vomit. He felt as if he could puke himself right up. Watching such lowdown broads, letting them send him off as if he was a sixteen-year-old punk who still had his cherry. How different Catherine was from them. She was decent. And look what she had and was giving up for him. And then his going to a dime girl show, and liking it, getting so hot. Ugh, but he had acted like a slimy bastard. Pride in his woman Catherine mounted in a rush of dizzy hot-blooded thoughts. Catherine so clean, where they were dirty. He was just a louse, unworthy of her.

He sneezed, coughed, full of fear. He was sick. He wanted to go home, get his clothes off and fall into bed. He was tired. His arms pained, and an ache wormed straight down his backbone. His feet were so leaden that walking was an effort. His underwear was sticky, his clothes heavy. To get home and in a bed of clean, white sheets, resting, sleeping endlessly, forgetting everything that was on his mind. He tried to walk fast, but slowed down. Too much for him. His heart was leaping. His feet were getting more soaked with every step.

He had just made a mess of every damn thing. The thought of Catherine, her love and devotion alone, gave him confidence, and he wasn't worthy of her, he had been false to her. He was through. Studs Lonigan, hang up your glove. Studs Lonigan, you're through. He was beaten and whipped and he did not know what to do. He could only crawl to Catherine, ask her to forgive and take care of a louse named Studs Lonigan.

He sneezed again, and his head pounded. He realized that he had a headache. A nauseous taste arose from his stomach. He had to get home. He walked through the tunnel leading underneath Michigan Boulevard to the Van Buren Illinois Central Station. Waiting for the train, he bought a newspaper and read a headline.

RIOT AS BANK FAILS

But he was too tired, too tired to read.

"South Chicago," an announcer barked.

Studs stagged through the doors to the long, narrow platform, slouched into a seat by a window. He sneezed and coughed, and damp, dirty, tired, he wished the train ride would end quickly. He touched his cheeks. Warm. Thirsty. Must have a fever. He was sick. Maybe he was going to die. Oh, God, please don't let him die. Please only let him get home to sleep, sleep, sleep. He let his chin sink on his chest. He felt as if he were going to vomit. He wanted to moan, and fought back his impulse.

"I was walking down Sixty-seventh Street, and he smiled at me. And he had such a nice smile. He! He! I didn't mean to smile, but I couldn't help myself. But then I walked right on like a good little girl, and he came along, and when I was looking into the window of a hat store, he stood there, and I smiled again. And he had such a nice smile," a girl in the seat in back of him was saying, and he heard her dimly.

Broads and people in the train, and, oh, he was sick. He was sick, he silently repeated to himself. His eyes closed. His head and body sagged. Opening his eyes, he saw the broad, wet expanse of Stony Island from the moving train window. Almost home. The broads in back talking. Soon now, a bed, clean white sheets. He got up, tried to walk straight to the end of the car. Leaning against the side of the car platform, he saw a flashing picture of Seventy-first Street. Oh, Christ, what was going to become of him?

"Bryn Mawr."

He stepped off the train, forced himself to walk west to the street, and he ran down Jeffery for about a hundred yards. He halted from exhaustion, stood gasping with his heart pounding like a dynamo. His cheeks were hot. His tongue felt coated. His underwear was wet with sweat. He could just drop right down on the sidewalk, and sleep, sleep. He walked feverishly on, his shoes sopping oozy bubbles with every step, his side cut with a pain, his over-stimulated heart a bombardment within his diaphragm. A feeling of congestion and pressure grew in his lungs. He sniffed. His nose drooled. He coughed up slimy green mucus.

He stopped and like a drunken man watched an automobile splash by. Suddenly, a cold chill iced his body, and the rain slapped against his cheeks, dripped from his hat. Dizzy, he staggered off the sidewalk and supported himself against a building, looking dazed at an apartment hotel building, seeing, as if in a nightmare, two men come out of it and walk rapidly toward Seventy-first Street. The building began to waver and dance before his eyes. Funny. The building was doing the shimmy. He shook his head, as if that gesture would clear his mind and permit him to see clearly. He lurched to the sidewalk, zigzagged, telling himself, Christ, God, Jesus Christ, God Almighty, he had to get home. Against his will, he closed his eyes, walked with lowered head. His shoulder slipped against a lamp-post, and, feeling himself falling, he opened his eyes like one awakening from sleep, circled the post with his arms, hung to it. He straightened up and walked on, his face burning, his body wracked with a succession of hot spells and chills. He could feel his shirt wringing wet against his back, and there was an unpleasant tightness in his crotch. With the sleeve of his raincoat, he wiped his dripping nose, streaking his upper lip. The rain beat on him, and he lurched up the steps of his father's building, set his shoulders against the door, strained, pushed, fell into the hallway, bruising the shin of his right leg. He crawled up the stairway on hands and knees, and lifted himself to his feet against the railing outside his door.

"William!" his mother exclaimed in shock as he stood before her at the door.

"Mom, I'm sick. Put me to bed," he said feebly, throwing himself weakly into the house.

As she closed the door, he crumbled up and his mother screamed.

16. Boy with His Hair Cut Short

MURIEL RUKEYSER

Muriel Rukeyser (1913–   ) was born in New York City, spent several years at Vassar, threw herself into the "student movement" during the depression, and found herself in Spain on the very day of the outbreak of General Franco's rebellion against the Spanish Republic. Since those gaudier days, she has engaged in many varieties of literary-cultural work, from photographs and film scripts to biography (Willard Gibbs, 1942) and college teaching (Sarah Lawrence). But always she has been a poet (Theory of Flight, U. S. 1, Selected Poems), and always a serious artist. Her poetic impulse has fortunately survived her earlier association with the far left, but even during those days Muriel Rukeyser's political commitments never overwhelmed her humanity, as we can see in this poem of a brother and sister united in the terror and self-deception of the unemployed.

From *U.S. 1* (New York: Covici-Friede, 1938), pp. 89–90. "Boy with His Hair Cut Short" Copyright 1938 by Muriel Rukeyser. Reprinted by permission of Monica McCall, Inc.

Sunday shuts down on this twentieth-century evening.
The L passes. Twilight and bulb define
the brown room, the overstuffed plum sofa,
the boy, and the girl's thin hands above his head.
A neighbor radio sings stocks, news, serenade.

He sits at the table, head down, the young clear neck exposed,
watching the drugstore sign from the tail of his eye;
tattoo, neon, until the eye blears, while his
solicitous tall sister, simple in blue, bending
behind him, cuts his hair with her cheap shears.

The arrow's electric red always reaches its mark,
successful neon! He coughs, impressed by that precision.
His child's forehead, forever protected by his cap,
is bleached against the lamplight as he turns his head
and steadies to let the snippets drop.

Erasing the failure of weeks with level fingers,
she sleeks the fine hair, combing: "You'll look fine tomorrow!
You'll surely find something, they can't keep turning you down;
the finest gentleman's not so trim as you!" Smiling, he raises
the adolescent forehead wrinkling ironic now.

He sees his decent suit laid out, new-pressed,
his carfare on the shelf. He lets his head fall, meeting
her earnest hopeless look, seeing the sharp blades splitting,
the darkened room, the impersonal sign, her motion,
the blue vein, bright on her temple, pitifully beating.

PART FIVE

Hitting Bottom:

ON THE ROAD, IN THE RING, ON THE BUM

---

17. You Can't Sleep Here

EDWARD NEWHOUSE

With the coming of the depression, a whole generation of young men fell out of the middle class. Some found themselves in the working class—either because it was easier to find a job driving a taxi than in a law office or because their new political commitments dictated that they join the disciplined ranks of the proletariat—while some wound up as hoboes. For a time it appeared that Edward Newhouse (1912–   ) might be the spokesman for all these disaffected young men, as Jack London in a sense had been a generation earlier, but after his second novel, This Is Your Day *(1937), whose hero was a young Communist organizer of upstate New York farmers, Newhouse disassociated himself from the Communist movement. He went on subsequently to become a successful writer*

From *You Can't Sleep Here* (New York: Macaulay, 1934), Chaps. VI and VII, pp. 76–89. Copyright 1934 by Edward Newhouse. Reprinted with the permission of the author.

of stories, many of them based on his experiences in World War II; but even in his precocious early writings there can be discerned elements of the sardonic manner which was later to prove ingratiating to The New Yorker *readers. In the selection which follows, the hero (who, it can be assumed, is not unlike young Edward Newhouse) has lost his newspaper reporter's job and most elements of his middle-class respectability; although he is sleeping in Central Park, he is finding his way not to the Bowery but to the revolutionary working class. The brash self-confidence of the young rebels of the early thirties, almost eerily prefiguring the Beats of the fifties, is perhaps best captured in the youthful author's autobiographical note on the dust jacket:*

I was born twenty-two years ago and came to New York at the age of 12. I attended public and high schools here and I was an indifferent student and captain of the track and soccer teams. In my spare time and during vacations I worked as errand boy, bellhop, grocery clerk, busboy, economic research worker, warehouse hand and factory sweeper. I have been active in the revolutionary movement as far back as I can remember. I quit college in my freshman year because I wasn't learning much and would have been expelled anyway. I took to riding freights through the South and Mexico and California and most of the other states. I have covered about twenty thousand miles on them. My first story appeared in the *New Masses* five years ago and I have been appearing in its pages regularly since. I picked up change by contributing to highbrow magazines and other sordid methods. I have been a staff member of the Labor Research Association, the *New Masses* and the *Daily Worker*. In 1934 I spent weeks living in a Queens Hooverville.

I did not sleep very well. It was still dark when I finally decided to get up but by the time I reached Fifth Avenue day was stirring. Near Madison my eyes lit on two bottles of milk on a doorstep. I took one and ducked into an alley to drink it. I could not finish the quart and had to leave a little at the bottom. It tasted good. I started walking down the street but went back and drank the remainder. Around the corner I saw the milkman.

The doorways of grocery stores were just beginning to fill. Drivers were leaving bread in boxes and rolls tied into gunny sacks. I found a chain store, made as though I were looking to see if they had opened, and tucked away a sweet rye.

This was the sort of section in which not even janitors were up and around before six and I returned to the park without meeting a pedestrian. The sweet rye was still warm from the oven, and savory, but it had no caraway seeds, which was a pity. I ate three-quarters of it and gave the rest away in crumbs to pigeons. An old squirrel came and took some of the rind.

I put in another hour of fitful sleeping and set out to find a Times. I had to walk till 55th Street before one of the newsstand men would let me look into the want ads. There wasn't anything likely listed. With the stubble I had I could not have applied anyway.

It was some time before they opened the doors of the big library. In the lavatory I looked into a mirror for the first time in days. My suit was crumpled and dusty. I shaved and washed carefully and went into the American History room for a book I always wanted to finish. After I had read a few pages I let my head rest on my forearms and had the best bit of sleep since the furnished room. I was dreaming unusually nice things but the severe lady librarian came down from the desk and awakened me. It was much more exasperating than the time in Penn Station. She appeared to relish rebuking me. She waited for me to cringe and apologize, I think.

The book was interesting but I could not go on. I got an idea to write a story and borrowed paper from one of the research workers. This is what I wrote:

PUNCH IN THE EYE.

I had been transferred to a branch library where they fired the bookbinder for coming in drunk, and when I returned it was all over. Miss Gilbert sat at her desk sorting the overdue list. She smiled wanly and blinked with the discolored eye. It wasn't a black eye yet. The center ring was lavender. The periphery was orange and yellow.

"Hello, Miss Gilbert," I said.

"Hello there. Freezing, isn't it?"

"Below zero in Chicago."

"That's where it comes from," she said "It's a northwesterly wind. No mountains in between to stop it. At that, we're only in the tail of the blizzard. Must be awful in Chicago. Goodness knows it's bad enough here."

"Not so bad."

I was wondering how she got it. She did not have to look at me to know I was wondering how she got it.

"You missed a lot of big doings here."

"Big doings at the other branch too," I said. "Someone broke the binding on the Funk and Wagnalls unabridged."

"And what?"

"And I had to fix it."

"That's not exciting. Wait'll you hear what happened to me."

"You were assaulted by four Hawaiians."

"No."

"Vice President Garner."

"No. Don't be silly. Miss Gordon will tell you a lot of gossip about it, the way she's telling everybody, but it won't be true so probably you'd like to know the truth, wouldn't you?"

"Like to?" I said. "I'd love to."

"Well, last Thursday a man came and settled down in the reference room this side of the Britannicas and fell asleep. Miss Tordik tapped him on the shoulder but he didn't budge so she started giggling, the little fool, and she comes to me, the way she always does when there's something disagreeable to be done. I said all right. I tapped him. He didn't move. I tapped him again. He stood up and yawned and hit me in the eye. That's what happened and you can ask Miss Tordik. He was a tall, dirty looking man."

"Just like that?"

"Just like that."

"The meanie."

"Scoff all you like," Miss Gilbert said, "but the thing didn't rest there, you can bet. I heard Miss Tordik scream and I became unconscious and when I came to, there were policemen here and they had him. Miss Gordon said he didn't resist or try to run away at all. She spoke to the officer and sent me home. Then in the afternoon they rang and told me the case was coming up Friday. I didn't want to go. They made me. I think the whole affair is shameful. The man was a maniac."

"No kidding?" I said.

"I think so. Outright demented. When the judge asked him if he had been intoxicated he said no, he'd never had a saner moment in his life. He told a tall story: said the previous night he couldn't get a bed at the Municipal Lodging House and they threw him off a bench in Washington Square. Imagine anyone being thrown out of Washington Square. He said that was at four o'clock in the morning and he had to walk around in the cold until the library opened.

"He said when the janitor hustled him out of the hallway of an apartment house he promised himself that the next person who awakened him he'd poke in the eye, that was his expression. I think that's what the magistrate referred to when he gave him the extra sixty days for contempt of court. But maybe it was because he smiled when I took the chair. 'And what do you find so vastly entertaining?' says the magistrate. 'Nothing,' he says, 'just struck me queer that this should have happened to Miss Gilbert when there's a dozen people in this very court room who had it coming to them a damn sight more.' And I sitting up there having my name spoken by the creature.

"You may think I'm prejudiced but I said to the court the electric chair is too good for a beast like that, and I'll stand by that opinion. He can't find work, he's no good to himself, and he's certainly no good to anyone else."

"Why not the guillotine?" I said. "Takes more men to operate. Times like this, that ought to be a consideration."

"No call for being facetious," Miss Gilbert said. "Anybody who really wants to work can find a job. Imagine, letting a man like that off with eighteen months hard labor."

I wrote the story rapidly and without correction. Reading it over, I knew it was just a way of working off steam and not good for anything. When I started I had an idea I would have it typed and sent off but I stuffed the longhand sheets into my pocket. The story tried to sound funny and the situation wasn't. I remembered Tommy's picking up an obituary notice from the copy desk and taking it back to the graduate of the Columbia School of Journalism who had written it, and hollering, Where's the conflict in this yarn, the pity and terror, the catharsis, the resolution of forces? We resolve our forces in this office, madam, or we stop wasting copy paper for which men had to cut down trees that live and flourish. I want this story to breathe and pulsate and tapdance and run the gamut of emotions from a to b. I want it to kick people in the nostrils. Do it over.

She had never heard the one about a to b and she had been a tractable girl and a good reporter, more useful to the paper than I, but she was first to go. Tommy said Glaser had tried to make her.

I returned to my book which was the local preacher's chronicle of events in an early Vermont settlement. He was a naïve and outspoken preacher who appeared to be in on the affairs of each household and these were engrossing enough. The consummation of his life work came in the final chapters where he blackmailed the rich and incestuous farmer of the parish into having a church built. Parenthetically he supplied much data on haying and minor chores and a treatment for the croup and two recipes for strawberry jam.

This compilation had been performed in the eighteenth century but currently, too, there was a cycle of back to the earth movies and fairly decent novels not as good as "Growth of the Soil." The people in these works were too tired and busy and uninformed to be greatly disturbed about things. They were so goddam cute and monolithic you almost forgot that to cook all those grand, simple dishes it was necessary to buy flour at the village A. & P. I did not know any of the authors but I would have liked to gather them into a room and ask how many had wheat or milk to sell or a mortgage coming due.

No. I had not captured the essence of the situation by having the librarian punched in the eye. You needed more than little wish-fulfillments like writing about punches in the eye and returns to the soil.

The flavor of the preacher's diary brought back the mellowness and exasperating conclusions of Benjamin Franklin's Autobiography, specifically the passages where young Benjamin decides to leave Boston but cannot openly do so on account of his family's opposition. "My friend Collins therefore undertook to manage a little for me. He agreed with the captain of a New York sloop for my passage, under the notion of my being a young acquaintance of his that had got a naughty girl with child, whose friends would compel me to marry her."

This being, altogether naturally, not nearly so reprehensible as "indiscrete disputations about religion." And then cautious Benjamin, after having avoided the snares of two young women on board who invited him to come and see them in New York, went ahead to "gain money by my industry and frugality" and to ask himself each morning, "What good shall I do this day?" For the sake of bourgeois ethics it was a shame Benjamin Franklin and the Vermont preacher did not possess the advantages I had just six months ago. They could have cleaned up so much more effectively and their books would have been the better for it and would have won for them maybe the Nobel Prize.

Woven into the blackmail chapter the preacher had a recipe that read more like a feature article about Oscar of the Waldorf than the meal of a Vermont Yankee. It had sliced onions frying in chicken fat and veal sliced thin and gravy prepared with spices whose taste I felt on the roof of my mouth and the inside of my cheeks. I was ravenously hungry and all but drooled over that page.

When evening came I thought I would rifle a slot machine with a wire I found after much search but I could not get into a subway station. I had expected it to be comparatively easy to ask someone for a nickel but it wasn't. I couldn't duck under the turnstile the way a kid would and I walked helplessly from Fifth Avenue to Grand Central to Times Square.

A desire came over me to imitate the hungry movie hero who strode into the expensive hotel dining room, ordered a meal with marvelous effrontery, had the manager called when it was over, threatened to make a soapbox oration to the paying guests if not let off, thus extricating himself with careless and scornful aplomb. My bundle was still checked at the library and would not hamper me. My face and hands were presentable but not my suit. It was doubtful if they would have seated me. And if they called my bluff I could not have said anything to the guests. Oh, couldn't I? But I wouldn't. I would simply get the bum's rush with probably a kick in the pants. They might have me arrested. Then I would sell Glaser a series exposing prison conditions.

I looked into the window of one of the big hotels on Seventh Avenue. The orchestra's drummer was visible. He did not have much to do. He kept his eyes on the conductor whom I could not see. After a while he began working the chimes. A woman looked out and rested her eyes on me but she took no notice. Although I certainly would not have paid any attention to her under other circumstances, this infuriated me. One corner of my mouth twitched and parted, the lower lip drawing down, the upper in a snarl. Still she did not see me but turned to her companion with the proud and possessive smile Mrs. Weiland used on Eileen.

I adjusted my necktie and jacket and went in at the main entrance. I hurried past the desk and the palm trees and stopped before the dining room. The headwaiter was seating a large party near the orchestra stand. I chose a small table near the window and did not wait to be led. My waiter was a lean and restrained and totally effaced Frenchman or Italian who bent stiffly from his hips and assented with his eyebrows. His gaze ran apprehensively over my clothing but my perfunctory manner and pronunciation of the antipasto and the Chauché Noir may have reassured him partly. I ordered the two dollar dinner without hesitation. Later I saw him consulting the headwaiter who shrugged his shoulder.

They played ingratiating, wily music with tiny, tart adumbrations by the piccolo. Humility was the conductor's personal stock in trade but his motions were not too coy and he sang in a warm and unobtrusive baritone. The wine was light and neutral and blended extremely well with the taste of the mushroom sauce. I ate slowly and thought how much better Eileen and Elizabeth danced than any woman on the floor and how much prettier they were. While eating, I gave very little thought to what would happen after the meal. Between courses I reflected but I was not afraid, only embarrassed. Once the responsibility had been transferred to the headwaiter my man operated flawlessly. He recommended a very successful Biscuit Tortoni. I was eating powerfully but not too much. The very small cinnamon buns punctuated courses. I drank more wine than I should have but my head was clear. Around my lungs and throat I had the constricted sensation little boys experience before an unavoidable fight.

"Would you mind calling the headwaiter," I said. Spencer Tracy in the movies had asked for the manager.

"Anything wrong, sir?" It was exactly what the movie waiter had said.

"No, no."

They returned together. I knew there wasn't going to be any soapbox oration.

"What is your customary procedure when a man can't pay his check?"

The waiter was wanted at another table and excused himself. The headwaiter's face set for a moment. He said, "Come with me."

The kitchen was full of steam and smells.

"I'd work it off," I said.

He was in a glowering fury and gave me a strong shove toward the pearl divers' row. A name was called from the doorway and he turned sharply and said, "Right this second. Give this man dishes, all you have. I'll be back."

About a dozen men were looking at me, a bellhop, cooks and dishwashers. I removed my coat and held it on my arm. As I neared the trough to take my place my neighbor, a one-eyed gnome, said, "Put that coat on and beat it through the end door if nobody stops you. There's two house dicks on their way now and you'll be sapped up, no expenses paid. Last guy who pulled that had to scrape himself off the alley walk with a trowel. Git."

I started for the end door. Their eyes followed me but no one intervened. In the alley I took a run and hopped a grating and ran along the hotel. I mingled with the crowd and arrived at the library in time to get my bundle.

Not everything went off like that. Fully a week passed before I worked out a method of getting into subway stations. I would wait until a train pulled in and people were hurrying through the turnstiles, then I would flash my open wallet before the change booth and walk in. The cashier generally assumed it was a pass but when he did call after me I would be nearly in the car. Once or twice he rushed out but the doors were closing and he did not bother to hold up the train. At the next station it was a matter of ten minutes to secure a handful of chocolates. One time a station master caught me but I said I had deposited three pennies and I was determined to get my money's worth. He said, Not at this station you don't.

For weeks my diet consisted of pilfered milk, rolls and chocolate. I could vary it only when one of my telephones came through. I stuffed up dozens of them with paper napkins from the automat and when they failed to discover this, change would accumulate. I did not starve but I was perpetually hungry.

Finding a place to sleep was always the greater problem. As a rule, I was reduced to the promontory in Central Park. I became inured to the discomfort but on the cooler nights I had to lie fully dressed and the condition of my suit lessened my chances at the agencies. I made the rounds in three or four of these places after I cleaned up at the comfort station behind the old reservoir or at the library. Once I did save enough nickels to have the suit pressed but after a few nights it looked worse than ever. Although I washed my linen often and desperately it never attained a laundry whiteness.

I rarely spoke to people. Much of my time was spent in the library, reading. Reminiscing became a passionate obsession and it made me grow abstracted in a sullen and inert manner. Too often I found myself muttering, and acting out imaginary situations. Geared as I had been to the tempo of the most exacting newspaper in town, inactivity oppressed instead of exhilarating.

To loaf entertainingly, I discovered, one needed a minimum of ready cash and a more or less suitable base of operations. Even Maugham's and Conrad's self-sufficient derelicts amused themselves as tolerably as they appeared to have, only some thousands of miles away from the scene of their defeats.

Much of my delving into the past concerned itself with the lost apartment I had furnished over a period of years. One morning I played Galahad to a governess by separating two viciously fighting boys who were her charges. After tears of mortification she described what demoniac imps these were, how jealous of each other, how her main job was keeping them from the baby whom they were forever attempting to bite. She could not imagine how they got that way, their parents were nice people, they lived in a magnificent mansion on Fifth Avenue, what an outrage three brats had to be kept in separate rooms while (with a glance at my clothing) people went homeless on park benches.

My accustomed reaction to commiseration was a rather

boastful air of You ain't seen the half of it, say, in the winter time and so on. But to this nurse I gave an account of the room and kitchenette I had, how perfectly appointed for my purposes they had been, the large luxurious carpet, the eight hundred hand-picked, familiar books to caress, the serapes and the couch which did not sag but soothed your body, the worn, warm slippers, the victrola and the short wave set, the closets stuffed with sweaters, tennis racquets, rich, long towels to wrap yourself into, the refrigerator full of Grade A milk and Roque-fort cheese spread when you blew in late at night and all the other things, the abundance.

The nurse listened courteously. The boys fell to scrapping again and while she was admonishing them I checked myself and left without saying goodbye. That was an unusual out-burst, the one occasion I recall of going into particulars about my past. I kept to myself, cultivating social life only in the form of open air meetings at Columbus Circle and on 86th Street. Here the Communists spoke and sold literature. They handed me leaflets. I read them and passed them on. A girl sold me the Communist Manifesto for a nickel. I signed up with one of the Unemployment Councils but nothing came of it.

The early days of July were full of rains and a thunderstorm but I found the storage room of an apartment house on the West Side to sleep in. In another part of that cellar I met a young Scotch terrier who had strap and collar but no master and he followed me about until I took hold of the strap. This revived his spirits and he committed himself into my charge by wagging his tail and smiling. In his more settled moments he looked as though his name were Marvin and I started calling him that. Butchers never refused to feed him. They threw the dog chunks of meat I wouldn't have scorned myself. In the park he slept between my shins, with the chin resting on my knees. He disturbed me by yelping when the water rats were hitting it up in the Indian cave. I used to see them scamper from the rocks into the inlet and their round bodies left wakes whose sight excited Marvin. In a little while I had him trained so he would stifle the yelps into little guttural and abdominal mumblings.

It was more difficult to keep him from growling when lovers settled on the bench below. He stopped only if I whispered nothings into the pointed black ears. On moonlit nights he was assailed by vague canine ecstasies which caused him to stir painfully and paw the canvas with his short forelegs.

One such night he became restive and chewed a hole in my trousers. I did not notice until next morning but that night I took him in my lap and whispered to quiet him. He licked my hand and gazed mistrustfully at the couple below. The girl wore a light print with organdy trimmings. She held onto the hand which cupped one of her breasts and looked more comfortable than her companion.

"There has never been anyone like you," he said.

"I love you," she said. "You're the nicest person in the world."

The dog growled and I whispered to quiet him. "Oh, Marvin, what pretty hair you have. You're the nicest male Scotch terrier in Central Park."

"Wasn't the concert marvelous?" she said.

"Only because we were together and because I knew we would be together when it was over."

"We will always be together, won't we, sweet?"

"Nothing could keep us apart."

The couple were kissing audibly but their tones were lowered. When he raised his voice again he was telling her of the records he had of Beethoven's Ninth, orthophonic, a complete collection, and why doesn't she come up to the house to hear them? She said that wouldn't be quite the thing at this hour and he said she didn't trust him, then there were tears and she said, all right but not for long.

18. From Flushing to Calvary

EDWARD DAHLBERG

Edward Dahlberg (1900–   ) was born in Boston, the illegiti-
mate offspring of an impoverished immigrant girl named Lizzie
Dahlberg. He studied for a time at the University of California,
and graduated from Columbia University in 1925. Of the inter-
vening years—by far the most important of his life—we have
several versions, all by Dahlberg himself, in some of the most
remarkable confessions of childhood ever set down by a literary
man. Lizzie Dahlberg was an itinerant barber before settling
down for some years in Kansas City, Missouri, where she
opened a barber shop that "is one of the early memories of
Harry S Truman." Raised partly in Jewish and Catholic or-
phanages, Dahlberg was able to say, with every apparent
justification, "I still think there was more health in the wild,
ruttish Kansas City streets than in my later experiences in
Paris, London, Florence and Brussels." In 1930 he published the
first fictionalized account of the lives of Lizzie and her son
"Lorry Lewis," and followed it in 1932 with From Flushing to
Calvary, *in one sense a sequel and in another a revision of the*
first. By this time Dahlberg had become deeply involved in the
Communist literary movement, and this second book was re-
viewed in the December 1932 New Masses *by Erskine Cald-*
well, who wrote: "We were dumped by a capitalist system on
hard ground, and here we lie. Our first step is now being
taken; we are scattered, broken, and bewildered; we are lifting
our heads and looking ahead into the future. From Flushing to

---

From *From Flushing to Calvary* (New York: Harcourt, Brace, 1932),
pp. 275–293. Copyright, 1932, by Edward Dahlberg. Reprinted by Permission of Harcourt, Brace & World, Inc.

*Calvary is the hard ground, the working model from which we hope to get away. . . . This is the clay for the mold. The next step is that of contact and teaching. Dahlberg's people are ripe for revolution." Whether they were or not, Dahlberg probably intended for his hero to be, as we can sense in the final pages of the book, which follow. But Dahlberg himself moved on from communism to other concerns, and in 1964 published as an autobiography—*Because I Was Flesh*—*a brilliantly reworked version of his novels of the thirties.*

Going up the steps, he ran into Carol Roonan.

She called him, her teeth, stupid wideapart kernels of bantamcorn:

"Heh, yer mother's in the hospital."

He had to wait till 3:00 for visiting hours. Then he was admitted with a herd of others into a 35-foot long charity ward. Lagging behind, he passed down the aisle, moving down each white enameled cot. His mother saw him coming toward her. His eyes suddenly shuttering over her pivoting head and face were a smeary kodak-lens.

Her lips, a tight and fist-clenched gasp, lumped out her chin.

He bent over to kiss her lips and handed her a paper-bag inside of which were three sunkist oranges.

Putting the sack on the table at the side of her cot, she fumbled for a handkerchief underneath her pillow, took it out and getting up close to it, spat into it.

Lorry sat down on the bed.

Across the aisle a woman groaned. Turning over on her other side the spring underneath her resounded like cymbals.

Lizzie opened up.

"Poor thing, she's a goner and she don't know it. Young little lady too. A taxidriver and two other men come to see her. She's got a cancer [Lizzie shook, made an epsom's salt's face], guess she had too fast a life."

Lorry stealthily craned his neck partways toward the cancer-patient.

A clean-shaven bony-faced man with stiff nerveless fuller-brush hair was limping down the aisle on a crutch. He hopped over to Lizzie's bed with a quick spruce wink and a neat haberdashery T-squared smile.

"Cheer up, Miss Lizzie, you'll be as fit as a fiddle in no time."

He hobbled from one cot to the other making his rounds.

Lizzie made a throat-laugh at him as he went on.

"A sign-painter, he fell two stories. His wife she comes once a week, primped and painted; she don't want to recognize nobody. She stuffs him up with cannedgoods all the time. He's a straight, honest, makes a dandy . . ."

The headnurse came over, rolled up Lizzie's sleeve, put a cotton dab of alcohol on her arm and gave her a hypodermic injection. Jabbed, she let out a scream.

Lorry's eyes glinted, lightninglike.

When the nurse went off, Lizzie's other arm slowly swam across her forehead wiping it.

"Nurse! Nurse!"

"Oh, nurse!"

Came from the other end of the ward.

"Nurse! Nurse!"

It went into a singsong, mounting and falling, in a nightmare vocal chant.

The cancer-patient groaned again.

Lizzie rang the bell for a bedpan.

"Just 24, he's got the dropsy. You can ring from morning till . . ."

The interne took her pulse, placed his instrument against her chest, and then went out.

A male attendant and a nurse wheeled in a man who had just been operated on. The nurse rang the curtain around his bed.

Propping herself up on her elbows, Lizzie took an orange out of the bag and told Lorry to eat it.

"Why don't you eat an orange, mother?"

She wiped her face, passing it off.

Watching Lorry studiously strip the peelings, her face broke, had the misery in it of broken bits of glass.

Lorry looked up at her.

"So, son, you ran away from your mother."

Then she cried, all of her throat and mouth cried.

He sat there staring, listening.

Then her chubby peglike fingers touched his hand; it unnerved him, shook him out of something.

Suddenly he wanted to weep, to push himself into a flood of tears. Then edging over toward her, as if he were trying to cross a line, her hand went up, away from his, inside her sheet. Her lips seemed to have gone somewhere inside, too. The kisses, like liquid tears, gulped back dry in his mouth. The rindy orangepeel smeared on his fingernails tasted bitteracid in his throat.

Then, as if she had her hands behind her back she recited to him how she had come to the hospital. After the little money she had was gone, she was thankful to have a bed and a bite in her mouth. She had to come; otherwise she would have been out in the streets. She explained to him how she had had to beg the doctor to lay the operation off till her son came. She didn't want to go under the knife without first seeing her flesh and blood.

Then she said:

"You know, I don't have to tell you, how much respect they give to a charity-case."

"Well, what's past is past."

Her chin was knobbed, slick, shiny.

A wheeltable was rolling down the aisle.

Lorry watched it with the sort of passive sitting-back interest of a moving-picture audience. It came to a halt in front of his mother's bed. The blood swam out of his cheeks.

The male attendant told her to get up.

Lizzie raised herself up, her face twisting.

The nurse watched, looking on.

"Miss Jenkins, I'd like to have a bedpan, please."

"You jest had one an hour ago."

Closing in on her the nurse pushed up against her as she gruntingly got up on the table.

Lying down flat on her back, her nose cowered over her mouth, she saw the animalflanks of it haunched against her face, her chin ledged out more. She looked up and around her in a kind of frightened twitter.

The italian woman next to Lizzie's bed reassured her.

"Thank you, Mrs. Gonfalo. I hope God'll help me."

Saltgargle tears swobbed her cheeks.

Lorry kissed her, kissed her three times with a jerky willful punctuated machine-movement.

With a towel turbaned around her head, she looked like a pope being wheeled out on a bier.

> *meet me*
> *at st. louis louis*
> *meet me*
> *at the fair*

Oh, Henry Smith, Kentucky Henry Smith, his sweet blue-grass eyes, oh, how she thought of Henry Smith. And that night on the *Chester* up the Mississippi on their way to St. Louis. How they laughed. Their laughter just about broke the springs of the bed in the cabin. Their kisses were long drinks of missouri wellwater, and their chuckles fizzed over their lips, and rippled like. Ah, Cecile Henty had taught her that, she knew so many dirty words. Wonder what had become of her? Cecile lived a day. And why not. But why not? And why,

where was she? She cried a little thinking that. Thinking what.
But what was the use.

Oh, Henry Smith, where was Henry Smith? Probably laying around with some skirt or chippy in St. Louis. Henry
would always have a woman, never fear that. But how they
roared, and how she roasted him, and how he tickled her. And
all the while the champagne waters of the Mississippi wound
and sudsied and churned underneath their laughter—oh, so
sweetly underneath, fizzed and rippled inside of her. Oh, dear,
how they boohooed again again and again. Oh, dear.

And when Henry was pleased with himself, he was such a
jolly fleshy billowing laughing man. Oh, he was so pleased
with himself that they both got to laughing so much that Henry
accidentally, and not on purpose, mind you, no, not Henry,
passed wind. They hadn't known one another long then—no,
not that way, and Henry was right put out with himself, and
she tried to pass it off, and change the subject. But he couldn't.
Oh, dear me, he couldn't change the subject. For on the main
deck the brassband was playing:

> *meet me*
> *at st. louis louis*
> *meet me*
> *at the fair*

And when there came toot toots from the flute and a boom
boom from the bassdrum, and Henry tried to hold down a little
mouse-like squealer, she just couldn't control herself. Oh, he
was so put out. The Kentucky gentleman in him was so out of
sorts, to let go of himself that way, and right out in public. It
was a good thing, she told him, it hadn't happened in the lady
barbershop, or she'd had to charge him up for three bottles of
hair tonic. But Henry was clean from the tip of his head to his
toes. You couldn't take that away from him. And when he was
rooming and boarding with her at the 8th-Street flat, she didn't

mind washing his socks. She didn't mind the body of them, oh, no, she never minded the body of them, because he was such a fine one. And the flesh of him was such a gentleman's.

Then the surgeon entered. Hurriedly she covered herself. The blanket encased and coffined her in. She wriggled against it. As the doctor took her pulse, she trembled; she shook like a leaf, the way she did when Saul had popped into K. C. The surgeon attempted to calm her, to quiet her. His concern soothed her and she breathed heavily, densely, with a thick phlegmish pity for herself. Suddenly she felt utterly exhausted. Her bones groaned against her flesh like the heavy wagon-wheels against the cobblestones underneath the 8th Street viaduct. Then she said, her lips, loose folded mumbling putty: "Doctor, is my heart all right? I know my lungs." He slapped her hand brightly, a whack of chirpy good health behind it. "You'll be o.k." Then he walked out.

Then Hervey crossed her mind, a squat little *w* of a man. Soon as she set eyes on him, she could tell he was no man. She could tell that by his bulby little nose. No man with such a little stinker's nose could do anything. Nothing could come of such a nose but . . . and then she had to laugh again. Oh, dear me, she couldn't help. Well, it didn't cost nothing to laugh.

Lizzie had to wipe her eyes. The eggskin whites of them were wet and warm. What a relief it was to laugh. Horse on Henry, all right.

Phew, what 4th of july weather, what a baking spell that was; and everybody was out on the water, the whole K. C. stew was on the *Chester*, the whole shooting-match. Everybody from the mayor down out for fireworks, B.P.O.E.s, oddfellers, masons, easternstars, 32nd degrees, elks, drummers, hot air merchants. And the band from the maindeck kept playing oldtimer airs and *Waltz Me Around Again, Willie*, and the river kept swishing up against the boat like haircutting scissors. And she was so phewy and hot and fanning herself, she had to get up every minute. And Henry, when it came to see what was going on, he was johnny-on-the-spot. But she couldn't fight nature. And every time she kept running. Henry, of course, he had to raise himself and use those blinkers of his. He said that was what they were for. Oh, he always had an answer.

But nobody could talk against her good name. She had always kept her head up wherever she went. She always knew her place. That was the main thing in the long run. Ask Cromwell, poor soul, he just grieved himself into the grave; or Wolkforth, her landlord; they'd give her the best of references any day.

But what was the use of going over bygones. He was nothing but an old rounder. Henry Smith, he'd never be anything but a steamboat man. Once she had to give him a piece of her mind. She bawled him out good and proper, too. She wasn't going to have no man butting into her place of business. It didn't look good to have a man hanging around a lady barbershop. It drove trade away. Mind you, once an out-of-towner, he was a big job and a dandy tipper, dropped in on a rainy day, and Henry who felt like cutting up had the nerve to tell him how he should dress himself. Cecile, of course, smelled something right away. Henry, he says to the stockman who was taking off his coat, collar, necktie, and wiping his boots against the spittoon, just before getting into the chair: "Mister, don't you wear rubbers; what, no umbrella, no raincoat, either, well, I declare." And when the customer answers him back: "No, sir," Henry pops up with: "Sure do take chances, don't you? Believe in letting nature take care of itself. Guess you're right." Why, Cecile she just doubled over.

Oh, well, what's past is past. All that foolishness wasn't worth repeating.

When she smelled the medical ward about her, she thought of hot aspirin gargles. The towel turbaned and tied around her head became unbearable. She fumbled with the safetypin at the back. The towel was a weight on her head. She had to unloosen it. Taking it off, she puffed to get air. With the safety-pin in her mouth, she felt like a feverish consumptive tailor threading a needle. Then she fluffed her hair to let the air pass through it. Every morning in the hospital she rubbed salve in her scalp to keep her hair in condition. The threads of single hairs had the shiny oiliness of a black-olive. On her stand was an almost full jar of Marsha facecream which she used on her skin morning and night.

Then she remembered the anaesthetic. And then her other operations. How she had suffered. When she saw the surgeon with big strapping viaduct shoulders enter, she cried. Cried and cried herself out. To be made for so much misfortune. Always to be butchered up and for what. Where was Henry now? Maybe. no. no. And the U. S. Major, he was such a prince. Cromwell, poor old soul, laying in the ground. Hagen, what a miserable end he had. And Lorry he didn't have a picnic, either. But God would help her. Other people had operations. Older, too. Every day didn't she read in the papers?

Then she prayed, absorbed as if she was paring or cutting her callouses down with her honed razor. She begged God to let her live; she hadn't begun to live yet. She deserved a little sunshine.

The nurse went out. A nurse with a pillwhite apron and cap went by. Her footsteps carried down the hallway. Then they went dead blank. Lizzie suddenly felt alone. There was nothing about her but thick cement slabs of silence. Nothing else touched her from the outside. She was still inside, a strange still-born obelisk hollowness was inside. She started to whimper to hear herself, to recognize herself. Her nose fell over her mouth.

Then the surgeon who had gone out reentered with a male attendant and a nurse. They wheeled her down the hall. The ceiling overhead slid past her like revolving convex and concave mirrors. The electriclights in the elevator flooded her eyes, were a crown of torches on her head. She sniveled and her breasts heaved and moved. As the elevator went up, she rolled up inside of herself, crouched away from it.

In the operating room they put her on a porcelain arctic white-enameled table. She felt so chill, so small and cornered, her head rolled up and sunk upon her breast, a human embryo, and she wanted the big Godlike doctors to help her. The surgeon patted her hand. The hand that touched her seemed to come from such a distance. It seemed so large, as if it were under a magnifying glass. Waiting and shaking, she suddenly went still. Her breath had become so remote, almost out of hearing, the drop of a pin. Looking about mutely, she tried to place herself. Blocks of space were sucking her up. She searched as if she was trying to locate something. For she didn't know where she had gone. Other surgeons and observers entered. Closehuddled massive shoulders of granite, they walled her in.

When they placed the ethercup over her nose she tried to help, to properly adjust it—as though everything would come out all right. After the ethercup was set she counted, carefully spelling and sounding out each number with the halting plodding earnestness of a secondgrade pupil reciting his arithmetic table of 2's. She breathed in deeply, taking way back in the mask of her head deep cool grotto-like draughts. The cup over her nose was a dark well turned upside down. The ether flowed down through her darkly, darkly, more darkly. She floated so heavily underneath it. For a moment she ceased to count. The surgeon reminded her. He touched her arm. It went numb, lifeless flesh that wasn't hers. The touch sawed her. The surgeon's voice quivered above her, a current electrifying the flat glasstop of a deep pond. She counted again. Louder and louder.

Then she was strangely and medically divided, one part of

her trailing away from the other. She was being unribboned, physically unravelled. She floated away from herself.

The ether sang through her mazed brain like rainy weeds in the wind. And then she sort of shook her head, to let it go at that—and then she attempted to wrench herself free, to rise up to the top and to pull herself together, to keep herself from going off in opposite directions.

She tried to knock off the ethercup. Why had she let them put it on her? She did not want it. For between her and the ethercup, there was Lorry outside, or downstairs, waiting, waiting, and she could not bear the thought of his waiting. Out there somewhere, far, far. And she could not stem the ether that was washing her away. The waves of ether swept her back, and she could not get to him. Lorry was out there and she could not reach him. Dimly she could hear circles and figures of talk. But their voices were distant, the wiry bass barranging cello echo running through telegraphpoles.

Then her breath, her conscious breath was lowered, the lowering of a lifeboat softly plashing into the sea. And then she had left it.

For the furniture a secondhand dealer let him have $8.00. He got another five for a pint brandybottle of medicine from Mrs. Schroeder.

He thought he would go away. Each day he set out to move on. But he didn't. He waited, waited; he didn't know what for.

One night he started up out of a groggy ferriswheel sleep. He had heard, he thought, hingecreaking of bones, his mother's gravebones roomily skidding like a key in a rusty lock. Sitting up in his b.v.d.s, he leaned forward toward the foot of the cot for his coat. He took out a postcard picture of his dead mother and held it between his fingers.

A low-pulsed 25-watt bulb shone on the pasteboard skin of her face. His head palsied rabbinically over it, his lips sputtering, hanging in an old man's gape. Lying down, he dug his nose, her nose in effigy, into the pillow, muffling the windy gasps. Then something springily softpadded, pawed across the side of his face.

Lunging into his pants and coat, his shoelaces trailing, like skims of black plaguy milk, he ran out.

Outside, underneath a sign, *Beds 25 and 35 cents,* a november bowery night flopped up against him, desolately wagging against one of his coatlapels.

A few days later, the last of november. A late afternoon, with some remnant-sale autumn sun over Union Square. A parade was coming down. There was singing, a marchtime hymnal procession. He couldn't make out the words. At first he thought it was a funeral. Standing next to a steamy peanut-wagon which was chirping and cheeping away, he watched.

Looking down, he thought he saw a peanut at his feet, he wasn't certain. The parade was on top of him, the voices swelling chorally. It was turning the corner. Gently he pushed the thing at his feet with his shoe. Bending down to pick it up, he felt the reassuring hard shell of it against his fingers. About to straighten up he saw something out of the corners of his eyes which looked to him like an auctioneer's red flag. Then it went sweeping down, bloodstreaming floppily. Something hit hard against his head.

Scuffling, shrieks, horns, motorcycles went sirening through him with the nightmare gallop of a fire-engine. Lying on the sidewalk, not budging, he felt as if he had a stinging nose-bleed. His head in his arms, he was afraid to look up. Then opening one eye, he saw the anthill parade crowd, splintered, flying off in all directions. Mounted cops were chasing, motor-cycle-police were mowing them back and down, paving the way for the horses. Over him three skyblue uniforms were kicking a man in the stomach. A woman, her hanging hair shrieking and spurting over her eyes in fingernail scratches, was punching out and pummeling, yanking with insane fingers the brassbuttons off their coats. A plainclothesman ran up, blackjacking her. They carried the two of them off toward a patrol-wagon which had just factorywhistled around the corner.

In a crouch, he staggered up, snooped around and ducked behind a row of street-cars standing still. Then running, his eyes peeling off the blocks, he bent his back way forward like a football player making an end run.

Wiping the blood on his coatsleeve, he went along a block or so in a drunken totter. Then he unclenched his fist. Bracing himself, he cracked the peanutshell between his teeth. Slowly he licked the reddish brown-papery skin with his tongue. Then he started to chew the oily meaty guineapig-shaped kernel. Holding himself back, as if to make it last as long as possible, he munched away at it, sort of counting time. He moistened it more, like Prunes used to do with his prunepits in the orphan-age, in order to get as much out of it as he could.

Coming toward Washington Square, he tightened his belt and started to sing an orphan-asylum hymn. The bruise on his head was clotting, and the blood was stingingly humming over the wound:

He-roes, up! On   to   the fight,   For that flag means

vic - t'ries new;   Not in num-bers lies your might,

'Tis God's spi - rit wars for you.

A few american banknote leaves hung on the washington square november-ash trees. They were the last bugletaps of summer. Some gusts of dusty wind flapped up around him, gray and as uniform as a railroad timetable of cities.

Treading along, his thin soles, callousburns against his feet, he thought he would go somewhere, but he didn't know where. He might be able to kick some go into himself. Vaguely, he believed, going, going somewhere, would be more possible for him than doing. But what could he push himself into, where could he drive himself? Cleveland, Chi, Frisco, L. A., they made him mutter with cold. They were the nastywet searsroebuck catalogue sheets of a leaky outhouse up against him.

Spitting out the dust and licking the tiny splinters of the kernel that had settled between his teeth, he went through the park rolling off another two lines of the maccabean stanza:

> *'neath its folds, defeat unknown,*
> *triumph, triumph crowns our glorious way*

19. The American Earthquake

EDMUND WILSON

*For at least a quarter of a century, Edmund Wilson (1895–   )
has been by common acknowledgment America's first literary
critic. Despite reservations about the depth of his understanding or the quality of his judgments, there is general accord on
his extraordinary versatility and skill in making a wide variety
of subject matters not merely interesting but intellectually exciting. It hardly seems necessary, therefore, to detail the work
in which Wilson has been engaged since his graduation from
Princeton in 1916. It is important however, to recall that, in addition to his serving as F. Scott Fitzgerald's "literary conscience," he has popularized among Americans the work of the
most difficult and recherché of the European avant garde and
has written for* The New Yorker *on everything from the Dead
Sea Scrolls to the cultural scene in French Canada. A first-rate
reporter, Edmund Wilson was observing the oddities of American behavior during the Boom with amused detachment, and
during the thirties he reported on the horrors of depression
America in* The Nation *and the* New Republic *with the eye
of one who had moved toward identification with Marxism and
sympathy (but never intellectual obeisance) to communism.
The piece which follows, a brilliant evocation of the "sea of
misery" surrounding Jane Addams's famous philanthropic headquarters in Chicago, is characteristic of his work in* The American Earthquake, *an essential book for students of American
history.*

From *The American Earthquake* (Garden City: Doubleday, 1938), pp.
447–464. Reprinted with the permission of the author.

Hull-House in 1932

The landscape has turned gray: the snow-fields gray like newspaper, the sky gray like pasteboard—then darkness; just a crack of gray, distinct as a break in a boiler, that separates darkening clouds—a black fortress with one smokestack: the Northern Indiana Public Utility Company—darkness, with light at long intervals—a sudden street with lighted stores and streetcars—then the darkness again: dim front of a frame house, dim signboards—a red electric globe on a barber's pole —bridges in the blackness, a shore?—black factories—long streets, with rows of lights that stretch away into darkness— a large blunt tower embroidered in coarse beadwork of red, green and gold lights—then the endless succession of cars speeding along the dark lake-front, with the lights at shorter intervals now—then a thing like a red-hot electric toaster as big as an office building, which turns out to be one of the features of next summer's World Fair.

But mostly black midland darkness. Chicago is one of the darkest of great cities. In the morning, the winter sun does not seem to give any light: it leaves the streets dull. It is more like a forge which has just been started up, with its fires just burning red, in an atmosphere darkened by coal-fumes. All the world seems made of gray fog—gray fog and white smoke—the great square white-and-gray buildings seem to have been pressed out of the saturated atmosphere. The smooth asphalt of the lake-side road seems solidified polished smoke. The lake itself, in the dawn, is of a strange stagnant substance like pearl that is becoming faintly liquid and luminous—opaque like everything else but more sensitive than asphalt or stone. The Merchandise Mart—the *biggest* building in the world, as the Empire State Building is the *highest*—is no tower, in the fog, but a mountain, to brood upon whose cubic content is to be amazed, desolated, stunned. The Chicago River, dull green, itself a work of engineering, runs backward along its original course, buckled with black iron bridges, which unclose, one after the other, each in two short fragments, as a tug drags car-barges under them, like the peristaltic movement of the stomach pushing a tough piece of food along. The sun for a time half-reveals these scenes, but its energies are only brief. The afternoon has scarcely established itself as an identifiable phenomenon when light succumbs to dullness, and the day lapses back into dark. The buildings seem mounds of soft darkness caked and carved out of swamp-mud and rubber-stamped here and there with red neon signs. A good many of the streets, one finds, aside from the thoroughfares, are dimly lighted or not at all; and even those that are adequately lighted lose themselves in blurred vistas of coal-smoke.

In that dull air, among those long low straight streets—the deadened civilization of industry, where people are kept just alive enough to see that the machines are running—the almost neutral brick walls of Hull-House have themselves an industrial plainness. The old big square high-windowed mansion of earlier family grandeur, embedded in the dormitories, eating halls, gymnasiums, nurseries and laundries that today pack a city block, has been chastened as well as expanded: it has something of both the monastery and the factory. The high Victorian rooms that open into one another through enormous arched and corniced doorways, though they still contain mahogany tables, sofas and faded Turkish rugs, are in general scantily and serviceably furnished. The white woodwork and the marble fireplace have been painted a sort of neutral drab green, so that the use of the house may not soil them. In the little polygon room, in which one imagines hanging pots of ferns and a comfortable window-seat, one sees a typewriter and a set of colored charts showing the shift of nationalties around Hull-House. Yet one finds also traces of a cult of art: copies of paintings and statues, a fragment of a Greek frieze. Behind the glass doors of bookcases are nineteenth-century sets of Ruskin and Augustus Hare's *Walks in Rome.* The hallway is lined with photographs of residents and friends of the house; and on the walls of the polygon room hang the patron saints and heroes of Hull-House: Kropotkin and Catherine Breshkovsky, Arnold Toynbee and Jacob Riis—and Jane Addams's father. Over the desk by the front door is a picture of Jane Addams herself, in a big-sleeved and high-collared gown of the nineties, a young woman, slender and winning and almost like an illustration for some old serial by William Dean Howells or Mrs. Burton Harrison in the *Century Magazine.*

A little girl with curvature of the spine, whose mother had died when she was a baby, she abjectly admired her father, a man of consequence in frontier Illinois, a friend of Lincoln and a member of the state legislature, who had a flour mill and a lumber mill on his place. Whenever there were strangers at Sunday school, she would try to walk out with her uncle so that her father should not be disgraced by people's knowing that such a fine man had a daughter with a crooked spine. When he took her one day to a mill which was surrounded by horrible little houses and explained to her, in answer to her questions, that the reason people lived in such houses was that they couldn't afford anything better, she told her father that, when she grew up, she should herself continue to live in a big house but that it should stand among the houses of poor people.

At college, in the late seventies, she belonged to a group of girls who vowed before they parted for their summer vacation that each would have read the whole of Gibbon before they met again in the fall. In a Greek oration she delivered, Bellerophon figured as the Idealism which alone could slay the Chimera of Social Evils; and for her graduation essay she chose Cassandra, doomed "always to be in the right and always disbelieved and rejected." She heard rumors of the doctrines of Darwin and borrowed scientific books from a brother-in-law who had studied medicine in Germany; and she resisted with invincible stubbornness the pressure brought to bear by her teachers to make her go into the missionary field. The year that she graduated from college, she inherited a part of her father's estate and gave the college a thousand dollars to spend on a scientific library.

She herself went to medical school; but her spinal trouble got worse, and she had to stop. She spent six months strapped to a bed. This gave her a lot of time for reading, with no uncomfortable feeling that she ought to be doing something else, and she was very glad to have it; but when she was able to get about again, she felt dreadfully fatigued and depressed. She tried Europe; but one day, in London, she went out for a bus-ride in the East End. As she looked down on the misery and squalor, she remembered De Quincey's *Vision of Sudden Death:* how, when confronted with a pair of lovers about to be run over by the mail coach in which he was traveling, he had found himself powerless to warn them till he had remembered the exact lines in the *Iliad* which describe the shout of Achilles; and she was suddenly filled with disgust for the artificial middle-class culture upon which she had been trying to nourish herself and which had equipped her to meet this horror with nothing but a literary allusion, and that derived from an opium-eater as far removed from life as herself.

What was the good of enjoying German operas and the pictures in Italian galleries? In the interval between two trips to Europe, she visited a Western farm on which she held a mortgage—it was one of the American investments which made her traveling possible. She found there a woman and her children almost starved by the drought and attempting to raise money on a promissory note for which she could offer as collateral nothing but a penful of pigs. The pigs were starved, too, and horrible: one was being eaten by the others, all hunched up and crowded together.

She gave the mortgages up and went back to Europe again, and there she saw some striking match-girls suffering from phossy jaw. She decided to return to Chicago and to found a settlement house—there had never yet been one in America. The "subjective necessity" for settlement work she analyzes as follows: "first, the desire to interpret democracy in social terms; secondly, the impulse beating at the very source of our lives, urging us to aid in the race progress; and thirdly, the Christian movement toward humanitarianism." But she did not exclude "the desire for a new form of social success due to the nicety of imagination, which refuses worldly pleasures unmixed with the joys of self-sacrifice" and "a love of approbation so vast that it is not content with the treble clapping of delicate hands, but wishes also to hear the bass notes from toughened palms." Her father had impressed upon her early that scrupulous mental integrity, the unwillingness to make pretenses which one knew inside one did not live up to, was practically the whole of morality.

In South Halsted Street in Chicago, where there were Italians, Germans, Russians and Jews, she tried to help relieve their difficulties; to teach English to those who had immigrated as well as to give the young generation some idea of the European tradition from which they had been cut off. But this led to looking into their living conditions; and the problems of their living conditions led to the industrial system. When it was a question of children of four spending their whole day indoors pulling out basting threads or pasting labels on boxes, she found that she felt it her duty to get some labor legislation put through. She got one of the Hull-House residents appointed factory inspector.

At the time of the Pullman strike in 1894, Miss Addams was surprised and dismayed to find Chicago split up into two fiercely antagonistic camps. She had known Mr. Pullman and had been impressed by the excellence of his intentions in building a model town for his employees. She tried to maintain relations with both camps; but by the time the strike was over, it turned out that she and Pullman were on different sides of the fence, and that he was highly indignant with her. The Socialists and other radicals tried to convince her that she ought to be one of them; but, though she carefully looked up socialism, she resisted them as she had the teachers who had tried to make her be a missionary. She could not bind herself to parties and principles: what she did had to be done independently, on a basis of day-by-day experience. And she had still so vivid an impression of the classless democracy of the Western frontier that it was difficult for her to imagine a general class conflict in the United States.

Yet the winter after the World's Fair Chicago was full of people left stranded with no employment; and she was assailed by a new sense of shame at being comfortable in the midst of misery. The activities carried on at Hull-House now began to seem to her futile; its philanthropy a specious way of reconciling one's own conscience to the social injustice from which one profited. She remembered that the effect on Tolstoy of a similar period of suffering in Moscow had been to make him degrade his own standard of living to that of the poor themselves. She was again incapacitated by a serious illness, but got well and decided to travel to Russia and discuss the problem with Tolstoy himself.

Miss Addams found the great moralist working in the hay-fields with the peasants and eating their black bread and porridge, while the Countess with her children and their governess had a regular upper-class dinner. He pulled out one of Miss Addams' big sleeves and said that there was enough material in it to make a frock for a little girl; and he asked whether she did not find "such a dress" a "barrier to the people." She tried to explain that, since big sleeves were the fashion, the working girls in Chicago were wearing even bigger ones than hers, and that you could hardly dress like a peasant on South Halsted Street, since the peasants there wore middle-class clothes. But she was abashed when he asked her who "fed" her and how she got her "shelter," and she had to confess that her income was derived from a large farm a hundred miles away from Chicago. "So you are an absentee landlord?" he said scathingly. "Do you think you will help the people more by adding yourself to the crowded city than you would by tilling your own soil?"

She went away feeling humbled, and, before she arrived at Bayreuth and could allow herself to enjoy the *Ring*, she resolved that when she got back to Hull-House, she would spend two hours every day in the bakery. Yet as soon as she was actually at home again and found the piles of correspondence and the people waiting to see her, she decided that this and not baking was the proper work of her life, and she forgot her Tolstoyan scruples.

Her efforts for labor legislation embittered the manufacturers against her; her attempts to get garbage and dead animals that had been left in the street removed embroiled her with the political machine: garbage-collecting was a racket, and the rackets seemed to go right on up. She was astonished to find that her opposition to reëlecting a corrupt alderman roused both pulpit and press against her. When Czolgosz assassinated McKinley, the editor of an anarchist paper was arrested and held incommunicado, not allowed to see even a lawyer. She protested, with the result that Hull-House was denounced as a hotbed of anarchy. When the agents of the Tsar succeeded in making Gorky a pariah in America by circulating the news that he and his companion were not properly married, she asked a Chicago paper to print an article in his defense and found that she was at once accused of being an immoral woman herself by interests that wanted to get her off the school board.

At last, when, in 1900, she saw the Passion Play at Oberammergau, it struck her for the first time that the real enemy of Jesus was the money power. The young agitator had antagonized the merchants by interfering with their trade in the temple, and hence the Pharisees, whose racket depended on the temple, too. Church and State had stood solid with the Pharisees; and the money power had bribed Judas to betray him.

When she advocated peace at the time of the war, she found that President Wilson bowed her out and that she was presently being trailed by detectives. And then, when the war was over, people were more intolerant than ever.

Hull-House had always stood for tolerance: all the parties and all the faiths had found asylum there and lived pretty harmoniously together. And it still stands planted with a proud irrelevance in the midst of those long dark streets—where its residents occasionally get beaten and robbed—only a few blocks from a corner made famous by a succession of gang murders. With its strong walls, its enclosed staircased courts, and a power plant of its own, it stands like a medieval château protected by a moat and portcullis.

Inside it there is peace and a sort of sanctity. Jane Addams at seventy-two still dominates her big house among the little ones—though she is supposed to have been forbidden by the doctors to spend more than four hours a day there—with her singular combination of the authority of a great lady and the humility of a saint. In the large refectory-like dining room with its copper and brass and bare brick, the quick glances of the "seeing eye" which fascinated young women in the nineties and excited them to go in for settlement work—that glance at once penetrating and shy—still lights its responses around her table. Through her vitality, Hull-House still lives—the expression of both pride and humility: the pride of a moral vision which cannot accept as its habitat any one of the little worlds of social and intellectual groupings; the humility of a spirit which, seeing so far, sees beyond itself, too, and feels itself lost amid the same uncertainties, thwarted by the same cross-purposes, as all of those struggling others.

All around the social workers of Hull-House there today stretches a sea of misery more appalling even than that which discouraged Miss Addams in the nineties. This winter even those families who had managed to hang on by their savings and earnings have been forced to apply for relief.

A relief worker's cross-section of an industrial suburb shows the sinking of the standard of living. The people here are mostly Poles. Every pressure has been brought to bear on them to induce them to spend their money on motor-cars, radios, overstuffed furniture and other unattractive luxuries; and they are caught now between two worlds, with no way of living comfortably in either. The most urgent problem, however, is how to be sure of living at all.

In one house, a girl of seventeen is interpreter for her mother, in whom the girl's stocky figure has expanded to enormous amorphous bulk, and she changes not only her language but her expression and gestures, her personality, in passing from English to Polish. She had till lately, at $2 a week, been doing all the housework for a real-estate man; but she decided he was imposing on her and quit. She is handsome and evidently high-spirited—Americanized during the whoopee period. Her brother had had a job on the conveyer at a bookbindery; but, due to a mechanical improvement, this job no longer exists: the boy has been laid off, with no prospect of reëmployment. The girl takes us up from the downstairs kitchen, where the family mostly live, and shows you the little-used floor above, which is papered with big blue, pink and magenta blossoms and furnished with all the things that the salesmen of the boom have sold them: a victrola and wadded chairs and couches, spotted with a pattern of oranges, which nobody seems ever to have sat in. On the walls, as in all these houses, exhibited in ornate gold frames, hang Slavic saints and Madonnas, bristling with spiky gold crowns, Byzantine embroidery and Polish inscriptions.

Elsewhere an old man is dying of a tumor, with no heat in the house, on a cold day. His pale bones of arms lie crooked like bent pins; nothing is heard in the house but his gasping. His old wife, her sharp Polish nose sticking out from under a bonnet-like cap, stands beside him, as silent as a ghost. Their granddaughter, who is married and wears well-fitting American street-clothes—an American middle-class woman, but today as badly off as they are—has just been to the relief station for coal.

In another place, a family of five have three small rooms in a basement, and they have sunk below any standard: the father grinningly and glaringly drunk in the middle of the morning, the mother stunned and discouraged by her struggle against poverty and filth. They live around the stove with their small dirty children, in the close sweetish sickish smell of cooking and boiling clothes. Where they sleep on two narrow cots, the bedclothes are old twisted gray rags that have not even been smoothed out flat. They do not know very much English, and they cannot explain to the relief worker what they have done about relief and insurance; they do not understand, themselves. All they know is that they are living in that dirty hole, from which they have not yet been expelled, and where the man, with a little liquor in him, can imagine himself the shrewd and sound father of a family, with the situation well under control. In another basement, however, the young husband has carpentered and painted the big cellar room which, with a tiny bedroom, is all they have, so that it almost resembles a human dwelling. He used to work for the Fruit-Growers' Express, but has been laid off a long time. The stout blond girl to whom he is married has had to be on her feet all day and, from the strain on her heart, has just had a collapse. They do not have any children, but they keep a canary in a cage. The young wife in another household has put kewpie dolls around in an otherwise bare apartment, and has made blue curtains for the cot in which her two children sleep. She and her husband are very fond of one another and very fond of the children. They are the kind of people who do not like to ask for relief, and they have put it off as long as they could, with the result that, though goodlooking and youthful, they are now pale and thin with undernourishment.

A pink clear-eyed innocent-eyed woman, alone in an immaculately kept kitchen, all white oilcloth and green-and-white linoleum and with the latest thing in big gleaming gas-ranges, flushes at the relief worker's questions. She is going to have a baby and has applied for money to pay the midwife. The relief worker offers her a doctor but she is used to having the midwife. An elderly couple from Zürich are living in an apartment equally immaculate, though far less completely equipped, amid blue-and-green chromolithographs of Swiss waterfalls and mountains and lakes. The woman is cooking a few slivers of onions on a tiny coal-stove, which was intended primarily for heat. The husband is out on the railroad tracks picking up pieces of coal in order to keep it going. The woman suddenly begins to cry as she is answering the relief worker's queries, then as suddenly stops. The husband, a little smiling man with Kaiser Wilhelm mustaches, comes back with a few pieces of coal: the railroad detectives have chased him away. He was formerly an industrial chemist and has recently turned his ingenuity to inventing little gambling toys. One of them, he says, he has a fair prospect of selling: you shoot a marble which drops into a hole and knocks up a little tin flap; "Swiss Navy" counts lowest and "America" a hundred per cent. In another place, the bookbinder who has lost his job through a technological improvement has a fellow in the musical field—a young violinist whose profession has been partly abolished by the talkies.

Above the straight criss-cross streets the small houses of brick and gray boards, the newer little two-story Noah's Arks, prick the sharp Roman Catholic spire and the bulbs of the Orthodox Church.

The single men are driven to flophouses. During the last year —September 30, 1931–September 30, 1932—50,000 have registered at the clearing house. Those who are not residents of Chicago are ordered to leave the city: if they got there by paying their fare, they are given a half-fare which will take them home. Others are sent to the asylum, the poorhouse, the veterans' home; referred to the blind pension, the juvenile court. About 500 men a month are disposed of in this way. The Oak Forest poorhouse, called "the Graveyard," has people sleeping in the corridors and turned 19,000 away last year. The rest are directed to the shelters, where they get two meals a day and a bed.

Among the high whitewashed walls of an obsolete furniture factory, the soiled yellow plaster and the scrawled and punctured blackboards of an old public school, the scraped-out offices and pompous paneling of a ghastly old disused courthouse; on the floors befouled with spittle, in the peppery-sweetish stink of food cooking, sulphur fumigations, bug exterminators, rank urinals doctored with creosote—ingredients of the general fetor that more or less prominently figure as one goes from floor to floor, from room to room, but all fuse in the predominant odor of stagnant and huddled humanity—these men eat their chicken-feed and slum amid the deafening clanking of trays and dump the slops in g.i. cans; wait for prize-fights or movies of Tarzan (provided to keep them out of the hands of the Communists or from holding meetings themselves) in so-called "recreation halls," on the walls of which they have chalked up "Hoover's Hotel"—big bare chambers smothered with smoke, strewn with newspapers like vacant lots, smeared like the pavements with phlegm. Here they sit in the lecture seats, squat on the steps of the platform, stretch out on the floor on old papers. In one room a great wall-legend reminds them: "The Blood of God Can Make the Vilest Clean," and they get routed to mess through a prayer meeting. When they come back to the recreation hall, they discover that a cheerful waltz has served merely as a bait to draw them to the harangue by an old Cicero policeman who says that he has been saved. They are obliged to send their clothes to be fumigated, and, if they are wet with the winter rain, ruined. They herd into steaming showers, the young men still building some flesh on straight frames, the old with flat chests, skinny arms and round sagging bellies; and they flop at last on the army cots or in the bunks in double tiers, where the windows which are shut to keep out the cold keep in the sour smell—men in slit union suits and holey socks, men tattooed with fancy pictures or the emblems of some service they have left—resting their bunioned feet taken out of flattened shoes or flat arches wound around with adhesive tape—lying with newspapers for pillows, their arms behind their heads or with a sheet pulled over their faces or wrapped up in blankets, rigid on their backs, their skin stretched tight over their jawbones so that these look like the jaws of the dead.

There is a clinic which does what it can to head off the venereal diseases. There is also a great deal of t.b., to which the Negroes have a fatal susceptibility; and in one shelter spinal meningitis got out of hand for a while and broke nine backs on its rack. Another common complaint of the flophouses is the poisoning that results from drinking a dilution of wood alcohol which the inmates buy for fifteen cents a pint, which looks and tastes, as somebody says, like a mixture of benzine, kerosene and milk, and which usually lands them in the infirmary or the psychopathic ward. And yet one man, given his choice between his bottle and admission to the shelter, refused to give up the bottle: he preferred to spend the night in the cold rather than surrender his only support in a life so aimless and hopeless. In the Salvation Army shelter, they will not take in steady drinkers, but the others do the best they can with them. In one, there is a hobbling cripple who comes in drunk every night. "I wouldn't be surprised," says the manager, "if a hearse drove up and a dead man got up and walked out and asked for a flop." One man turned up "lousy as a pet coon—so lousy nobody would go near-um and they put-um in the stable with the horse for the night, and the horse tried to get away. The next morning they gave-um a shower and scrubbed-um with a long-handled brush." But most of the cases in the infirmaries—from exhaustion to bad kidneys and body sores—come down to the same basic disease: starvation.

Razor-slashings and shootings bring in other patients—though the prospect of a day of work a week, with its brief liberation from the shelters, is said to have diminished these. The bad characters are sent to the bull-pens in the basement, where, crowded together, in fetid air, they sleep on hard benches with their coats under their heads. Newcomers for whom there is no room have to be dumped down among them.

Yet Chicago has apparently been particularly efficient in providing and running these shelters. At best, it is not unlike the life of barracks—but without the common work and purpose which give a certain momentum to even a dull campaign. In the shelters, there is nothing to coöperate on and nothing to look forward to, no developments, no chance of success. The old man is ending his life without a home and with no hope of one; the wage-earner who has hitherto been self-dependent now finds himself dropped down among casuals and gradually acquires their attitude; the young man who comes to maturity during the workless period of the depression never learns the habit of work. (There are few actual hoboes here: the hobo can do better by begging or stealing.)

In so far as they are unable to adapt themselves, they must live under a continual oppression of fear or guilt or despair. One sees among them faces that are shocking in their contrast to their environment here: men who look as if they had never had a day's ill health or done a day's careless work in their lives. Now they jump at the opportunity of spending a day a week clearing the rubbish off vacant lots or cleaning the streets underneath the Loop tracks. This is the only thing that stands between them and that complete loss of independence which can obliterate personality itself—which degrades them to the primal dismal undifferentiated city grayness, depriving them even of the glow of life that has formerly set them off from the fog and the pavements and the sodden old newspapers, rubbing them down to nothing, forcing them out of life.

Yet none of these single-men's shelters produces such an impression of horror as the Angelus Building on South Wabash Avenue, where families of homeless Negroes have taken refuge. This neighborhood was once fairly well-to-do; but at the present time, left behind by the city's growth in other directions, it presents a desolation that is worse than the slums. When the snow in the darkening afternoon has come to seem as dingy as the dusk and the sky as cold and tangible as the snow—as if the neutral general medium of the city were condensing in such a way as to make it hard to move and exist—the houses, interminably scattered along the straight miles of the street, monotonous without being uniform, awkward or cheap attempts at various types of respectable architecture in gray limestone, colorless boards or red brick, all seem—whether inhabited or not—equally abandoned now. The windowless slots of one open into a hollow shell: it has been gutted of even its partitions; the Romanesque prongs of another make it look like a blackened pulled tooth; on the brownstone façade of a third, some distance above the ground, is stuck a pretentious doorway, from under which, like a lower jaw, the flight of front steps has been knocked. And, as a suitable climax to this, the Angelus Building looms blackly on the corner of its block: seven stories, thick with dark windows, caged in a dingy mesh of fire-escapes like mattress-springs on a junk-heap, hunched up, hunchback-proportioned, jam-crammed in its dumbness and darkness with miserable wriggling life.

It was built in 1892 and was once the Ozark Hotel, popular

at the time of the old World's Fair. In the dim little entrance hall, the smudged and roughened mosaic, the plaster pattern of molding, the fancy black grill of the elevator, most of it broken off, do not recall former splendor—they are abject, mere chips and shreds of the finery of a section now dead, trodden down into the waste where they lie. There is darkness in the hundred cells: the tenants cannot pay for light; and cold: the heating system no longer works. It is a firetrap which has burned several times—the last time several people were burned to death. And, now, since it is not good for anything else, its owner has turned it over to the Negroes, who flock into the tight-packed apartments and get along there as best they can on such money as they collect from the charities.

There are former domestic servants and porters, former mill-hands and stockyard workers; there are prostitutes and hoodlums next door to respectable former laundresses and Baptist preachers. One veteran of the war, once foreman of the Sunkist Pie Company, now lives in cold and darkness with his widowed mother, even the furniture which he had been buying for $285 the outfit and on which he had paid all but the last installment of $50.20, taken away by the furniture company. For light, they burn kerosene lamps, and for warmth, small coal-stoves and charcoal buckets. The water-closets do not flush, and the water stands in the bathtubs.

The children go to play in the dark halls or along the narrow iron galleries of an abysmal central shaft, which, lighted faintly through glass at the top, is foggy and stifling with coal-smoke like a nightmare of jail or Hell. In the silence of this dreadful shaft, sudden breakages and bangs occur—then all is deathly still again. The two top floors have been stripped by fire and by the tenants' tearing things out to burn or sell: apartments have lost their doors and plumbing pipes lie uncovered. These two floors have been condemned and deserted. Relief workers who have visited the Angelus Building have come away so overwhelmed with horror that they have made efforts to have

the whole place condemned—to the piteous distress of the occupants, who consider it an all-right-enough place when you've
got nowhere else to go. And where to send these sixty-seven
Negro families? Brought to America in the holds of slave-ships
and afterwards released from their slavery with the chance of
improving their lot, they are now being driven back into the
black cavern of the Angelus Building, where differing standards of living, won sometimes by the hard work of generations, are all being reduced to zero.

Those who want to keep clear of the jail-like shelters get
along as they can in the streets and huddle at night under
the Loop or build shacks on empty lots. On whatever waste-
places they are permitted to live, the scabby-looking barnacles
appear, knocked together from old tar-paper and tin, old car-
bodies, old packing boxes, with old stovepipes leaning askew,
amid the blackened weeds in the snow and the bones of old
rubbish piles. One "Hooverville" on Harrison Street flies a tattered black rag like the flag of despair.

The inhabitants of these wretched settlements chiefly forage
from the city dumps, as do many of those whom charity will
not help or who for one reason or another will not go to it or
for whom the relief they get is inadequate. There is not a
garbage-dump in Chicago which is not diligently haunted by
the hungry. Last summer in the hot weather, when the smell
was sickening and the flies were thick, there were a hundred
people a day coming to one of the dumps, falling on the heap
of refuse as soon as the truck had pulled out and digging in it
with sticks and hands. They would devour all the pulp that
was left on the old slices of watermelon and cantelope till the
rinds were as thin as paper; and they would take away and
wash and cook discarded turnips, onions and potatoes. Meat is
a more difficult matter, but they salvage a good deal of that,
too. The best is the butcher's meat which has been frozen and
has not spoiled. If they can find only meat that is spoiled, they

can sometimes cut out the worst parts, or they scald it and sprinkle it with soda to neutralize the taste and the smell. Fish spoils too quickly, so it is likely to be impossible—though some people have made fish-head soup. Soup has also been made out of chicken claws.

A private incinerator at Thirty-fifth and La Salle Streets which disposes of the garbage from restaurants and hotels, has been regularly visited by people, in groups of as many as twenty at a time, who pounce upon anything that looks edible before it is thrown into the furnace. The women complained to investigators that the men took an unfair advantage by jumping on the truck before it was unloaded; but a code was eventually established which provided that different sets of people should come at different times every day, so that everybody would be given a chance. Another dump at Thirty-first Street and Cicero Avenue has been the center of a Hooverville of three hundred people.

The family of a laid-off dishwasher lived on food from the dump for two years. They had to cook it on the gas of the people downstairs, since their own had been shut off. Their little girl got ptomaine poisoning. Two veterans of the war, who had been expelled from Washington with the bonus army and made their homes in the fireboxes of an old kiln, were dependent on the dump for some time, though a buddy of theirs found he could do better by panhandling at people's doors. One widow with a child of nine, who had formerly made $18 a week in a factory and who has since been living on $4 a week relief and two or three hours' work a day at fifty cents an hour, has tried to get along without garbage but has had to fall back on it frequently during a period of three years. Another widow, who used to do housework and laundry but who was finally left without any work, fed herself and her fourteen-year-old son on garbage. Before she picked up the meat, she would always take off her glasses so that she would not be able to see the maggots; but it sometimes made the boy so sick to look at this offal and smell it that he could not bring himself to eat. He weighed only eighty-two pounds.

Many people in the Hooverville on Cicero Avenue have been poisoned from eating the garbage. One man ate a can of bad crab-meat thrown away by a chain store, and was later found putrefying.

On the endlessly stretching latitude of West Congress Street —lit only on one side at long intervals by livid low-power lamps—along which huge cubes of buildings are infrequently belted by lighted-up floors and where black and blind ranks of trucks stand posted in front of dark factories, some anonymous hand has chalked up on a wall: "VOTE RED. THE PEOPLE ARE GOOFY."

20. Somebody in Boots

NELSON ALGREN

Nelson Algren (1909–   ) was born in Detroit of oddly mixed but typically American Scandinavian-Jewish parentage. He took a degree in journalism at the University of Illinois, and when the depression struck, he went on the bum, drifting through the Southwest, working on the WPA Federal Writers' Project, serving as co-editor of Anvil *with Jack Conroy. He has told the story of how he came to write his first book:*
I went right up to Vanguard Press and met James Henle. And he said, 'What'll you need? What would you do? How would you write a novel?' I said, 'I'd go back to the Southwest.' He said, 'What would you need to do that?' I said, 'I need thirty dollars a month.' I mean I knew it would cost that much. You get room and board

From *Somebody in Boots* (New York: Vanguard Press, 1935), Chap. VIII, pp. 124–151. Reprinted with the permission of the author.

for twenty dollars a month and that leaves ten dollars a month for three months, a total of one hundred dollars. I wrote *Somebody in Boots* on that. I didn't finish it in three months, but I delivered it. It was delivered in 1935. That was the only work I did between graduation and 1936 when the WPA opened up. I got married in 1936 and the book wasn't a success at all, so I didn't try writing another novel until 1940. I got divorced then.[1]

In fact the book sold only 750 copies, and is hardly known today. It is to be hoped that this situation will be corrected,[2] for although Somebody in Boots *displays the weakness of Algren's later, more famous books* (The Man with the Golden Arm, A Walk on the Wild Side) *and his stories—a sentimental romanticizing of those at the bottom of the social pile—it also has their strengths in abundance. With its mordant, bleak humor, its relentless exploration of a social reality passed over by more squeamish souls, its refusal to pretty up the central figure in order to make him conform to certain stereotypes of the virtuous proletarian, it demands rereading as a raw, undoctored, and elementally vigorous portrayal of boxcar existence in the depths of the depression.*

The people were moving about, moving about. It seemed to Cass that no one knew why. Sometimes it seemed to him that men were all, somehow, blind; that they went from city to city in darkness.

By the winter of 1931 Cass knew that disaster had come to the world above him. For all through the South that winter, East and West, the trains gathered people like flies. Whole families piled into cattle-cars, women rode in reefers; old men rode the brakebeams, holding steel rods above the wheels with fingers palsied by age. Several times Cass saw pregnant women riding in empties.

---

[1] H. E. F. Donohue, *Conversations with Nelson Algren* (1964), p. 6.
[2] *Somebody in Boots* is now (1966) available in a paperback edition (New York: Berkley Publishing Corporation).

"It's the big trouble everywhere," a girl told him. Wherever he went men spoke of "the big trouble."

And even though there were now faces always about him, some moving east and some west, yet he himself went alone. All men went alone; no two went together.

Faces changed. One spoke of Seattle, one of Memphis, another of ripening wheat in Kansas. But whatever they said, Cass felt that they were lying; he felt somehow that these faces had never seen the cities and fields, that they only thought they had seen them.

And the voices always lying, always boasting or lying voices, they all came to sound alike to him, as voices sound in rain. Their words were encrusted with a thin film of white spittle, like the spittle on the lips of the pervert in the park.

Wherever he walked that winter, whether in New Orleans along icy docks or on Railroad Street in Baton Rouge, he saw the vast army of America's homeless ones; the boys and old women, the old men and young girls, a ragged parade of dull gray faces, begging, thieving, hawking, selling and whoring. Faces haggard, and hungry, and cold, and afraid; as they passed, booted men followed and watched. Springfield, Decatur, Little Rock, Fort Smith; Beaumont, Houston, Austin, San Marcos. Then, San Antonio.

Cass got into San Antonio on the third night of January of 1931; and 1931 hit San Antonio with rain, sleet and hail. He slept under newspaper that night in a wheelless S. P. passenger coach standing on a siding outside the S. P. yards. It smelled foul within, but its windows were boarded and its floor was dry.

All night rain tapped against the windows; a timid rat came to nibble something at the far end of the coach, and Cass rustled his paper to scare him away.

When he rose in the morning he felt hunger like a wound behind his navel; so he came to his feet slowly, having learned that hunger spun his head like a top whenever he came too swiftly to his feet. Outside a false dawn was breaking over a dripping water-tank, and beyond the tank lay the city. He tied his shoes standing against a pile of car-wheels through which stunt burdock was still trying to grow; then he pushed through fields of buffalo grass knee-high and stiff with frost, until he came to a street.

Nogalitos Street.

"If ah could rustle me up two bucks in this pesthole," he promised himself, "ah'd get me tattooed all over."

He decided to look for that beanery where, three years before, he had eaten with a boy named Thomas Clay. Or had it really been Thomas Clancy? Cass pondered this ancient question as he walked.

Night-clouds hung heavily, threatening snow. A child's face peered wanly from a window as he passed, like the face of a sick child peering. As he passed the false dawn died, the streets became black as pitch once more. He could not find the old beanery, nor any similar place, though he sought along the streets for long.

When he turned down Pedro avenue into Navarro it was seven o'clock—and three blocks away, unevenly scissored there from a gray mist, a soup line seemed a thousand-humped serpent winding. Regularly and minutely the dark line jerked, was still with waiting, then wormed six convulsive inches through one narrow door. Its humps were the heads of homeless men, centipede legs were arms in rags. Its hungering mouth was a thousand mouths; even from three blocks away Cass felt that dreadful humility with which homeless men wait for food. A feeling as though of some disgraceful defeat came to him. On the curb gray sparrows flirted their tails, and pecked where horses late had passed.

Once, far ahead of the place where Cass stood in the queue, at the place where the queue found the door, someone shouted something in anger or pain, and a mocking response came from within. A little flurry of excitement ran up and down the line, many laughed together and a single cry went up, weakly and thinly striving up into the unseen sky. Fog wrapped the cry, and Cass saw the bum who had cried out: he was walking swiftly away down Navarro. At the corner his angry figure turned, Cass could see it only dimly, the voice came muffled by mist.

"Do a man have to wait all mornin' in line to git a tin plate o' cow-donick? I kin get garbage out o' any old can."

But even Cass knew better than that. He knew that once a week, on Saturday, all open garbage was sprayed by the city. (In order to keep paupers from poisoning themselves on Sunday, which was the Sabbath.) So to the sullen shoulders in front of him, to a flat-backed head on a hairy neck he said, "They're puttin' stink-oil on the grab-cans now. That guy won't find even crap left clean. Ah seen 'em sprayin' it on last summer, back o' Commerce Street in Dallas. It was green kind o', looked like to me."

The flat-backed head did not turn to reply. But three sparrows rose in a single flight and the head turned then slowly to follow that rising. Cass's throat contracted when he saw the man's face. Disaster or disease had torn or eaten the nose away until only the nostrils now remained. Cass had seen faces beaten expressionless by defeat, faces hungry and hopeless and sick with long shame—but this was the mask of death itself. He touched his own nose and found it running. He smeared phlegm off on the back of his hand and looked down at his wrists. They were blue-black with dirt and cold, and the reddish hairs on the backs of his fingers seemed frozen around the roots.

"That stuff they're puttin' on the cans is coal-oil, bub," a voice behind him informed. "*I* read about it in the paper, that's how *I* learned. Coal-oil, so kids 'll quit gettin' sick from eatin' slop."

The noseless man spoke nasally.

"Yeh, they want the kids to starve healthy-like is why they doin' it."

The fog began to lift above the mission. Two of the sparrows returned to the curb.

When Cass was only a few feet from the building, a door opened and a smell from within came billowing out. It sugged up his nostrils in one thick and sticky woosh. In one moment hunger went out of him. Like blood through a bag, hunger drained out. Had it not been for remembering coal-oil on the cans Cass would have followed the bum who had cried out in protest. Instead he tried to close his senses when he came into the place. He reached for a plate, found an empty place at a bench, and sat down among a dozen other ragged once-men.

"I Am The Way And The Light," a wall-sign informed him. "Christ Died For Your Sins," said another.

Cass looked down at his plate. The thing upon it was formed like a meat-ball, and it well might have been all of that; but it wambled about in a thin yellow swill, a kind of diarrheal brown gravy. Cass thought of cow-dung dropped thinly and long. "Cow-donick" the man in the fog had called this meat, and the recollection did not help Cass greatly. After moderating its odor with salt and hot pepper, he yet could not down the stenchful stuff. One bite, wholly vile, convinced him that the man had been right. He swallowed, retched half-way, and paused one moment to reflect: the meat was as rank as something a half-starved street-cur would have to regurgitate twice before downing. The coffee had been ground out of chicory and some cheap dry cereal; he swashed it down hastily to cleanse his mouth of the meat, found it both hot and good. It was bitter as medicine, but invigorating, and he felt a little stronger after drinking. When he learned that he could have a second cup he reached for it eagerly.

Over the brim of his cup he regarded a squat and foreign-appearing fellow valiantly struggling with that with which he had himself struggled. For some reason the man kept tilting his plate on a level with his eyes, first to one side and then to the other, as though unable to make up his mind about something. He did this three times while Cass watched, till the brown-yellow soup began slopping over the edge and the thing in the middle began walking, as though on very short legs, about the periphery of the tin. He set it down quite carefully then, and with a deliberated accuracy spat in the plate's center. Then he rose from the bench to flee for coffee, belching hugely as he fled.

Cass drained his cup and rose to leave the Jesus-Feeds-All mission, but at the door he learned that to pay for his meal he would have to chop wood in the yard for a while. This did not take him longer than twenty minutes; when he was through his hunger had returned. He resolved to give the alleys a try before returning to the mission. He could only get one more meal in the place anyhow. The "Jesus-Feeds-All" mission served no one man more than twice, if he were transient. After two meals you went somewhere else. And "somewhere else" was down the nearest alley.

Beside Cass, as he found the street, the squat-necked man fell into step. He walked with his fists jammed in his pockets and his cap pulled low over his eyes; for a minute he said nothing.

"Looks like a hunky," Cass thought. "If it weren't fo' furriners times'd be better."

"Are you a hunky, fella?" he asked.

The fellow replied in a voice so broken and guttural that at first Cass could not quite understand.

"No, not hunky. Litvak from Memel is all. You know? Carl Jusitska, that is my name."

Then Carl Jusitska spoke of his life as they walked. He had once been a steel-worker in Latvia, a place somewhere in Europe, and there he had had a wife and four boy-children. Today he did not know where this family was, because of a red-haired man who had come one day to the rolling mill where he had worked. The red-haired one was an American, and the foreman had brought him into the yard where Carl was sitting among other workers, all eating dinners from tin dinner-pails. The foreman had told his men that they must all listen hard, for this was a wise man he had brought, even though the wise one did not use the tongue very well. So each man listened hard as he was able; and the American told them young workers were needed in *Dee*-troit, a place somewhere in America. All workers who came there would receive such fine wages that very soon after they arrived each man would send for his wife and his family and all his small brothers to come to *Dee*-troit also. And when he told how much money each man would earn in that far place the men were a little suspicious; they could scarcely believe. Carl had been a little suspicious too, but the more he thought it over the truer it all had sounded. Then the red-haired one had finished speaking abruptly and had gone swiftly away; no one knew where to exactly, he was not seen again anywhere. And the more Carl had thought it over the truer it all had sounded. He had come to America, and had sent for his family.

"For one year I am scab," he said, "I get reech. Not unnerstan'. Then unnerstan': I am scab. I join oonion. I strike, I am fire. No *joo*stice. I am poor once more." He pushed back his cap and pointed to a line of gray about his temples. "See—I get old in thees America. No monies anymore, anywhere. You tink Mary gone home? You tink where I could find she?"

Cass walked a little faster. He didn't like hunkies.

To their left, for a block, loomed a long low factory, silent now where machines once rumbled. Its windows had been broken out, there was nothing inside now save silence and rust.

"Mebbe Matvey Karskoff send Mary monies to come home to Memel. Mebbe Mary take such monies an' go. Matvey like Mary for long long time."

Cass was hungry. He was cold. He didn't like hunkies. He wiped his nose on the back of his hand.

"*Look*"—Carl took his shoulder so fiercely that he had to stop. "*Look*, keed—we eat togedder, leev togedder, sleep to-gedder—everee night for twelve long year—an' now, no more.

Wonse in ol' time, long time, time afore we marry, Mary say, "Oney you is what I lof'. Because Mary say thees ting to me we marry. Now—no more. Now when it get night I tink Mary in bed wit Matvey. I look in many windows to see. In same bed I tinkin'—windows, houses, rooms inside wit' beds. So walk, walk, all night walk. Same bed, Mary. Same bed, Matvey."

Cass took the hand off his shoulder. He wanted something to eat, right away. He saw the swart alien face a foot from his own, and for one second he wanted to hurt it, to strike it between the eyes so that it would cry out quickly and strike back blindly. He wanted to kick it till it bled. He wanted to see its mouth broken in with pain.

"Git along, bum," he said. "Whyn't you go back where you come from?"

Carl Jusitska turned swiftly and went off in the opposite direction. His hip bumped and scraped the bricks of the factory's wall as he went, as though he could no longer see clearly the street whereon he walked. Cass's eyes followed till the man from Memel was lost in an eddying swirl of traffic. Then Cass tightened the thin and greasy cord that held up trousers once his brother's, and he listened to the protesting grumble of wind within his bowels. In a slow glissade his stomach caved in and turned half-way over—it seemed for one moment that he had no stomach at all, only a head going up like a balloon, buzzing and bounding through space up and up, till it burst in a bubble of blackness and left him standing with his back braced tensely against the bricks of the wall. His eyes felt dry, with a burning and granular dryness.

"Ah'm *really* hungry now," he thought, and the thought frightened him, for in this city men could not beg on the streets even covertly.

He tried mooching twice. The first moochee gave him a half-filled sack of tobacco. But the second looked around for the law, and Cass ran into an alley. He went down the alley only a little way, and he came to a grab-can where the coal-oil had dried.

Now came the night-hours, when men walked up and down. All night Cass went through streets and alleyways, smelling and pawing and stooping over.

"Look!" (His belly seemed now to whisper its need.) "Look in that *big* can, down below." He tried to turn the can on end, to dump its refuse out, but he lacked strength. So he dug deep down, blindly groping beside high-piled ashes till his fingers sank into something soft and warm. When he pulled his hand out it was caked to the wrist, with human dung.

Cass did not feel disgust that time. He saw his hand with eyes which were dry and burning, and no longer capable of disgust. He smelled, with a nose which nothing could now offend. He scraped his fingers half-heartedly against ashes and fence. And Belly whispered, "Look! Look *behind* the ashes!" But there was nothing behind the ashes to eat, there was nothing there save a few drifted leaves. So Cass sat down on the leaves, between the high-piled ashes and the fence, and he pulled his cap down low over his eyes, and he slept.

Early the following morning he went into a small bakery on Durango Street, to beg for bread. The woman behind the counter looked at him for one moment as though she thought he might strike her; and then she looked sorry for having thought that. But she had just given the last of the old stuff to the mission, she said. "The-Jesus-Feeds-All mission. 'Cause that's where they're feedin' the homeless now, an' it's where *you* ought to go."

Half an hour later, in the rear of a delicatessen on Zarzamora Street, Cass pulled a half-loaf of raisin bread out of a can. Save for one small corner, it was untouched by coal-oil. In the bottom of its crust were small toothmarks, so that he did not eat all the way down despite his hunger.

"Ah'd like to get me tattooed sometime," Cass planned as he gnawed in the alley.

A while later Cass had a great piece of luck. He found a head of lettuce the inner leaves of which were still fresh and green. That *was* luck. It was in back of a fruit store that that happened, and he hung around the place for an hour after the finding in the hope of another head. A boy came out of the store carrying a crate of bananas, but he put the crate on a wagon, and he hauled the wagon to the corner, and then he turned that corner out of sight.

On the evening of Cass's second day in San Antonio the garbage cans were sprayed again. So it was then time to be moving on.

He had had his fill of San Antonio. Or rather, not his fill.

He returned to his wheelless passenger coach and found two men sleeping where he had slept. When they wakened he jungled up with them over a fire near the Soupline tracks. Both men were older than himself, and they seemed unwilling to speak much to him. But they gave him potatoes and coffee and a cut of plug-tobacco. Toward midnight a westbound stock-run began humming the rails, and all three rose from their fire to go. Cass saw the headlight a mile down the track, heard her working steam with the brake-shoes slack. Then she whistled, once, the headlight began growing larger every second—and he raced with the other 'boes to catch her before she gained such speed as to make catching difficult or impossible. He swung up a ladder, cracked a seal—and dove.

It was warm in the reefer with the other two. They pulled the trap down over their heads, shoved a spike in the lock to prevent the trap locking, and slept.

Hours later, under flood-lights far ahead, Cass saw six bulls in slickers come out of a Harvey Café. They walked limned sharply against those lights; they laughed as they went toward the tracks. Across the thunder of approaching wheels their laughter, like six bells in storm, tinkled thin and silvery. As the first car rolled beneath the lights the first of the bulls swung himself up its ladder; climbing, his body swayed and powerfully flexed as though on hips forged of rock and rubber. Then easily as five jungle-cats, with the same steel swing of rock-and-rubber torsoes, the others followed and advanced.

All six were young men; they were all of them hard. The one who led drew a flashlight; the others gripped small colts. Their high-heeled boots had steel-spiked soles that they might not slip on the icy spine.

Other men saw.

A quarter of a mile away, from where they crouched on a rocking roof, they saw and ran. Caps yanked low over their foreheads, bodies bent in challenge to the slant rain beating, bums raced down the narrow spine away from the men who walked in light. The cars were coated with ice and rain, they ran in mist and a swaying dark. The planking, as though in alliance against them with rain and bulls, kept buckling beneath their feet. Between cars a four-foot gap—no time to measure gaps tonight—just *jump!* Already the flood-beams were bathing the cars that made up the train's center section. *"Jump you lame-leg son of a bitch, jump or we'll shove y' over."*

At the side, autos waited. The six on the top shagged the 'boes down the side, into the arms of their deputies. The bounty on bums was a dollar a head here; the detectives split with their aides. No use playing 'possum tonight, lousers— deputy's baby needs new shoes.

Some of the bums huddled stubbornly in reefer pits, thinking no bull would trouble to come down after—even when a flashray made their darkness bright. Such a bum didn't know what a bull was getting just for climbing down in after him. And when a bull did come down it went worse with the bum. Working methodically and with a devastating thoroughness, the police yanked men out of reefers like dish rags out of deep sinks. Then, with a car packed to the hood, with a deputy on each running board and a constable on the fender, they raced toward the city with sirens blasting the January sky. The only chance a 'bo had was to keep travelling back in the hope that by the time the last cars came under the lights the train would have gained such speed as to force the bulls to abandon it.

Cass heard the wheels begin a steadily-rising roar.

The homeless had a special fear of this place. It was here, near Uvalde City, that the hungriest jailhouse and the cruelest bulls in all southern Texas were located. There had been an epidemic in the place, and its fame had spread among transients far and wide as a place sedulously to be avoided.

Racing against the racing wheels, the bums ran toward the cab's green light. Fifty feet down one narrow board— a blind leap then into rocking space—and fifty feet to the unseen gap once more. Through fog Cass saw the green side-light eight cars ahead. Someone behind kept treading his heels, and one ahead was lame. Then the dark split, and the men in hoods were bearing down. Men on the cab car! *"Jump you club-foot son of a bitch, you're holding all us back."* The deputies appeared to the 'boes like an army with flashlights approaching through mist—bums veered and stumbled, Lame-Leg missed, and the others saw, and the wheels went up and the wheels went down; and four raced ahead where there had been five. When the bulls started firing, none of the transients paused; two got to a ladder and scrabbled away into mist. One flung himself over the side and then lay very still till they picked him up. Cass ran on—till steel clanged against steel inches to his left. Then he flung himself blindly down a reefer pit, grabbed cold iron as he dropped, and let go with both hands.

His fall was broken. Feet first he smashed down onto a softness. He thought of dead men, of snakes and of dung— "Who's in here?" he asked, looking down at the thing on the floor at his feet. There was no reply. He saw a girl or a woman, he couldn't tell which, with something or someone dim bending over. Then a match scratched, and a voice called out. He saw a Negro face two feet from his own, then the match died, and the calling ceased; there was no sound then above that of the wheels.

"Whyn't she git out o' mah way, 'stead o' layin' stretched out right in mah way?" Cass asked. He discerned the face on the floor. The woman was white.

"Now you sure done it. Skwar down on her belly you hit, wid her belly big uz a barrel." The Negro flapped his lips hurriedly, one on top of the other; his voice was that of a northern Negro. "White boy, you ort git slapped clean to Jesus."

To Cass it was all unreal as nightmare, for the thing had happened too quickly to be understood clearly. He had only run from men who were enemies; but apparently he had just killed two poor reefer-bums, a woman and the child she carried.

The Negro cupped a brief flare, in the basket of his hands, over the face of the stricken bum. When her eyes opened he asked, "How are yo'? Are yo' hurt bad, yo' think?" For reply her eyes shifted accusingly to Cass's sooty phiz bending above her. His face had eyes that seemed almost closed now, and a mouth like that of a small boy getting ready to cry. "I know who to blame for this all right," her eyes seemed to say to Cass.

"Ah'm right sorry, Miss," Cass said, feeling genuinely solicitous for the small white face on the floor. He saw that she was a girl in her twenties. Her face was pimpled, and coated with coal dust; on the left side of the throat ran a twisted pink scar tissue, like a scar left by scalding water. He saw her clutching at her pain till she tore her skirt at the crotch; he thought of the black girl left alone on the prairie. "Ah'm always doin' wrong," he thought. "Sometimes ah mean it an' sometimes ah don't." He felt a helpless bewilderment. Then he looked again at the girl, to where her fingers clutched her pain, and all his innards seemed suddenly to sag . . . blood was there slowly, at the deep seam there, darkening blue cloth. Her fingers fumbled where pain like burning girdle bound her now; the dark matting between her thighs was becoming dyed with a red wetness. The match flickered out.

The Negro spoke sharply.

"Take her head, I've got her feet. We've got to get her out of this hole perty damned pronto." The acrid odor of blood rose pungently in the rocking chamber.

When Cass lifted her head she began screaming again; and frightened as though a dead woman had screamed, he fell forward and almost dropped her. He braced his back against the steel screening, and shut his eyes for a moment to steady himself. The screening was wet with snow or rain; the car was rolling fast.

"Quick! We're pullin'!"

In the tiny chamber the Negro's voice rang and reechoed. Cass fancied that in the darkness then the womb of this girl was already opening, gaping red and terribly.

He had never seen a child born, he had always feared to be near such a sight. His fingers, weak like a drunkard's fingers, kept slipping and fumbling about her neck as though momently he might let her fall. He had no strength left. From hunger and idleness his hands had become hands of cotton. The Negro flung the woman over his shoulder much as one would a half-filled flour sack, and in the wink of an eye was clinging by one hand to the grating's top; he began butting the trap-door with the back of his head.

"Should ah come up theah an' open it fo' yo', mister?" Cass asked.

With one sharp and peremptory push of the head, the trap flew back wide to the sky. Slant rain flecked again into Cass's face, into his eyes and down his ears. The Negro and the woman were gone. Cass imagined them, over his head working cautiously back, the black man bent and swaying beneath his white burden. . . .

Minutes later shadows darkened the opening over Cass's head. The Negro was coming down once more, and the woman's arms were about him. From his shoulder her face descended reproachfully on Cass. Cass stood looking up with hair in his eyes, understanding that it was too late—too late because he had made it too late. When he reached the floor the Negro brushed Cass aside.

"Couldn't make it. Couldn't take a chance the way she's moving now. Have to wait till she slows, that's all."

Cass climbed the grating to close the heavy trap. He tugged manfully, but he was weak as noodle-water, and the swinging hood seemed to weigh more like a thousand pounds than the one hundred and fifty that it was. Then recalling with something of shame what the Negro had done without use of his arms, Cass strove heroically; with both fists he caught hold and strained frantically upward till it actually came half way—then his fingers seemed to melt, the hood balanced for one split second above him, he ducked—and it crashed. There came a small click from the outside then; and the reefer was black as pitch.

The Negro started climbing when that small click came. Cass watched from below with a desperate hope.

"You ort to get slapped clean back to wherever you come from," the Negro called down, and descended as quickly as he had gone up. Cass didn't have to be told what he'd done.

Slam a steel reefer all night from inside, nobody walking the spine will hear. Shout till you're hoarse and beat the sides with a shoe, nobody outside will hear a sound. Might as well just lie still, save your breath, hope for luck. Maybe they'll unload the car at the next division point; maybe a brakie will look down in. Maybe he saw you jump down and knows all the time that you're sealed there. Maybe someone else saw; maybe a yardman or maybe the shack; maybe some bull or maybe some switchman. Maybe a hostler will peer down and say, "Did we have you scared for a minute, boys?"

And maybe you'll stand for three weeks on a siding and get shipped three times across the state of Texas before someone looks down in. But by then it's a little late of course. More than one brakeman has opened a reefer long-sealed to find on its floor just two shoes, a rag, and one skeleton.

The wheels roared, rails sang and a long smoke poured. To Cass it seemed that the wheels were singing a song full of mockery. *"Ho! Ho! We were waiting long. Ho! Ho! We've caught three more. Lousers, lousers—caught three more!"* The wheels ground to a stop, waited like live things very still; and then, with monotonous mockery, rolled on.

It was cold in the reefer. Cold and dark. Cass measured the night by the times that the wheels stopped. Measured the hours by the song the wheels sang. The woman slept. This was Del Rio perhaps, perhaps Sanderson. In the musty air of the chamber the smell of the white woman and the smell of the black man mixed. The woman had an odor faintly like something sour; the Negro smelled salty-sweet. Cass felt his head wobbling with weariness, then the Negro said, "Matches." He was standing above Cass with his shirt unbuttoned; Cass stood up quickly to find him a match. As he fumbled he was surprised to notice that the Negro was only a boy no older than himself.

"Here—matches."

The Negro took off his shirt to make a pillow for the woman's head. Squatting, he tore the lining out of his shoe and made a torch of it in the second before the match failed. The woman looked up in terror, and then pain pulled her mouth into an oblong 'O'. Cass cringed at her howling. It was as though he were being struck for what he had done. He held the torch above her, and it trembled in his hand. The Negro wiped a jack-knife on an unclean rag . . .

The thing which Cass saw cut free that night in the S. P. reefer chamber looked like nothing so much as a length of pink sausage at first. Then it went black all over and looked like nothing at all. Holding it awkwardly, the rude torch burning in his hand, Cass felt that he held so much filth. He had a crazy desire to touch the small flame to the thing, to stomp it down into the cracks of the flooring, into the darkness there. He wrapped it in a wet newspaper instead, and he laid it down in the corner.

The Negro tried to staunch the woman with his cap. The floor became a cess-pen running with blood, stinking of urine and strewn with rags. When Cass touched the rain-wet screening he fancied he touched blood even there. Once, being either too dazed to turn her head or too weak to lift it, she vomited down her own breast. Pieces of stuff dribbled the corners of her mouth. Trying to retch a second time, her head merely bobbed weakly. Cass saw that her right eye kept crossing, being too weak to focus.

"She ain't hardly no older'n me or you," he said to the Negro. And now the woman became so quiet and still Cass thought for one moment that she were dead. Then her mouth gaped, slowly, and she began to breathe heavily. Cass sank into the corner opposite the thing wrapped in paper. The pit began to stink as though a dozen mangy curs had drenched the floor knee-deep.

Once in the night the mother woke, and the Negro asked Cass for the matches once more.

Cass said, "Here—Matches," thus giving the other a nickname along with the box.

In the corner the child, dead as decay, moved with the long car's swaying. Sometimes it seemed to raise itself, sometimes it rolled toward the wall. Once, when the car buckled violently, it worked whole inches toward him just as though it lived. Cass thought then that, it being so strangely dead, it knew whom to blame for its death. He felt that it would crawl like that soon again, that in hate it would bite him with small teeth like a rat's teeth. He lacked the courage to rewrap it in the paper. He just shut his eyes, and let it bounce, and listened to its mother's muttering. As he listened there came briefly, out of a meaningless babble, clear words.

"I dreamed the mines were burning. I saw them all aflame. Let me go now to the place I used to be."

After that she fell once more into babbling; after that she slept.

"She got on in Sabinal right before dark," the Negro said,

"I was in a empty up front when she come down the track. When I seen how she was I helped her up, an' she gimme a cig'rette. 'Goin' to Laredo,' she says 'ol' man's in the jailhouse down there again.' Then a shack come along an' told us we'd better duck an' stay ducked, that federal men was comin' on in Uvalde. An' they sure come on, didn't they? That's when we found this reefer. It was jest gettin' dark then." He talked on and on, until the words mixed in Cass's brain into a mumbling as meaningless as the mother's.

With a start Cass came awake, he did not know what had waked him so suddenly; he could not return to sleep. He remained tense and strained, in spite of himself, as though he were waiting for something; he didn't know what. His uneasiness increasing, he climbed the grating with the futile notion that the trap might not have locked after all.

Cass recalled the other time he'd been sealed in. That had been only three months before, but it seemed now like three years. And now he could feel nothing save his own utter weariness and his own great guilt. Thirst, shame, and hunger were less now than his guilt. Every time his eyes closed and his nerves relaxed for a second, his brain leaped up shouting, "Look out! Look out! You'll be getting a boot if you don't look out!"

And guilt hung like a dark stone about his neck, heavy, heavy like hunger, . . . and all utter weariness dragging him down, . . . down into . . . darkness and cold hunger, heavy, dark, down and heavy into. . . .

When the reefer was opened out from above all three slept. In the bluish light of a flash-ray a stubbled face looked mildly down. Mountain breeze with fog-laden night wind off of prairie, and a looking-down face all covered with stubbles.

"Jeezus K. Reist. What a vile stink. What y'all been doin' down there anyhow? *Say,* is thet a *womern* y'all got down there?"

Matches shook the girl gently, and Cass picked up the small thing in the corner. Then, Matches and the mother first, the unnatural parade went up the grating. When the brakie saw the stillborn child in Cass's arms, his mouth went eggshaped with amazement.

It was yet dark night. From the roof of the car Cass saw two Mexican hostlers knocking cinders and ashes from the fire-box of a dead engine. They were dressed to the ears to keep off the heat, and fire played weirdly upon their features. Cass wondered whether the fire-box which they were cleaning was the one that had pulled them from San Antonio. If it was they had been in the reefer but six hours. He followed Matches and the brakeman down the tracks to a little suburban freight station.

There in the silent depot west of Ysleta they stood looking down at the suffering woman. The scar tissue on her throat had turned to a pasty gray. "It's longer than mine, but mine went deeper," Cass mused, holding the dead infant in one hand and tracing his own scar with the other. The brakeman put a coat beneath the mother, lying along a hardwood bench; then he walked toward the door backwards, his face still thick with wonder.

Cass wished desperately to rid himself of the thing in his hand; when the woman half-opened one eye he held it out to her with a tentative gesture. But the eye closed and the Negro spoke angrily, "You ought to get bounced back to where you come from, that's what." He took the body from Cass and wrapped it at the feet of its mother. "I've got to get out o' here, now," he said. "Ain't nothin' else I can do, an' I'll sure get in deep trouble if I stay. That dumb shack'll bring the law back with him. So you'd best scram with me, clown." He stuffed the shirt which the girl had used for a pillow into his pocket. "Mebbe you figger on walkin' alone?"

The question was a challenge.

"Well, yo' comin'?" he persisted.

"Yeah, ah reck'n ah'll trot along with y'all fo' a space," Cass answered.

Outside it was raining again. On either side of the tracks

stretched the prairie, half-seen under fog. A cow-bell tinkled, near at hand and coming nearer. The Negro drew a battered pack of cigarettes out of his pocket and offered one to Cass.

"I took 'em off'n her in the depot," he explained. "All we done for her was worth it, don't you think? 'Speshully you." He smiled a little at his jibe, as only very tired men smile. Cass had to grin a little too; he'd sure been a clown all right.

"But mebbe she'll die," he thought, "Mebbe that feller in jail is waitin' on her. Mebbe he was plannin' to git out 'fore the kid was born. Mebbe. . . ." He made a wry face and spat. In the darkness the spittle caught a clump of scrub cedar and hung long and whitely in mist for a moment. Then it dropped. Beside him the Negro plodded along like a sick mule in a muddy furrow. Twice they paused to light cigarettes. After they had had three apiece Cass suggested timidly, "Mebbe we ought to save some fo' later on. Them's the fifteen-cent-a-pack kind ah think." The Negro walked on for several minutes before replying. Then, "Say, yo' know why they made Camels in the first place?" he asked.

Cass didn't know.

"To keep niggers an' Jews from smokin' Ol' Strikes, that's why."

They both laughed, without strength. It was a good joke— "Niggers an' Jews." You could turn the joke around if you wanted to, too, if you smoked a different kind. Only when, in his mind, Cass tried to turn it around, the thought blurred oddly and skipped away.

Matches stopped, stood on one leg like a heron, braced one hand on Cass's shoulder and slipped off his right shoe; the one from which he had torn the lining for a torch. He wore no socks, and Cass saw that the foot was encrusted with a brown and fish-like scale. He rubbed it with his knuckles till brownish chips brittled off onto the S. P. ties.

"It itches," he said. "It itches like the crabs."

Cass volunteered advice: "Y'all ought to wear a white sock on that, on *anythin'* like that."

When they reached El Paso they found the streets almost deserted. But morning was breaking over Juarez; and an empty truck came rolling by as though to herald an empty dawn. Neither knew where this city's breadline, if any, was to be found; they walked aimlessly.

They stopped in a doorway while Matches took off his shoe again to scrape his knuckles against his toes. Behind him, throwing a sickly greenish glow across a flight of uncarpeted stairs that led up to nowhere, an unshaded night-bulb still burned feebly. Once a woman passed the door, head down and hurrying in the rain.

"I'm tired as a old sick hound," Matches said as he scraped. "Aint you?" Cass said "Yeah. Yo' look tired kind o'. Reckon last night was a mite too much fo' yo'. Mahself, ah ain't been eatin' so reg'lar o' late." He looked up, and there was a woman there with them, standing as though she had already been there for several minutes. Just standing beside him, looking down at the same sick black foot at which he was looking, her face framed in a shawl and with one bright raindrop trickling down her cheek toward her open throat. A white woman, tall, smiling a strange half-smile. Under her arm were newspapers wet as her cheeks; the green flow from the night-light bathed her head as she stood. As though his foot then were something obscene Matches thrust it hurriedly down the throat of the shoe. Cass's eyes followed the slow raindrop down the cheek. In the long moment before it came to her throat he became conscious of his own increasing excitement. Though he did not see that throat until that drop came to it, yet his heart pounded before he saw, in anticipated horror. And both himself and Matches saw the same thing at the same moment: *Pink scar tissue down the side of the neck like a scar left by scalding water*—and terror hit both with one blow, they ran wildly out of the hall-way and down the street.

At the corner Matches caught up to Cass. They stood to-gether peering back through the rain, but there was nothing behind them save the grief-stricken houses on the long Southern street; and one dark doorway looking blindly out upon a mist-wet world.

"Holy Creepin' Jesus, man, didn't she *look* like her though?" Matches gasped. He was breathing heavily and favoring one foot as he stood. "But I only got scared 'cause you did, that's why. I didn't even think about that other till you turned rabbit on me like that. Holy God-'n-Jesus man, I thought I'd never catch you with this leg of mine. You shouldn't ought to scare a fellow that way. Why, she were only some little scurve who lived in that place, that was all; even if she were scarred up a little."

"Ah guess mebbe ah had that other on mah mind a little still," Cass confessed. "She sho' gimme a turrible fright for a minute."

His heart was still racing; they lit the last of the cigarettes together. The morning fog was lifting, and the sun came through.

"If I jest had a sock," Matches complained, "a sock like you said. I think that'd keep it from rubbin' some, don't you? But I always get the dirty end of the stick. I shouldn't of tore out that linin'."

Cass perceived that weariness had stripped his friend of the self-reliant air which he had seen in him the night before. Matches seemed, of a sudden, devoid of all will. When Cass asked him how old he was he replied, "Nineteen, I guess."

Cass said, "That's how old I am too I guess."

They were walking down a street lined with old elms, and at the end of the street they came to a park. It had a picket fence going around and around, and swings for small girls and slides for small boys and teeter-totters for bigger children. Cass could not remember ever having seen anything quite like this park before. They found a gate and entered there.

It was noon and growing warm. The boys found a stretch of dry ground beneath a tree, and Cass lay down. The small grass bent itself between his fingers, long shadows trembled in the light.

"Ah'd better shake this shine," Cass cautioned himself.

Surreptitiously, Matches tried bathing his foot by wriggling his toes like fingers beneath the still dripping boughs of some near-by winter shrubbery. He did this a long time, then declared his foot healed and lay down beside Cass.

"But a sock. If oney I had a sock now," his eyes closed as he muttered, and in a moment he was sleeping soundly, one arm in a ragged sleeve outflung and the other shielding his eyes; as though even in sleep he feared to be struck.

"Ah ought to git me a coat fo' the night that's comin'." Cass thought, watching sun-shadow between half-closed lids. Sun-shadow made him think of wet lengths of yellow ribbon stretched flat aslant the grass to dry. Some lengths were narrow and some were quite wide, some intertwined and became one, then wriggled into many, all yellow-wet and delicate across green shadow-grass.

Matches wriggled his toes in sleep. Cass's own feet had gone sockless for months, he too was very tired; but just as he felt himself dozing off he became aware of someone coming toward them. A silver badge above pointed boots swung up a winding cindered path twirling a club on a cord like a swagger-stick. Cass saw the boots coming, shoved Matches once and fled; from behind high shrubbery then, he watched: Boots nudged Matches till he rolled over groaning like a sick man. Sweat on his forehead gleamed in the sun, his open mouth drooled saliva in his sleep—he woke with a jerk, with his eyes bugging out. There was, for one moment, no flicker of recognition in them.

"This is white folks' park, nigger. Get goin' 'fore I fan yore fanny."

Boots twirled his club-on-a-cord significantly, boy-fashion, threatening.

Cass waited on the street for Matches. He'd like to josh the nigger a little now. But when Matches rejoined him they walked on in silence, and Cass said nothing at all.

On a street lined with radios competitively blasting the air into splinters, they sat down on a Keep-Our-City-Clean box.

Both were hungry enough to chew their own tongues, but they were both too weary to think consistently even about food. Cass rested his feet on the curbstone and watched the gutter-flow swirl past. Much was being borne on that tide; a frayed cigar-butt came past first, then a red beer-cork; and then, its pages flung wide in a disgraceful death, a copy of *Hollywood Gossip* came by. It lay flat on its back, a whore-like thing. Cass sniped the cigar and the magazine, crushed tobacco onto a dry page, and rolled a rude cigarette. Smoking, he glanced at the dry pages of the magazine. One page bore a picture of Douglas Flatass, Jr. in a stove-pipe hat, hugging two girls in one-piece bathing suits. Out of this fellow Cass fashioned four long cigarettes, but the figures of the girls in the bathing suits he preserved, studying them as he smoked. A small frown came between his eyes; he squinted narrowly. Six weeks without a haircut, three weeks without a shave—he had not had a square meal for weeks and he had not slept lying down for five full days. He tossed his head back jerkily, flouncing hair out of his eyes, and he ripped one of the paper girls up the middle. He had an odd feeling when he did that; and after he had rolled another cigarette he looked through the book for more girls' pictures. But there was no other dry page, and he began to feel more tired than ever. He offered Matches a cigarette, but the boy did not take it. He merely sat holding his kinky head in his hands, and would not even shake his head to say that he didn't wish to smoke now.

Cass recalled vaguely as he sat that a day or a week before he had eaten meat in some place where there had been fog on the streets. Or he had not eaten meat. He couldn't remember; and he couldn't remember the name of that place, though his mind sought it sleepily and long. Somehow, much seemed to depend upon the remembering: Chicago, Springfield, St. Louis. Memory was a jumble of steel rails, city sounds, sunlight on boxcars and fog on a half-forgotten street. So he dropped the magazine in the gutterflow, wiped his nose on the back of his hand, and poked Matches.

Apparently the encounter in the park had taken the last bit out of the Negro, for he walked beside Cass now as though he were half-helpless. When Cass turned, he turned; when Cass paused for traffic, he paused; when Cass hurried forward, Matches hurried forward beside him. Only once as they went did the Negro speak coherently.

"Bummin' takes everythin' out of a feller, don't it?" he asked as they turned a corner into Mesa Avenue.

Cass agreed readily that it did. "Yeah, sho' do. Bummin's knocked all the tallow clean out o' mah pole." To himself he thought, "Ah better shake this shine."

When they reached the next Keep-Our-City-Clean box Matches wanted to remove his shoe again; but his fingers slipped around his ankle like a little child's fingers. So Cass took it off for him, kneeling as the other sat. He pulled a wad of newspaper out of the box and padded it into the shoe's torn places. Beside him a bare-footed Mexican boy, holding a small brown girl by the hand, stood and watched with a cynic's air. A woman with furred shoulders went by on high heels, her head in the air and her nose sniffing elegantly, as though about to spew green phlegm sunward. As he struggled to get the shoe back on Matches' foot someone behind him spat toward the gutter over his shoulder; he saw the gob, like a speckled bug, being borne away on the current. People were gathering behind him; it was time to be getting on.

They had not gone half a block farther when Matches stopped and complained, half-accusingly, to Cass. "It hurts. You just made it worse you did. Now it hurts worst. You ought to get slapped clean to Jesus." They could not stop, there was no place here to stop, and Matches continued to complain with a rising irascibility.

"If oney I had a sock. A *white* sock, mind you. Have *you* got that kind?"

That was the last thing he said to show that he knew that Cass was still with him; after that he seemed slowly to lose awareness, he became like a man mildly drunk or doped. Cass had not known what havoc the simple fact of overtiredness could work. Only a few short hours before he had almost feared this boy; now there plodded beside him only a sick pickaninny who depended on him, Cass, to lead him about and to put on his shoes. Cass felt something of a mild responsibility.

Matches stopped dead still and planted himself directly in front of a bespectacled youth with books in both hands. The boy looked frightened at Matches' glance; and when Cass looked at Matches he too became a little afraid; Matches' eyes were fever-bright and burning hollowly. Cass took his arm, but he wouldn't budge an inch.

"*You*. Gimme that sock." He took Specs by the lapel, and the boy dropped a book. When he straightened up, after retrieving it, his voice quavered shrilly as a frightened school girl's.

"Saaaay—I'll call a cop on you, nigger." And he raised his voice in a long wailing plea, "Ohhhhh, officer!"

This time *two* silver badges, two rows of brass buttons, two pair of pointed boots shining in the sun.

"Here, niggers—at it again? All right, Smitty, take 'em both along."

Cass cocked his head, half-unable to believe what he had just heard. Slowly then he understood: a white man who walked with a 'nigger' was a 'nigger' too. He recognized the park bull as the other bull took his arm, and he said, "Ah'm not no nigger," but the bull made no reply.

Cass wasn't afraid, somehow. He was a little too tired to be afraid. Going to jail was all a part of this life; no one escaped it for very long and he'd been pretty lucky for a long time now. What he didn't like, what got him by the short hairs, was that crack about being a nigger. He saw the big park bull start reaching for Matches when Matches was still five feet away, and Specs stood in between. The boy ducked wildly when the cop's paw came over his shoulder—to seize Matches' shirt and pull him free of the sidewalk with a yank which ripped the sleazy cloth down to the navel. Matches came so straight forward that his head would have rammed the cop's Sam Browne belt, had not the cop stiff-armed him with his open palm.

Cass glanced at the bull who was holding his wrist.

"Ah'm not no nigger," he repeated; but the cop didn't seem to hear.

With the eyes of the gathering crowd upon himself and Matches, Cass thought of his scar, and turned his head away; as he turned, Matches screamed, like the black girl had screamed.

"You got no right! You got no right!"

It was shameful to see the Negro so, his shirt in tatters so that his navel showed through, screaming nonsense at a cop as though he had lost his mind. A man in the crowd laughed, harshly, and a girl fled titillating, "Oooooooo—what I *saw*." The big bull started shaking Matches, to stifle that foolish screaming in the street. Matches' arms flailed stiffly against the brass buttons. A ragged end of his sleeve caught the cop's star and left it hanging lopsidedly.

"You got no right! You let me go!"

Someone behind Cass said, "Quit shakin' him, off'cer, he's only a kid."

"You got no right!"—the fingers clawed weakly upward, the club-on-a-cord whizzed in a gleaming circle a foot above his head, the fingers reached up for it, and the club came down. It came down slantwise across the temple, with the hissing sound of a large stone thrown through a thin paper wall—a brief sound, sharp and ripping and cold; Matches stood very still for one long moment. He had stopped screaming rather suddenly. A dark star appeared on his temple, and his head began sagging a little, like a wounded fighting-cock's head. Hands caught him under the arm-pits as he fell; white hands held him tentatively, offering him out to the bull like a limp dishrag.

Cass whimpered.

"My, wasn't that *brave*," a woman mocked from the crowd.

As the bull half-carried and half-dragged Matches toward the patrol, a boy's voice called him.

"Oh, Officer."

This time the cop's eyes were shifting uneasily. Without fixing his gaze on any one face he asked, "Well, who wants to see me?"

No reply—till he turned. The woman's voice came again:

"No one, officer my dear. Who would? You smell most awful vile."

"Who said 'at to me?" he bluffed loudly. "Who said 'at, huh?" His face looked ready to burst with its bluff. Then he saw laughter starting and got inside the patrol with Matches to escape it. The other officer followed with Cass in front of a chorus of catcalls and jeerwails. Cass heard only one thing clearly: Just as the door slammed someone shouted in, "Niggerlickers—that's all cops is. That's all they do—that's all they *can* do. Big tough niggerlickers, and that's all they *do* do."

Matches' eyes opened, but he did not speak. On either side of him sat a bull. Cass, sitting opposite, watched the Negro revive and wondered whether he understood all that had happened. Although his own hands were free, Matches' were thumbcuffed; Cass was torn between regret for having walked with the Negro, and with pity for seeing him beaten.

The big bull guarding the door looked over to Cass and spoke warningly. He was still out of breath, and a bit bewildered, it seemed.

"This'll go mighty hard with you two boys. Mighty hard, I can say that now. Almost a riot call it was, an' a riot call al'ays goes harder"—he gasped for breath. "Lots o' trouble you boys made—trouble in the park first. . . ."

His rump-like face was streaked with sweat. As though to reassure himself of the penalty they were certain to have incurred, he spoke to the other bull.

"A riot call al'ays makes it twicet as bad, don't it Arthur, huh?"

Arthur nodded. He was thin, and freckled, and looked unhappy.

"See what Arthur says? Ya almost instergated a riot, that's jest what I'm sayin'—an' ya'll get ninety days each fer it sure, or elts"—he gasped again for breath—"or elts I'm not yer witness!"

In spite of exhaustion, Cass went sick with fear then. He hadn't reckoned on ninety days.

"He jest wanted a sock on account his foot is so bad," he said. "Honest, mister, that foot look ready to drop off'n his laig."

The silver badge looked at Cass with a huge and expressionless, a moon-like wonder. The big thick brain behind the eyes began to move slowly, like a heavy door opening onto a room long closed. Then his face looked cunning-cruel, as understanding at last came into it. And he guffawed. Thwacking his thigh resoundingly he yawped his face so near to Cass's that Cass smelled the foulness of his breath like the breath from a privy.

"He jest wanted a sock! He jest wanted a sock! Hey, Arthur, do ya get it, Art? He jest wanted a *sock*, an' ain't that what I given him?" He went off into whole gales of laughter, his body shaking to its very fingertips. "Say, Art—d'ye get it?—He jest wanted a sock!" Arthur smiled a bit wanly, a bit indulgently, and said nothing at all.

"Ho! Ho! Ho! He wanted a sock, a *clean* sock—an' aint that jest what I given him? Ho! Ho! Ho!"

Outside the late afternoon sun was waking trembling checkered patterns on low stone buildings rushing past.

They were going to jail; they were going to eat. They were going to have a place to lie down.

Cass said, "Ah'm not no nigger," and looked over to Matches accusingly.

Matches only smiled. Then, "You're ridin' jest the same, ain't you?" he asked.

But the little bull named Arthur only sighed.

21. Dempsey, Dempsey

HORACE GREGORY

"No matter what others may think of my work I should like to have said of me what was said of Baudelaire, a far greater poet than I: 'He belonged to no school. He copied no one, but he used everyone that suited him, making what he had taken his own and something new.'" Nothing could be more characteristic of Horace Gregory (1898–   ) than these words, with their combination of modesty and hard-won self-confidence. In truth, he has always been his own man. When the Crash came, the Milwaukee-born poet brought out his first volume of poetry, Chelsea Rooming-House (1930), and the titles of his subsequent volumes of the thirties, No Retreat (1933) and Chorus for Survival (1935), were in themselves testimony to his allegiances during the period. But while Gregory was heart and soul with the underdog and the victimized ("Dempsey, Dempsey" is a classic of its kind), and often in accord with his Communist fellow contributors to the New Masses, he belonged to no school and was no man's kept poet. In the decades since the thirties, Gregory's poetic reputation has grown, slowly but surely. Now retired from many years of teaching at Sarah Lawrence College, he is extremely active not only as poet, but also as critic, translator, and literary journalist. In 1965, he was honored with the Bollingen award, the most prestigious prize that can be received by an American poet.

From *Collected Poems* (New York: Holt, Rinehart and Winston, 1964), pp. 5–6. "Dempsey, Dempsey" copyright © 1941 by Horace Gregory. Reprinted by permission of Holt, Rinehart and Winston, Inc.

Everybody give the big boy a hand,
a big hand for the big boy, Dempsey,
failure king of the U.S.A.

Maybe the big boy's coming back,
there's a million boys that want to come back
with hell in their eyes and a terrible sock
that almost connects.
They've got to come back, out of the street,
out of some lowdown, lousy job
or take a count with Dempsey.

When he's on his knees for a count
and a million dollars cold,
a million boys go down with him
yelling:
        Hit him again Dempsey,
kill him for me Dempsey,
Christ' sake Dempsey,
my God they're killing Dempsey,
it's Dempsey down, Dempsey, Dempsey.

The million men and a million boys,
come out of hell and crawling back,
maybe they don't know what they're saying,
maybe they don't dare
but they know what they mean:
Knock down the big boss,
o, my little Dempsey,
my beautiful Dempsey
with that God in heaven smile
and quick, god's body leaping,
not afraid, leaping, rising—
hit him again, he cut my pay check, Dempsey.
My God, Dempsey's down—

he cut my pay check—
Dempsey's down, down,
the bastards are killing Dempsey.
Listen, they made me go to war
and somebody did something wrong to my wife
while I was gone.
Hit him again Dempsey, don't be a quitter
like I am Dempsey,
o, for Jesus Christ, I'm out.
I can't get up, I'm dead, my legs
are dead, see, I'm no good,
they got me and I'm out,
down for the count.
I've quit, quit again,
only God save Dempsey, make him get up again,
Dempsey, Dempsey.

22. Waiting for Nothing

TOM KROMER

Of the millions seared by the flames of the depression, an occasional victim managed to free himself from the fire, if only to cry out once to the rest of the world before lapsing back into silence. Such a one was Tom Kromer (1906–　), the son of factory workers, whose father died when he was twenty and left him with three sisters and a brother to look out for, but

From *Waiting for Nothing* (New York: Alfred A. Knopf, 1935), Chap. XI, pp. 163–177. Copyright 1935 by Alfred A. Knopf, Inc. Reprinted by permission of the publisher.

also with a mother who insisted on education for her children "so they wouldn't have to worry about the factory closing down." He managed, with odd jobs, to get through three years at Marshall University in Huntington, West Virginia, by 1929. After the Crash, he headed for the Kansas wheatfields, then back East; no luck at either end, so he rode the rods to California and found nothing there either. But he was writing, on scraps of paper, as he bummed across the country, about the agonies of the stiff, and he was discovered by Lincoln Steffens. Waiting for Nothing was published in 1935 and acclaimed by Fred T. Marsh in the New York Herald Tribune Books as "one of the most extraordinary documents I have run across." Kromer headed in to the University of New Mexico, but his health had already been damaged, and he had to exchange the university for a tuberculosis sanitorium. He married, and with his wife published a little magazine in Albuquerque for a number of years, but continued to be plagued by illness. It is doubtful that he will be heard from again, but he deserves to be considered by a new generation, who should read in its entirety this Gorkyesque cry from the lower depths, the remarkably honest, unvarnished, unliterary, unpolitical utterance of a man who barely survived to tell us of certain American horrors.

It is night, and we are in this jungle. This is our home tonight. Our home is a garbage heap. Around us are piles of tin cans and broken bottles. Between the piles are fires. A man and a woman huddle by the fire to our right. A baby gasps in the woman's arms. It has the croup. It coughs until it is black in the face. The woman is scared. She pounds it on the back. It catches its breath for a little while, but that is all. You cannot cure a baby of the croup by pounding it on the back with your hand.

The man walks back and forth between the piles of garbage. His shoulders are hunched. He clasps his hands behind him.

Up and down he walks. Up and down. He has a look on his
face. I know that look. I have had that look on my own face.
You can tell what a stiff is thinking when you see that look on
his face. He is thinking he wishes to Jesus Christ he could get
his hands on a gat. But he will not get his hands on a gat. A gat
costs money. He has no money. He is a lousy stiff. He will
never have any money.

Where are they going? I do not know. They do not know.
He hunts for work, and he is a damn fool. There is no work.
He cannot leave his wife and kids to starve to death alone, so
he brings them with him. Now he can watch them starve to
death. What can he do? Nothing but what he is doing. If he
hides out on a dark street and gives it to some bastard on the
head, they will put him in and throw the keys away if they
catch him. He knows that. So he stays away from dark streets
and cooks up jungle slop for his wife and kid between the
piles of garbage.

I look around this jungle filled with fires. They are a pitiful
sight, these stiffs with their ragged clothes and their sunken
cheeks. They crouch around their fires. They are cooking up.
They take their baloney butts out of their packs and put them
in their skillets to cook. They huddle around their fires in the
night. Tomorrow they will huddle around their fires, and the
next night, and the next. It will not be here. The bulls will not
let a stiff stay in one place long. But it will be the same. A
garbage heap looks the same no matter where it is.

We are five men at this fire I am at. We take turns stumbling
into the dark in search of wood. Wood is scarce. The stiffs keep
a jungle cleaned of wood. I am groping my way through the
dark in search of wood when I stumble into this barbed wire
fence. My hands are scratched and torn from the barbs, but I
do not mind. I do not mind because I can see that we are fixed
for wood for the night. We will not have to leave our warm
fire again to go chasing through the night after wood. A good
barbed wire fence has poles to hold it up. A couple of good

stout poles will burn a long time. What do I care if this is someone's fence? To hell with everybody! We are five men. We are cold. We must have a fire. It takes wood to make a fire. I take this piece of iron pipe and pry the staples loose.

This is good wood. It makes a good blaze. We do not have to huddle so close now. It is warm, too, except when the wind whistles hard against our backs. Then we shiver and turn our backs to the fire and watch these rats that scamper back and forth in the shadows. These are no ordinary rats. They are big rats. But I am too smart for these rats. I have me a big piece of canvas. This is not to keep me warm. It is to keep these rats from biting a chunk out of my nose when I sleep. But it does not keep out the sound and the feel of them as they sprawl all over you. A good-sized rat tramps hard. You can feel their weight as they press on top of you. You can hear them sniffing as they try to get in. But when I pull my canvas up around my head, they cannot get into me.

"Sniff and crawl all you damn please," I say. "You can't get into me."

When I look at these stiffs by the fire, I am looking at a graveyard. There is hardly room to move between the tombstones. There are no epitaphs carved in marble here. The tombstones are men. The epitaphs are chiseled in sunken shadows on their cheeks. These are dead men. They are ghosts that walk the streets by day. They are ghosts sleeping with yesterday's newspapers thrown around them for covers at night. I can see that these are ghosts that groan and toss through the night. I watch. From time to time a white splotch gets up off the ground. He cannot rest for the rats and the cold. This is a restless ghost. Or maybe it is the gnawing pain in his belly that makes him restless and sleepless. The ground is hard. Damp and hard. There are many things will make a restless ghost at night in a jungle. I am a restless ghost myself.

I look from face to face about our fire. We are not strangers. The fire has brought us together. We do not ask questions about each other. There is nothing to ask. We are here. We are here because we have no other place to go. From hollow, dark-rimmed eyes they watch the fire. Their shoulders sag and stoop. Men come to look like this when night after night they hunt for twigs through the dark to throw on a jungle fire. This hunchbacked guy across from me squats on his legs and talks. His voice is flat and singsong.

"I hit this state in 1915 with a hundred bucks I made in the harvest in Kansas. I pulled off this drag and made for a saloon in town. It was cold riding those rails, and I needed a drink to warm me up. Before I knew it, I was drunk and nasty. This spick lunged up against me at the bar, and I pushed him away. I never liked a greaser, anyway. Before I knew it, we were going after each other with our knives. I jabbed him one in the ribs. He dropped his knife to the floor and yelled. He wasn't hurt bad. Just a jab, but it scared him. Someone grabbed me and pinned my arms from behind. I thought they were ganging me. I was big and strong then. My back was hunched, but strong. I pulled away and let this guy have it. I got him right through the heart. He sagged to the floor. His hands rubbed against my face as he fell. Not hard. Just light. Light and soft like a woman's or a ghost's. I dream about those hands rubbing against my face light and soft when I sleep. I didn't know this guy was a deputy until they locked me up in the jug.

"Well, I got twenty years. That is a long time. It is a lifetime. I wrote my mother I was going down on a construction job in Mexico. That's the last time they ever heard from me. I wanted them to think that I had died down there. Fifteen years in the big house is the stretch I did. It ruined me. It would have ruined anybody. I was like I am now when I got out. My blood is all turned to water. I can't stand the cold any more. My blood is all turned to water.

"I bummed around on the rattlers after I got out. A bindle stiff was all I was. That's all there was to do. I was an old man. Then I got this crazy notion to go home and see how things looked. I hopped myself a drag and headed east. Well, it was the same old town. You know the type. Hardly a new building put up in years. I didn't hang around town much. The first thing I did was to go out to the cemetery. I was hunting a grave. My mother's grave. I didn't hunt long until I found what I was looking for. I knew it would be there. Fifteen years is a long time. I had a sister in that town, and a brother, but I had seen all I came to see. I turned around and walked back to the tracks. There was a west-bound due out of there at night. I nailed it."

He finishes. We do not say anything. We just sit here and stare into the fire. There are a lot of things will put a guy on the fritz. One minute you are sitting on top of the world, and the next you are sitting around a jungle fire telling about it. The rest of these guys could tell their stories too, if they wanted to. They have stories to tell. But they do not say anything. Some stiffs do not tell their stories. They walk up and down the garbage heaps at night with the look on their face.

We hear the sound of voices over at the other side of the tracks. They are coming our way. We raise our heads. More frozen stiffs hunting a warm fire, we think. But there is no such luck for us. Four men are hot-footing it over the tracks. They swing blackjacks in their hands. From their hips swing gats in holsters. It is the bulls. By God, a man can't even crawl into a filthy garbage heap for the bulls.

"Line up, you lousy bums," the leader says.

He swings his blackjack high. He is aching for a chance to bring it down on some stiff's head.

We line up. There are twenty of us. We are twenty, and they are four, but what can we do? We kill one of these bastards, and we stretch. They kill one of us, and they get a raise in pay. A stiff hasn't got a chance. They know a stiff hasn't got a chance.

"Hold up your hands," this leader snaps.

We hold up our hands, and they go through our pockets. They do not find anything. It makes them sore.

"I have a good notion to knock every one of you sons of bitches in the head and leave you for the rats," this guy says. "You are nothin' but a bunch of sewer rats, anyway."

He glances around the jungle. He sees our suppers that cook on the fires. He walks from one fire to the other and kicks everything over on the ground. I want to pull this bastard's guts out with my bare hands. We are twenty hungry stiffs in a jungle. We had to work hard to get that grub. A stiff always has to work hard to rustle up his grub. It is almost ready to eat, and he kicks it over on the ground.

"Get out on the highway before we sap you up," this guy says.

"You are a bastard," says this guy with the wife and kid, "a no-good bastard."

This bull walks up to this stiff and brings his blackjack down on the top of his head. It makes a thudding sound when it lands. He topples to the ground. The blood spurts from the cut in his head. He gets to his feet and staggers around the fire. This woman with the kid starts to cry. We close in towards these bulls. We fumble on the ground for sticks and rocks.

"Let's hang the sons of bitches," says this old stiff, "let's skin the bastards alive."

These bulls see that we mean business. They go for their gats in their holsters. They cover us.

"I will bore the first bastard that lays a hand on me," this leader says.

We stop crowding in. What can we do when they have us covered with these gats? There is nothing we can do.

"Hit it down the pike as fast as you can go, and don't come back," says this bull.

We head down the road. It is the cold night for us with our blistered feet and our empty bellies.

Five miles down this road there is a water tank. Sometimes

the drags stop there for water. If we are lucky, we can nail a drag out of there tonight. We walk. We have covered a mile when the man and the woman with the kid drop out. It is a rough walk over the ties in the night, and they are tired and hungry. They flop down on the side of the road to sleep. We go on. We can hear the baby strangling for breath behind us. We can hear the woman slap it on the back.

We stumble over the ties. It is too dark to see them. We get over to the side of the tracks and walk. The burrs come up through the soles of my shoes, but I go on. I cannot stop. If I stop, I will not be able to get started again. My feet will swell. I trudge on, and when I take a step it drives the sharp points of the burrs far into my feet. I straighten my pack over my back and limp. I look at the stars in the sky above, and I see no comfort there. I think of that poor bastard lying back there in the weeds with his wife and kid.

"Oh, God," I say, "if there is a God, why should these things be?"

We hobble for hours with our heavy packs before we reach the tank. We flop to the ground beneath it. We pull off our soleless shoes and rest our blistered feet. We lie here like men that are dead, and look at the sky overhead. We talk back and forth through the night. We talk and we do not care whether anyone is listening or not. We do not care. We have to talk. That is the only way we can get our thoughts out of our minds. This hunchback tells his troubles to the stiff in the ragged red sweater. This guy in the red sweater does not care about the troubles of this hunchback, but he sees in his troubles some of his own. So he listens. This hunchback is not talking for himself. He talks for all of us. Our troubles are the same.

"For three years," says this old stiff, "I have laid in the cold and the dark like this. Is this goin' to last forever? Ain't things never goin' to be different? How long is a guy supposed to put up with this?"

"You'll croak in a jungle, and I'll croak in a jungle," this hunchback says. "Times'll never get any better. They will get worse. I got a paper in my pocket." He taps the newspaper in his pocket. "There is an editorial in this paper. It says this depression is good for people's health. It says people eat too much, anyway. It says this depression is gettin' people back to God. Says it will teach them the true values of life."

"The bastards," says this stiff gnawing on the green baloney butt, "the lousy bastards. I can just see the guy that wrote that editorial. I can see his wife and kids, too. They set at their tables. A flunky in a uniform stands back of their chairs to hand them what they want at the table. They ride around all day in their Rolls-Royces. Will you ever see that guy in a soup-line? You will not. But the bastard will write this tripe for people to read. True values of life, by God! If this guy wants to get back to God so much, why don't he swap his Rolls-Royce for a rusty tin bucket and get in line? The bastard."

"He says you can live on nothin' but wheat," this hunchback says. "He says this depression is nothin' to get excited about. People will not starve. There is plenty of wheat. If a guy says he is hungry, give him a bushel of wheat."

"Where is the wheat?" this old stiff says. "When I come through Kansas, they was burnin' the goddam stuff in the stoves because it was cheaper than coal. Out here they stand in line for hours for a stale loaf of broad. Where is the wheat, is what I want to know."

"Try and get it," this stiff says, "just try and get it. They will throw you in so fast your head will swim."

Far away we hear this drag whistle in the night. It is a lonesome and dreary moan. We put on our shoes and go out to the tracks and wait. We lie down on the tracks and place our ears to the rails. We can hear the purr that rumbles through them. We look at each other and shake our heads. Too fast. If she does not stop for water at this tank, she is too hot to catch on the fly. A stiff just can't nail this one on the fly. We are old-timers. We know by the sing in the rails when a drag is too hot. We go back to our bindles and sit down. If she does not stop, there will be another drag tomorrow. What is a day to us, or a month or a year? We are not going any place.

We see her belch round the bend. She is not going to stop here, that is sure.

"She is coming round the bend," this kid yells. "Ain't you stiffs goin' to nail her?"

We shake our heads. Too fast. We know. We can tell by the puff, and the sparks that fly from her stacks.

He hits it over to the tracks and waits. Is this damn punk going to try to nail this one? If he does, he is crazy. But what the hell? All punks are crazy. They make it harder for us old ones. This drag whistles. She is batting plenty. The engine and a dozen cars pass us before we know it. She can't waste any time slowing up for a bunch of stiffs. This kid stands there by the tracks and watches her whiz by. He is making up his mind whether to nail it or not. He is a damn fool to even think about nailing this one. I have seen too many guys with stumps for legs to even think about nailing this one. I can still walk. That is something.

I sit here on my bindle and watch him. He is only a shadow by the tracks. The cars whiz by. He runs along beside her. He makes a dive for this step, the rear step. What is this damn fool diving for the rear step for? Don't he know enough to nail the front end of a car? She swings him high, and in between the cars. He loses his grip. He smashes against the couplings. He screams. He is under. Oh, Jesus Christ, he is under! He is under those wheels. We run over. He lies there beside the tracks. He is cut to ribbons. Where his right arm and leg were, there are only two red gashes. The blood spurts out of the stumps. It oozes to the ground and makes a pool in the cinders.

We drag him over to the side. He is through. I can see that he is through. His eyes are half shut. They are dopey-looking. There is a grin on his face. It is a foolish, sheepish grin. No

stiff likes to have a drag throw him. It hurts a stiff's pride to
have a drag throw him. It hurts this kid's pride, too, so he has
a sheepish grin on his face, and him with his two stumps oozing
blood to the cinders.

I lean over him.

"Want a cigarette, buddy?" I say.

"Hello, there," he says. "Sure, I want a cigarette."

I put it between his teeth and light it.

"My arm feels funny," he says. "Kind of numb and tingly.
That old drag was balling the jack. I must have bumped it
pretty hard."

"You got a rough bump," I say, "but you will be all right in
a minute. She was a hot one, all right."

"She was plenty hot, all right," he says. "I thought I was a
goner when I slipped."

He does not know he is hurt. He cannot see his two stumps
that are oozing blood on the cinders. I lean over so he cannot
see. What is the use to let him know? He will be gone in a
minute. There is nothing we can do. His troubles will soon
be over.

I watch him. I am sick all over. I am watching a kid die.
It is hard enough to watch anybody die. I even hate to watch
an old stiff die, even when I know he is better off dead. But a
kid is different. You kind of expect a kid to live instead of die.

There is no color in his face now. All the color is on the
ground mixed with the cinders. He closes his eyes. The cigarette drops out of his mouth. He quivers. Just a quiver like
he is cold. That is all. He is gone. I unfold a newspaper and
cover up his face.

We sit there in the dark and look at each other. ✦

PART SIX

Concern and Hope:

VETS, NEGROES, CIO, TVA, CCC

---

23. Veterans on the March

JACK DOUGLAS

Nothing is known about Jack Douglas—the name was probably a pseudonym—other than the obvious fact that he was an able Communist journalist who executed with verve a book-length history and Marxist interpretation of the historic Bonus March on Washington in the Summer of 1932. Both Communists and fascists vied for the favor of the ex-serviceman, but his march fizzled out into a footnote to history, and the New Deal bought him off (several years later when at least 446 vets on a make-work project around Key West were trapped and drowned in a hurricane, Ernest Hemingway wrote an enraged piece for the New Masses entitled "Who Murdered The Vets?"). In his fore-word to the Douglas book John Dos Passos wrote: "The March was a spontaneous movement of protest, arising in virtually

---

From *Veterans on the March* (New York: Workers Library Publishers, 1934), Chap. X, pp. 65–69. Copyright 1934 by Workers Library Publishers. Reprinted with the permission of New Century Publishers, Inc.

every one of the forty-eight states. Times were hard. The vets were broke, they couldn't get work. Congress had voted them a Bonus and the politicians had buttered them up for years for their votes; they felt that they were entitled to their Bonus now that they needed it so badly and that, as all the businessmen's lobbies were getting handouts of the taxpayers' money, it was up to them to go to Washington and make their demands in person. Any good American had a right to a square deal, hadn't he? In the March they showed an astonishing aptitude for democratic organization. They beat their way across the continent almost without delay or disorder and settled themselves on Anacostia flats. But having done that they were completely unable to cope with the problems offered by their situation; most of them were so anxious to be considered regular hundred percenters that they fell a prey to all sorts of schemers and orators, and the B.E.F. allowed itself to be dissolved without accomplishing its aims or formulating any real fundamental social demands."

Joe Angelo's Story

Scattered through widely separated parts of Washington, the population of a new village had already accumulated in the city. Clothed in remnants of clothing, dirty, weary, unhappy but determined, they were coming in—men, women and children.

These ex-servicemen and their families were part of the army of ex-employed made by the depression which began in 1929. Except that these, with their army service in common and having money due them from the government, had Washington as their goal. Among them were many who, without this last hope that lay in the money due them from the government, might not have had the courage to leave their home places. Many a family was kept together by this last hope; instead of breaking up, some going to institutions and some to become homeless wanderers, they stuck together for the trip to Washington, feeling that if they could once get to the government, they would at least be given what was due them.

No one knew yet whether the gathering of veterans would turn into a prolonged encampment or whether the vets would leave after making their demonstration before Congress. They themselves did not yet know what they would do. In spite of the cross barrages of political and police maneuvers of the newly formed Committee of Seven, Glassford, club-swinging M. P.'s, Secret Service men, Congress, Commissioners of the District of Columbia, the White House, Veterans Bureau and War Department, they were doing what they could to turn their makeshift shelters into homes. Temporary homes they were to be; they themselves wanted to return to their own communities as soon as they got the Bonus, and again make real homes for themselves.

Meanwhile they made themselves as comfortable as they could, patching and fixing the walls of their shacks, dugouts or empty buildings. Most of them were by now in the Anacostia Camp, but many groups were scattered throughout the city. In their spare time, of which there was plenty, they scouted through the neighboring lots and dumps for building materials, discarded pots and pans, and whatever they could find of homey things and conveniences. Housewives of Washington, getting over their first fears of the newcomers, gave them things they no longer needed themselves.

There was a good deal of resentment about the treatment of Bill Vitti, a 39-year old miner from Oregon, who was ordered out of the mess line at the 8th and I Streets encampment for not wearing his identification badge. When he protested, the entire official body of the B. E. F. got together and, under the supervision of a Metropolitan Police Captain, decided that Vitti had to be punished.

Vitti said, "I told the M. P. that my badge was on my coat at the barracks. But the M. P. wouldn't let me eat and ordered me out of the line. I wasn't the only one in line without a badge. And all the men, including the M. P., recognized me. Why, I came all the way from the coast with the boys—I wasn't an outsider. Why should I have to have a badge to eat?"

But "Orders are orders," said Waters, even though he admitted Vitti had come all the way from Portland and said he knew the men recognized him. After crossing the continent with his comrades, Bill Vitti walked the streets alone, 3,500 miles from home.

The rank and filers were in no way organized to protest a thing of this sort. The entire management of the Bonus Marchers was in the hands of the leaders, from the laying out of general policies down to making decisions about everyday details. Everybody felt they would soon get their Bonus and would soon be home again; they were greatly impressed by their own numbers. All they cared about was their Bonus. That was all they wanted.

If some of their leaders later turned out to be crooked—if there was graft of any sort—that didn't matter so much. They were used to that in their home towns. The rank and file were, at the beginning of the encampment in Washington, for the most part indifferent or actually unconscious of the political machinations of their leaders. Waters said he was leading them in a fight for the Bonus—O. K. Glassford got them food and supplies—O. K.

Meanwhile they went about tidying things up and trying to get comfortable. They told each other what they would do with their Bonus money—if they got it. A vet from Portland, Oregon, who had served in the Navy, said he not only wanted his Bonus: "I've got to have it. There's the wife and baby to think about."

Someone started a laugh when he brought around the story of how fifty-five Minnesota veterans had arrived the night before in a box car billed as "Livestock." The bill of lading specified that the car was Pennsylvania Railroad, No. 36865—

destination, Washington, contents, livestock, 55 veterans—origination, Canton, Minnesota.

A kinsman of Abraham Lincoln was among the Marchers, Charles Frederick Lincoln, sixth cousin of the Civil War President, a slight man, deeply tanned by the exposure of the March, had joined a Pacific coast group at Los Angeles.

Over and over again they told stories of starvation and misery back home: of children fainting at school for lack of food, of men being picked up in the streets, dying of starvation.

Joe Angelo, leader of the Camden, N. J. contingent, was a thin, wiry, excitable little man with swarthy, sunken cheeks under his bumpy cheek bones and shiny eyes. He told how his group had come to town.

This was one of the contingents which had started more or less spontaneously, with few political ideas either in its rank and file or at its head. Angelo described the trip: "I just said 'fall in' and we started. I walked most of the way here and I'm trying to get some order into the outfit. We want the Bonus and we want conditions restored the way they used to be."

Angelo told of the desperate straits of most of the Camden vets. He told how, a week before starting, he had helped to bury a hungry veteran alive. Then they advertised the stunt and people paid to look through a funnel at the man in the grave.

Some time later the same stunt was tried in one of the Bonus camps. Joe Angelo was the one buried. Some others stayed on top of the grave and collected money from curious visitors. After he had been buried a while the police interfered and made his partners dig him up. Angelo got only a few cents for his trouble. Someone had run off with the money. "Poor Angelo," said a lady who lived in a house near the camp, where the vets sometimes went for water, "and he's such a good-natured fellow—so ready to oblige everybody."

The final story about Angelo fits in here: One night, about fourteen years back, Joe Angelo went on patrol in no man's land in France, in a detail of five led by Col. George O. Patton, in charge of light tanks. A shell struck. All but Angelo and Col. Patton were killed. Col. Patton was badly wounded. Angelo, risking his life in the shell fire, went out into the open to drag him to a shell hole, and stayed with him all night. For this, Angelo was cited for exceptional bravery outside the line of duty and given the Distinguished Service Cross.

When the Bonus Marchers were driven out of Washington by soldiers, Patton, now Major Patton, was in charge of the cavalry which evacuated them. One of the Bonus Marchers, whose home was burned that night by the soldiers under Major Patton, was Joe Angelo. But, as the papers said, "It was his painful duty." Duty was duty; business was business; getting a war fought was one thing—paying for it, another.

Adding insult to injury, Major Patton told reporters, "Undoubtedly the man saved my life, but his several accounts of the incident vary from the true facts."

24. 12 Million Black Voices

RICHARD WRIGHT

Richard Wright (1908-1960) was born to a farm worker on a plantation near Natchez, Mississippi, and died in Paris, a world-renowned man of letters. He was raised with great difficulty by his mother, a rural schoolteacher, who became totally paralyzed before he was nine; he was then placed in an asylum, and later was shipped off to relatives. (These years

From 12 *Million Black Voices* (New York: The Viking Press, 1941), pp. 130–147. Copyright 1941 by Richard Wright. Reprinted by permission of the Viking Press, Inc., and of Ernest Benn Ltd.

he wrote about in the story of his childhood, Black Boy.) *An unruly youngster, he made his way to Memphis, where he became a postoffice clerk; here he discovered the writings of H. L. Mencken. After bumming around the country, he hit Chicago in 1934, joined the John Reed Club there, and got taken onto the Federal Writers' Project on the strength of a few published poems. From there he went on to New York, where he wrote the WPA* Guide to Harlem, *became a contributor to the* New Masses, *and won the* Story *magazine $500 prize for his magnificent long story, "Uncle Tom's Children," which served as the title story of a remarkable collection of novellas. But it was only with the publication of* Native Son *in 1940 that Wright gained international recognition as one of the most powerful writers of his generation. The following year he brought out 12* Million Black Voices, *illustrated with nearly a hundred stunning photographs from the file of 65,000 pictures in the Farm Security Administration collection. It is noteworthy that his text, the closing pages of which are republished here, was not in any way distorted by his Communist allegiance (which he foreswore in a memorable statement in 1944, at the very peak of Communist popularity in the U.S.). What is more, his rage at his people's fate is informed by a pity, compassion, and faith as relevant now as when the book was first created.*

The Bosses of the Buildings would have the world believe that we black folk, after these three hundred years, have locked in our veins blood of a queer kind that makes us act in this "special pattern." In their classrooms and laboratories they attempt to harness science in defense of their attitudes and practices, and never do they so vigorously assail us as "trouble-makers" as when we say that we are "this way" because we are made to live "this way." They say we speak treasonably when we declare that human life is plastic, that human nature is malleable, that men possess the dignity and meaning of the environmental and institutional forms through which they are lucky or unlucky enough to express themselves. They solemnly assert that we seek to overthrow the government by violence when we say that we live in this manner because the Black Belt which cradles our lives is created by the hands and brains of men who have decreed that we must live differently. They brand us as revolutionists when we say that we are not allowed to react to life with an honest and frontal vision.

We live on, and our music makes the feet of the whole world dance, even the feet of the children of the poor white workers who live beyond the line that marks the boundary of our lives. Where we cannot go, our tunes, songs, slang, and jokes go. Some of the white boys and girls, starved prisoners of urban homes, even forget the hatred of their parents when they hear our sensual, wailing blue melodies. The common people of the nation grow to love our songs so much that a few of us make our living by creating a haven of song for those who are weary of the barren world of steel and stone reared by the Bosses of the Buildings. But only a few of those who dance and sing with us suspect the rawness of life out of which our laughing-crying tunes and quick dance-steps come; they do not know that our songs and dances are our banner of hope flung desperately up in the face of a world that has pushed us to the wall.

Despite our new worldliness, despite our rhythms, our colorful speech, and our songs, we keep our churches alive. In fact, we have built more of them than ever here on the city pavements, for it is only when we are within the walls of our churches that we are wholly ourselves, that we keep alive a sense of our personalities in relation to the total world in which we live, that we maintain a quiet and constant communion with all that is deepest in us. Our going to church of a Sunday is like placing one's ear to another's chest to hear the unquenchable murmur of the human heart. In our collective outpourings of song and prayer, the fluid emotions of others make us feel the strength in ourselves. We build great churches, some of the greatest in terms of membership—some of our churches have more than 20,000 members—ever built in the history of Western civilization. Our churches are where we dip our tired bodies in cool springs of hope, where we retain our wholeness and humanity despite the blows of death from the Bosses of the Buildings.

Our churches are centers of social and community life, for we have virtually no other mode of communion and we are usually forbidden to worship God in the temples of the Bosses of the Buildings. The church is the door through which we first walked into Western civilization; religion is the form in which America first allowed our personalities to be expressed. Our churches provide social activities for us, cook and serve meals, organize baseball and basketball teams, operate stores and businesses, and conduct social agencies. Our first newspapers and magazines are launched from our churches.

In the Black Belts of the northern cities, our women are the most circumscribed and tragic objects to be found in our lives, and it is to the churches that our black women cling for emotional security and the release of their personalities. Because their orbit of life is narrow—from their kitchenette to the white folk's kitchen and back home again—they love the church more than do our men, who find a large measure of the expression of their lives in the mills and factories. Surrounding our black women are many almost insuperable barriers: they are black, they are women, they are workers; they are triply anchored and restricted in their movements within and without the Black Belts.

So they keep thousands of Little Bethels and Pilgrims and Calvarys and White Rocks and Good Hopes and Mount Olives going with their nickels and dimes. Nurtured in the close and intimate folk culture of the South, where each person knew the others, where the basic emotions of life were shared by all, many of them sometimes feel that the elaborate ritual of our big churches is too cold and formal for them. To retain the ardent religious emotionalism of which they are so fond, many of them will group themselves about a lonely young black preacher and help him to establish what is called a "store front" church, in which they are still able to perform their religious rituals on the fervid levels of the plantation revival. Sometimes, even in crowded northern cities, elderly black women, hungry for the South but afraid to return, will culti-vate tiny vegetable gardens in the narrow squares of ground in front of their hovels. More than even that of the American Indian, the consciousness of vast sections of our black women lies beyond the boundaries of the modern world, though they live and work in that world daily.

Outside of the church, many of our black women drift to ruin and death on the pavements of the city; they are sold, by white men as well as by black, for sex purposes. As a whole, they must go to work at an earlier age than any other section of the nation's population. For every 5 white girls between the ages of ten and fifteen who must work, 25 of our black girls must work; for every 5 white mothers who must leave their children unattended at home in order to work, 25 of our black mothers must leave their children unattended at home in order to work. As modernity and complexity spread through the cities, our black women find that their jobs grow fewer. Many white folk send their soiled clothes to the laundry and hire Japanese, Chinese, and Filipinos as servants to do their domestic work.

Many of our children scorn us; they say that we still wear the red bandanna about our heads, that we are still Uncle Toms. We lean upon our God and scold our children and try to drag them to church with us, but just as we once, years ago, left the plantation to roam the South, so now they leave us for the city pavements. But deep down in us we are glad that our children feel the world hard enough to yearn to wrestle with it. We, the mothers and fathers of the black children, try to hold them back from death, but if we persuade them to stay, or if they come back because we call them, we will pour out our pity upon them. Always our deepest love is toward those children of ours who turn their backs upon our way of life, for our instincts tell us that those brave ones who struggle against death are the ones who bring new life into the world, even though they die to do so, even though our hearts are broken when they die.

We watch strange moods fill our children, and our hearts swell with pain. The streets, with their noise and flaring lights, the taverns, the automobiles, and the poolrooms claim them, and no voice of ours can call them back. They spend their nights away from home; they forget our ways of life, our language, our God. Their swift speech and impatient eyes make us feel weak and foolish. We cannot keep them in school; more than 1,000,000 of our black boys and girls of high school age are not in school. We fall upon our knees and pray for them, but in vain. The city has beaten us, evaded us; but they, with young bodies filled with warm blood, feel bitter and frustrated at the sight of the alluring hopes and prizes denied them. It is not their eagerness to fight that makes us afraid, but that they go to death on the city pavements faster than even disease and starvation can take them. As the courts and the morgues become crowded with our lost children, the hearts of the officials of the city grow cold toward us. As our jobs begin to fail in another depression, our lives and the lives of our children grow so frightful that even some of our educated black leaders are afraid to make known to the nation how we exist. They became ashamed of us and tell us to hide our wounds. And many white people who know how we live are afraid of us, fearing that we may rise up against them.

The sands of our simple folk lives run out on the cold city

pavements. Winter winds blow, and we feel that our time is nearing its end. Our final days are full of apprehension, for our children grapple with the city. We cannot bear to look at them; they struggle against great odds. Our tired eyes turn away as we hear the tumult of battle. . . .

WE ARE THE CHILDREN of the black sharecroppers, the first-born of the city tenements.

We have tramped down a road three hundred years long. We have been shunted to and fro by cataclysmic social changes.

We are a folk born of cultural devastation, slavery, physical suffering, unrequited longing, abrupt emancipation, migration, disillusionment, bewilderment, joblessness, and insecurity—all enacted within a *short* space of historical time!

There are millions of us and we are moving in all directions. All our lives we have been catapulted into arenas where, had we thought consciously of invading them, we would have hung back. A sense of constant change has stolen silently into our lives and has become operative in our personalities as a law of living.

There are some of us who feel our hurts so deeply that we find it impossible to work with whites; we feel that it is futile to hope or dream in terms of American life. Our distrust is so great that we form intensely racial and nationalistic organizations and advocate the establishment of a separate state, a forty-ninth state, in which we black folk would live.

There are even today among us groups that forlornly plan a return to Africa.

There are others of us who feel the need of the protection of a strong nation so keenly that we admire the harsh and imperialistic policies of Japan and ardently hope that the Japanese will assume the leadership of the "darker races."

As our consciousness changes, as we come of age, as we shed our folk swaddling-clothes, so run our lives in a hundred directions.

Today, all of us black folk are not poor. A few of us have money. We make it as the white folk make theirs, but our money-making is restricted to our own people. Many of us black folk have managed to send our children to school, and a few of our children are now professional and business men whose standards of living approximate those of middle-class whites. Some of us own small businesses; others devote their lives to law and medicine.

But the majority of us still toil on the plantations, work in heavy industry, and labor in the kitchens of the Lords of the Land and the Bosses of the Buildings.

The general dislocation of life during the depression caused many white workers to learn through chronic privation that they could not protect their standards of living so long as we blacks were excluded from their unions. Many hundreds of thousands of them found that they could not fight successfully for increased wages and union recognition unless we stood shoulder to shoulder with them. As a consequence, many of us have recently become members of steel, auto, packing, and tobacco unions.

In 1929, when millions of us black folk were jobless, many unemployed white workers joined with us on a national scale to urge relief measures and adequate housing. The influence of this united effort spread even into the South where black and white sharecroppers were caught in the throes of futile conflict.

The fears of black and white lessened in the face of the slowly widening acceptance of an identity of interests. When the depression was at its severest, the courts of many cities, at the instigation of the Bosses of the Buildings, sent armed marshals to evict our jobless black families for their inability to pay rent for the rotting kitchenettes. Organized into groups, we black folk smashed the marshals' locks, picked up the paltry sticks of furniture, and replaced the evicted families. Having hurdled fear's first barrier, we found that many white workers were eager to have us in their organizations, and we were proud to feel that at last our strength was sufficient to awaken in others a desire to work with us. These men differed from those whom we had known on the plantations; they were not "po' white trash." We invited them into our homes and broke our scanty bread with them, and this was our supreme gesture of trust. In this way we encountered for the first time in our lives the full effect of those forces that tended to reshape our folk consciousness, and a few of us stepped forth and accepted within the confines of our personalities the death of our old folk lives, an acceptance of a death that enabled us to cross class and racial lines, a death that made us free.

Not all black folk, however, reacted to the depression in this manner. There were hundreds of thousands of us who saw that we bought our groceries from white clerks, that we paid our insurance to white agents, that we paid our rent to white realtors, that our children were taught in school by white teachers, that we were served in hospitals by white doctors, that we asked jobs of white bosses, that we paid our fares on busses and street cars to white conductors; in short, that we had no word to say about anything that happened in our lives. In 1935, inarticulate black men and women, filled with a naive, peasant anger, rioted in Harlem's business district and wrought a property damage of more than $2,000,000!

But our most qualitatively significant progress was organized and conducted through peaceful channels. In many large cities there were sturdy minorities of us, both black and white, who banded together in disciplined, class-conscious groups and created new organs of action and expression. We were able to seize nine black boys in a jail in Scottsboro, Alabama, lift them so high in our collective hands, focus such a battery of comment and interpretation upon them, that they became symbols to all the world of the plight of black folk in America.

If we had been allowed to participate in the vital processes of America's national growth, what would have been the texture of our lives, the pattern of our traditions, the routine of our customs, the state of our arts, the code of our laws, the function of our government! Whatever others may say, we black folk say that America would have been stronger and greater!

Standing now at the apex of the twentieth century, we look back over the road we have traveled and compare it with the road over which the white folk have traveled, and we see that three hundred years in the history of our lives are equivalent to two thousand years in the history of the lives of whites! The many historical phases which whites have traversed voluntarily and gradually during the course of Western civilization we black folk have traversed through swift compulsion. During the three hundred years we have been in the New World, we have experienced all the various types of family life, all the many adjustments to rural and urban life, and today, weary but still eager, we stand ready to accept more change.

Imagine European history from the days of Christ to the present telescoped into three hundred years and you can comprehend the drama which our consciousness has experienced! Brutal, bloody, crowded with suffering and abrupt transitions, the lives of us black folk represent the most magical and meaningful picture of human experience in the Western world. Hurled from our native African homes into the very center of the most complex and highly industrialized civilization the world has ever known, we stand today with a consciousness and memory such as few people possess.

We black folk, our history and our present being, are a mirror of all the manifold experiences of America. What we want, what we represent, what we endure is what America *is*. If we black folk perish, America will perish. If America has forgotten her past, then let her look into the mirror of our consciousness and she will see the *living* past living in the present, for our memories go back, through our black folk of today, through the recollections of our black parents, and through the tales of slavery told by our black grandparents, to the time when none of us, black or white, lived in this fertile land.

The differences between black folk and white folk are not blood or color, and the ties that bind us are deeper than those that separate us. The common road of hope which we all have traveled has brought us into a stronger kinship than any words, laws, or legal claims.

Look at us and know us and you will know yourselves, for *we* are *you*, looking back at you from the dark mirror of our lives!

What do we black folk want?

We want what others have, the right to share in the upward march of American life, the only life we remember or have ever known.

The Lords of the Land say: "We will not grant this!"

We answer: "We ask you to grant us nothing. We are winning our heritage, though our toll in suffering is great!"

The Bosses of the Buildings say: "Your problem is beyond solution!"

We answer: "Our problem is being solved. We are crossing the line you dared us to cross, though we pay in the coin of death!"

The seasons of the plantation no longer dictate the lives of many of us; hundreds of thousands of us are moving into the sphere of conscious history.

We are with the new tide. We stand at the crossroads. We watch each new procession. The hot wires carry urgent appeals. Print compels us. Voices are speaking. Men are moving! And we shall be with them. . . .

25. Speech from a Forthcoming Play

E. E. CUMMINGS

No one could have been less the public notion of the Harvard type than e e cummings (1894–1961), despite the fact that he had been born in Cambridge, the son of a Harvard professor, and went on to take two degrees there himself before racing off to World War I and the experiences in a French prison camp that led to The Enormous Room. *A congenital nonconformist, a bitterly mocking enemy of systems, iconoclastic to the end, he was at the same time a romantic anarchist in his poetry, his painting, and his prose. It is perhaps not without significance that the poem which follows originally appeared not in the* New Masses *but in* Partisan Review, *which by 1938 had turned away from blind obedience to the Soviet Union and American Stalinists and toward (in the reminiscing words of William Phillips, one of its founding editors) "purity in politics and impurity in literature." Nor is it without significance that this assault on the liberal cant and governmentalese of the patriots of the thirties, as well as on the monstrous tradition of the lynch mob, should have come not from an admirer of the Soviet system or a professional lover of minorities, but from an aristocratic individualist never enchanted with Russian communism or the special charms of ethnic or racial groupings. Indeed, the only rivals of Richard Wright as a chronicler of oppression and stoic resistance were not his fellow Negro writers of the period, but William Faulkner,*

Erskine Caldwell—and the e e cummings of "Speech from a Forthcoming Play."

by virtue of by virtue, I,
by hereby virtue of the hereby powers vested in hereby me,
do hereby declare and say that in the opinion of this court you
    are completely guilty of any crime or crimes of which you
    are absolutely innocent;
and in the name of this great hypocrisy,
which, as you hereby know, can do no wrong,
being a society based upon the equality of importunity, irre-
    spective of andsoforth andsoforth or andsoforth, with lib-
    erty and justice for all,
I hereby affirm that to the best of my knowledge and belief
    you have been conclusively proved,
in flagrante delicto, with full benefit of testimony,
to have committed a foul degenerate heinous and inhuman
    offense against your innocent and unsuspecting fellow-
    citizens, not to mention their lives their fortunes and their
    sacred andsoforth,
namely and to wit,
that hereby you were black in color at the time of your hereby
birth.
In consideration of which, I,
by hereby virtue of andsoforth,
do hereby extend to hereby you, on behalf of the government
    of the Benighted States of Hysterica, that glorious andso-
    forth alternative which is the illustrious andsoforth pre-
    rogative of every andsoforth citizen; and which is in ac-
    cordance with the dictates of justice and of mercy, as
    revealed to our forefathers in the Declaration of Interde-
    pendence; and which, in the ultraenlightened opinion of
    the supercivilized majority of the superhuman andsoforth
    race, constitutes a glowing andsoforth nucleus andsoforth
    of radiant andsoforth andsoforth:

e pluribus eunuch, or to make a long story brief,

I give you the choice of either being dead or of not being alive, nolens volens, whichever you prefer.

And in the sacred name of commonsense, I,

by hereby virtue and by hereby andsoforth and by hereby whathaveyou,

do hereby pronounce and decree that hereby you shall be punished for said crime or crimes according to that unwritten law which, according to all rightthinking people, governs the action of all rightthinking people;

namely and to wit,

that you shall have your right eye suitably excised with a very dull penknife, and placed in your mouth which has previously been opened with a hatchet;

that you shall be soaked with gasoline,

hanged with a rope,

lighted with a match,

cut down while you are alive,

slit up the middle by good women,

stamped on by little children,

and made to kiss the flag by strong men.

Finally: it is the irrevocable verdict of this impeccable court, in due session assembled, that your organ of generation, having been suitably tinged and bedewed with the liquid and solid excrement of all lawabiding citizens in general and of all patriotic persons in particular, shall be forcefully proffered to your own mother, who shall immediately and joyfully eat thereof under penalty of death.

In hoke signo:

God save the people From the people!

God save All of the people for Some of the people!

God save Some of the people All of the time, and all of the people will take care of themselves.

AMEN.

26. Industrial Valley

RUTH MCKENNEY

*Ruth McKenney (1911–   ) was as much a radical in her
youth as she was a humorist. The Mishawaka, Ohio, girl reporter who came to the big city during the depression and took
it by storm with her funny* New Yorker *pieces regarded these
sketches merely as a way "to make a living." Despite the fact
that* My Sister Eileen *(1939) was an international success as a
book, on Broadway, and on the screen, Miss McKenney's serious interest was in communism and in writing fiction and nonfiction which would be alive with social purpose. Late in the
thirties she served as an editor of the* New Masses *and contributed a column called "Nothing Personal." In 1943 she published a massive proletarian novel,* Jake Home, *which she herself later characterized with biting accuracy as "pious." By
1950, however, her disillusionment with American communism
had reached the point where she was ready to write about it
(in* Love Story), *and in the years since, her writing has been
primarily in the vein which originally won her a vast and admiring audience. Nevertheless, she did produce, during her
years as a true believer, one book—*Industrial Valley*—which
still retains both power and pungency. Winner of the Writers'
Congress prize as the best nonfiction book of 1938–1939, it
was, in her words, "the true story of what happened to Akron,
Ohio, from 1932 to 1936." The reader should be cautioned that
the truth is somewhat stretched to render heroic the role
played by the Communist party in arousing the workers from*

---

their depression lethargy, but the segment which follows does give due honor to the primacy of the Akron rubber workers in initiating the historic and tremendously exciting sitdown movement of the CIO.

The First Sitdown—January 29-31, 1936

The mountaineer workers of Akron were fond of Alex Eigenmacht, the bullet-headed, blue-eyed Hungarian who ran the union print shop out near the Firestone plant. They liked him because he was the best story-teller in town. Even the gaudy movies hadn't spoiled the taste of the sons of the Southern hills for a good tale deftly spun. And Alex—rubberworkers had difficulty pronouncing his last name, so he went simply by his first—had a real talent for reciting the stories of his improbably adventurous life.

Union rubberworkers used to turn up an hour or so early at Alex's little office, and while they waited for the last of their leaflets to come off the little press out in the composing room, they listened solemnly, with just the ghost of pleased grins on their broad mouths, to tall tales of Alex fighting in the Austrian mountains; Alex in the Hungarian Red Army; Alex eluding—by the merest hairbreadth—German spies; Alex escaping the White Terror by the very skin of his teeth.

One day four truck-tire builders from Firestone ambled into the print-shop office to pick up some union notices. Alex was in an expansive mood and he began, in his poetic, slightly accented English, to tell them the story of the beginning of the World War.

Like some adventurous men, Alex had a talent for being in the right place at precisely the right moment. He had been a union printer in Serajevo the day the Austrian Crown Prince was blown to bits by the fatal bomb. A passionate Serbian nationalist, along with other members of his union, he had fought to prevent Serbia capitulating to the Austrian ultimatum.

"The men who threw that bomb," Alex told the listening rubberworkers, "were men fighting for freedom. My union decided to protest against the government's arresting them and trying them for murder." This was a new slant on old history and the Firestone union men leaned forward and said, "Yeah, go on."

The printers couldn't actually walk out on strike, Alex said, because they had heard that their boss had a whole crew of scabs lined up ready to take their places at a moment's notice. Besides, if they actually struck, they were quite likely to be arrested and thrown in jail. The times were tense and the Serbian government was trying to do everything to prevent the inevitable war.

"So we had an inside strike," Alex said casually. "We just sat around by our machines, and, by God, nobody could come in and take our jobs, and they couldn't arrest us either. We were on the job."

Alex went on, telling about engineers who struck and finally the mobilization. The pressman brought in the notices and the tirebuilders shook hands and said they liked the story.

Nearly three months later, on the cold winter day of January 28, 1936, Alex was startled to hear the door of his office banging in the wind. He went out to greet his old friends from the Firestone truck-tire department. Their faces were cracked with the wind, and they wore heavy scarfs and thick mittens and lumber-jackets.

"Sit down, sit down," Alex said pleasantly. "Pull up next to the radiator and warm yourselves up."

"Nope," one of them replied. "No time. Look, Alex, will you do us a favor?"

Alex had courtly continental manners. He said he would be delighted, it was an honor, what could he do?

"Tell us about that time in that town where the World War started when you guys struck but didn't walk out."

Alex hesitated, trying to recall the story. Then he nodded. "Sure," he said, "but what's up?"

"Just tell us," a big tirebuilder said.

So Alex, considerably bewildered by the air of mystery and excitement written all over the faces of these big tirebuilders, told them the story again, this time in great detail. They stopped him to ask questions.

"Well, didn't the boss try to throw you out?"

"He couldn't," Alex replied. "He was afraid of hurting his expensive machinery if there was any fighting inside."

"Uhmm," men in the little group said, and added, "Go on." When he was through, the tirebuilders pulled their scarfs tight around their ears, jerked their woolen caps down to their eyes. "Thank you," they said briskly and without another word, slammed out the door.

Left alone, Alex drummed on his desk with a pencil, put a thoughtful finger to his nose. Finally, he called up the Firestone local headquarters and asked, in the course of a casual conversation, if there was any trouble in the truck-tire department.

"Boy," said the man from union headquarters, "is there! Trouble and plenty of it!"

"What's it all about?" Alex asked pleasantly.

"Well, you know about how they tried to cut the base rate up there forty per cent to speed the boys up some more?" the union man said.

"Yeah," Alex replied, "so I heard. I was surprised at that. They usually don't trifle much with those babies in the truck-tire department. They're tough."

"You said it," the union man agreed. "Well, anyway, the boys raised holy hell about it, and finally we got Murphy—the factory super—to agree to only an eleven per cent cut."

"Yeah," Alex said. "So?"

"So the boys was still sore," the union man explained. "Sorer than hell. They've been speedin' them up for months now something terrible. My God, it's worth your life to work up there. Nobody but them big husky babies could take it. There isn't one of them in there under six feet two, and they all weigh better than two hundred and, believe me, they ain't fat, not the way they work."

"Yeah, yeah," Alex agreed.

"Well, so this eleven per cent cut didn't go so good. The boys figure if they don't stop this speedup now, they'll all be in the ashcan by the time they're thirty-five. The pace is something awful. Anyway, you know all the boys are scared now of this eight-hour-day thing, and they figure if they let the company get away with this cut, why, they'll start to think they can do anything and end up putting in the eight-hour day."

"Yeah. So?" Alex said.

"O.K., so the boys got together and decided to stall on the rate. You know, they got that group payment stuff up there, so when all the boys slow down, why, they can't cut their wages, see?"

"Yeah, sure."

"So last week Murphy sends a rat in to make the time," the union man went on. "You know the system. If a guy comes in and works like hell and even does sloppy work, the company don't care, and if he makes the base rate on the new schedule, why, then the whole outfit has to make it."

"Yeah, yeah," Alex said impatiently.

"O.K.," the union man went on. "So this skunk comes in and starts making time on the boys. Well, the second night he's in there, it's on the night shift, why, the boys begin to get pretty sore. Things begin to look as though this rat is going to get popped by some of the guys with bad tempers. So Clay Dicks comes over. He's the union committeeman in that department. Clay figures there's going to be trouble, and he wants to quiet the boys down, because he thinks it's not so good having union men slugging rats right in the shop. The company would probably use it as an excuse to fire them."

"Sure," Alex agreed.

"So Dicks tries to smooth the boys down. But obviously this skunk has been tipped off by the management, because he starts to pick on Dicks. Calls Clay a son-of-a-bitch and a lot more—plenty more."

"So?" Alex said, interested. Mountain men, he knew, did not take kindly to insults.

"Yeah. So Clay holds himself in pretty good. He gets the fellows back on their machines, and he says to this rat, 'I'll see you outside after the shift.' That don't suit the skunk so good, he wants to fight right then, which is just what Clay figures. This guy is out to get him canned, because he's the union committeeman."

"So?" Alex said again, getting excited.

"O.K. When the shift is over, Clay rings out at the timehouse. You know how that is. There's a little courtyard there just before the gates. Clay was figuring on meeting the rat right outside the fence and giving it to him. But all of a sudden, as he was walking toward the gate, this rat turns up and slugs Clay a dirty one, from the back."

"Uhmm."

"Yeah, so Clay takes a fall and then he gets up and gives it to this guy. Boy, the fellows said he just knocked the living daylights out of him, bounced him six feet across the ground."

"Good," Alex said, pleased.

"Not so good," his friend replied, "because, Jesus, Clay hardly had time to lay a hand on this dirty dog when suddenly from nowhere at all, mind you, just by coincidence, who should happen to be strolling around in the middle of the night but a big bunch of factory guards."

"My," said Alex.

"Yeah, so they pounce on Clay, and of course let the other

guy go, and Murphy suspends Clay for a whole week, no pay, for fighting on company grounds, which is mighty convenient for Murphy, because here is the truck-tire department without their union committeeman just when they were trying to negotiate about this wage cut."

"Bad business."

"So the fellows is sore. Boy, they're boiling mad," the union man went on. "They're holding meetings here all the time, and Murphy says absolutely he won't take Dicks back, and the boys said he's got to, or else."

"Else what?" Alex inquired.

"I don't know," the union man replied, his voice suddenly blank.

"Yeah," Alex answered. "Well, thanks a lot." After he hung up he sat at his desk, drumming with his fingers, and staring out into the swirling snow. It was four o'clock. Alex bundled himself up in his heavy coat and went home.

The snow fell in patches all afternoon, and toward dusk, the winds grew fiercer. The six to twelve shift at Firestone came stamping into the factory, their ears wrapped in home-knit scarfs. The lights flashed on all over the great factory, and at six-fifteen the steady clatter and crash and whir of the early evening shift blotted out every human sound in the rubber shop.

Outside, in the gathering darkness, automobiles went carefully past the Firestone plant, poking their way along on the slippery windswept streets. People who lived in Akron were used to seeing the big rubber plants of southernmost Main Street, so only a few, as they rode by, even glanced at the great pile of yellow brick buildings. But passing strangers stared, and were filled with unrest. For the Firestone rubber shops, on the dusk of a winter's evening, were a commanding and beautiful sight. Arising black against a pale sky, they were illuminated by a thousand lights twinkling from their windows, making a soft glow on the snow-covered yards around them.

On this bitter night in January, the drafty hall of the union headquarters across the street from the Firestone plant was partly filled with restless tirebuilders. They were huddled, most of them still wearing their heavy lumberjackets, around a fat stove at one end of the big room. A naked electric light bulb hung on a long cord from the ceiling, making a pool of yellow light near the stove. No pictures, no bulletins, no notices hung on the walls, except a badly lettered, homemade sign off in one corner, stating, "Buy union-made goods."

The men were talking quietly but with fierce excitement. They had just decided to give Murphy one more chance: Reinstate Dicks and give him back pay for his time lost, or else.

"He'll say 'or else what' and that would be bad," one of the men objected. He was, like his friends, tall above the average with tremendous shoulders, but very thin and gaunt, with deep hollows in his young weatherbeaten face and at his big neck bones.

"Yeah, that's right," someone answered from the outer circle around the stove. "We don't want to give him no hint. This has got to come off quick and easy. It's got to be a big surprise. That's what was the matter last year. We was all the time talkin' and didn't do nothin'."

"Yeah," a tirebuilder whose heavy boots were sizzling against the very belly of the stove replied, "yeah, and we let a lot of guys do the talkin' for us. This time we run it ourselves, and we don't tell nobody, and we don't ask nobody if it suits them either."

"Yep," the men in the circle murmured. They sat quietly in their wooden chairs, close to the smelly stove, thinking. They seemed tired. Mostly blond men, freckled on the high cheekbones, with blue eyes, big red ears covered with soft blond fuzz, big heavy noses and wide mouths, they had still, after years away from their mountains, the look of outdoor men. Awkward in repose, their big feet reached out in a dozen queer angles. But even as they lounged silently, their lanky bodies revealed swiftness of action, power in motion.

And indeed these men who sat now, brooding, were said by expert industrial engineers to be the most highly skilled workmen in American mass industry. They built truck tires, partly by machine, partly by hand. They worked at a speed unequaled even in the auto shops. Their tires shoed the busses and heavy motor vans of the world.

In the quiet, the faces of these men were profoundly unhappy. They had been pushed into making plans for desperate action, a final resistance against the way of their lives. Most of them were married, and had three or four young children. During the past years many of them had been off and on relief as they were taken on and laid off again at the factory. Since they were the aristocrats of the rubber shops, they made about $25 a week when they worked—if they worked. They could not feed their growing families on this average annual wage of a thousand dollars or less. With the eight-hour day in the offing, every fourth man would lose his job forever.

Just before midnight the men in the union hall buttoned their jackets and crossed the street to ring in. Murphy had said "No" again to a hasty telephone call. Their minds were made up. The signals were arranged. Everything was ready. Some of the men had trouble slipping their timecards into the punch. They were nervous and their throats felt dry. This was really a hell of a thing they were going to do. Nobody had ever done such a thing before—at least not in this country. It made a man sort of upset.

Promptly at midnight the truck-tire department started work. Under pools of light, the big men stood at their machines. A wheel slowly revolved, as they wound on strips of heavy rubber and fabric. Their hands flashed. Helpers came in quietly and laid piles of carefully folded material beside their machines. Just over their heads, a conveyor belt clattered slowly by. Suspended from the belt were huge thick hooks. Every few minutes, one of the darting hands ripped the finished tire from the machine, slammed it on a hook, and went back to the revolving wheel. Foremen walked slowly up and down the long lines of tirebuilders, checking material, glancing at the finished tires, sending machine repairmen to a faltering wheel.

No human sound came from this vast room. The clatter and shriek and roar of the conveyor belt and the revolving wheels, the drone of motors, the broken rush and squeaking halt of electric factory trucks, drowned out even a brief salute of one worker to another.

But as a flashing hand reached up to slam a tire on the hook, the worker had half a second when his body came near to the tirebuilder on the next machine.

"Two o'clock," a man muttered as he swung up his tire. The tirebuilder next to him did not look up from the revolving wheel. His hands never stopped their expert, rapid motions. He hardly nodded. But when his tire went up to the conveyor belt he said, his face a blank, with such a tight mouth that he might merely have been shifting his wad of chewing tobacco, "Two o'clock."

The man at the next machine never even looked his way. But, a moment later, and this was strange, for he was such an expert workman, he dropped his heavy tire tool. It clattered to the floor quite near the fourth machine. The foreman looked up, his ears trained to pick out of the constant uproar a different, unexpected noise. But he only saw a tirebuilder picking up his tool, brushing against a friend.

"Two o'clock," the clumsy tirebuilder murmured.

After the first hour, the foremen on the truck-tire floor were considerably annoyed when it appeared that two of their best workmen were apparently suffering from kidney trouble. At least they left the floor to go to the washroom; this was nearly unheard of the first hour. A tirebuilder could hardly afford to go to the washroom so early on the shift, because if he went more than once, his pay for the night would take a bad cut.

When they came back, one of them nodded, the barest kind of jerk of the head. Downstairs, in the auto tires, a man on the top machine was saying, as he reached over to grab material, "Two o'clock." And next to him, an auto tirebuilder was dropping his tool and picking it up, saying, through hardly moving lips, "Two o'clock."

A little after one-thirty, a foreman on the truck-tire floor went downstairs to talk to the super on the auto floor. "Everything O.K.?" he asked, shouting in his friend's ear, to be heard.

"I guess so," the foreman from auto tires replied. The two men stood together watching the rows of flashing hands, the rhythmically moving backs. The noise sounded in their ears as familiar music. They knew every variation and could separate the proper drone of the motors from a sudden brief whine of a machine gone sour. Tonight the noise sounded all right.

"I got the jitters, I guess," the super from upstairs said, shaking his big shocky head like a puzzled hunting dog.

"Me, too," the head from the auto tires answered. "I keep feeling there's something phony going on here. But I don't know. The fellows ain't talking any. They're making fast time tonight."

"It's goddamned funny they ain't talking," the upstairs foreman growled. "The last two nights they've been howling about this Dicks guy. Tonight they're as quiet as a bunch of ghosts."

"Yeah," the auto super replied. "I got a feeling somethin's wrong. Them guys is watching us right now."

The two foremen stared at the tirebuilders. Their hands wove the usual quick pattern. Their heads were bent over their piles. To a stranger's eye, they were lost in their work, each man a picture of useful concentration. But to the two foremen, there was something wrong. They felt the side-glances of these men. They felt the impact of a quick flash of eyes. They sensed hostility.

"Listen," the foreman from upstairs said, "if anything goes wrong, I'll close up the fire doors right away. You do the same."

"What's going to go wrong?" the auto super said.

"Nothing," the truck head growled, "but if it should, we don't want nothing to spread."

"Yeah." The auto foreman stood unhappily in the doorway as the upstairs super left. His eyes wandered from one hefty tirebuilder to another. Nothing wrong, he could see. But he felt queer. In his bones, he knew something was coming off. Jesus, it gave a man the creeps watching those guys at their machines and knowing they were watching you back, and hating you, and planning some goddamned trick to upset the shift and maybe lose you your job. He walked down the line, brushing past a dozen tirebuilders. They didn't even look up, but he could feel their backs stiffen as he passed. The sons-of-bitches, they were up to something. But what? What?

It was 1:45 A.M. on January 29, 1936.

Upstairs the foreman passed down the lines, his ears cocked for a murmur, for the barest whisper. He was determined to hustle the first guy he caught even muttering right off the floor and out the gate. Something was mighty wrong tonight; everybody on this whole line was sort of holding his breath. Zero hour. He smiled grimly. Zero hour for what? He was sure getting the jitters lately. But, my God, the company didn't realize how sore these boys were at the rate cut, and you couldn't tell them thick-headed guys in the front office. No, all they'd say was "We hold you accountable for unbroken production in your department." Jesus, was that the way to treat a good loyal company man, threaten to can him if anything went wrong?

The foreman paced slowly past his workmen, his eyes darting in and out of the machines, eager for any betraying gesture. He heard no word, and he saw no gesture. The hands flashed,

the backs bent, the arms reached out in monotonous perfec-
tion. The foreman went back to his little desk and sat squirming on the smooth-seated swivel chair. He felt profoundly
disturbed. Something, he knew, was coming off. But what?
For God's sake, what?

It was 1:57 A.M. January 29, 1936.

The tirebuilders worked in smooth frenzy, sweat around
their necks, under their arms. The belt clattered, the insuffer-
able racket and din and monotonous clash and uproar went
on in steady rhythm. The clock on the south wall, a big plain
clock, hesitated, its minute hand jumped to two. A tirebuilder
at the end of the line looked up, saw the hand jump. The
foreman was sitting quietly staring at the lines of men working
under the vast pools of light. Outside, in the winter night, the
streets were empty, and the whir of the factory sounded
faintly on the snow-swept yard.

The tirebuilder at the end of the line gulped. His hands
stopped their quick weaving motions. Every man on the line
stiffened. All over the vast room, hands hestitated. The foreman
saw the falter, felt it instantly. He jumped up, but he stood
beside his desk, his eyes darting quickly from one line to
another.

This was it, then. But what was happening? Where was it
starting? He stood perfectly still, his heart beating furiously,
his throat feeling dry, watching the hesitating hands, watching
the broken rhythm.

Then the tirebuilder at the end of the line walked three steps
to the master safety switch and, drawing a deep breath, he
pulled up the heavy wooden handle. With this signal, in perfect synchronization, with the rhythm they had learned in a
great mass-production industry, the tirebuilders stepped back
from their machines.

Instantly, the noise stopped. The whole room lay in perfect
silence. The tirebuilders stood in long lines, touching each
other, perfectly motionless, deafened by the silence. A moment

ago there had been the weaving hands, the revolving wheels, the clanking belt, the moving hooks, the flashing tire tools. Now there was absolute stillness, no motion anywhere, no sound.

Out of the terrifying quiet came the wondering voice of a big tirebuilder near the windows: "Jesus Christ, it's like the end of the world."

He broke the spell, the magic moment of stillness. For now his awed words said the same thing to every man, "We done it! We stopped the belt! By God, we done it!" And men began to cheer hysterically, to shout and howl in the fresh silence. Men wrapped long sinewy arms around their neighbors' shoulders, screaming, "We done it! We done it!"

For the first time in history, American mass-production workers had stopped a conveyor belt and halted the inexorable movement of factory machinery.

"John Brown's body," somebody chanted above the cries. The others took it up. "But his soul," they sang, and some of them were nearly weeping, racked with sudden and deep emotion, "but his soul goes marchin' on."

Downstairs, the echo of the song burst on the first quiet. Men heard the faint music and picked up the familiar words. They leaned out the windows into the cold winter's night air. "He is trampling out the vintage where the grapes of wrath are stored," they sang.

Across the street, in the union hall, men ran to the door and heard the faint faraway song, and said, full of wonder and a deep pride, "Jesus Christ! They done it! Listen to 'em! They're singing! They're singing!"

Over the snow-swept yard, in the winds of January, the song floated out to the whole valley, a song that promised never to die away, a song that promised to live on, fresh and unafraid, in the hearts of workingmen, a song that promised to spread from Akron to Detroit, to New York, and across the whole land of America.

"Glory, Glory, Hallelujah!" the tirebuilders sang. "And his soul goes marchin' on."

The foremen heard the song and retreated. They locked the fire doors and, five minutes later, opened them on demand. They were amazed by the organization of these revolting workmen. After the first hysteria had died down, the confusion disappeared at once. The ringleader, the man who switched the current off, climbed on the foreman's desk and shouted, "O.K., fellows. Now any of you guys here who ain't with us can get the hell out right now. Go home and stay home and don't let's see your yellow-livered face around here again. Anybody want to leave?"

Nobody did. "O.K.," the speaker went on. "Now we got a lot of things to do. First, we got to have a committee to visit other departments, and let's have some volunteers who ain't chicken-livered." The whole truck-tire department wanted to go. The leader picked half a dozen. "You go downstairs and combine with the auto boys' committee and, listen, it's up to you guys to shut this whole goddamned plant down, see?"

"O.K.," the speaker continued quickly. "Now we got to have a committee to police the floor. We don't want no machinery broken we can get blamed for, and we got to keep the place clean. No gamblin' for money either, and absolutely no drinking. We frisk everybody who comes in, for bottles. We don't take nobody's word for it. A couple of drunks would make this sitdown strike look punk."

"Sitdown strike," the crowd repeated. It was a good phrase. The tirebuilders had never heard it before. They liked it.

"That's what I call it," the speaker said, "because we're sittin' down, ain't we, instead of working?"

"Yeah," the men answered and grinned.

"Now," the leader went on. "We're going to elect a committee to talk to Murphy. We figure we got to stay shut down until Murphy takes back Dicks and fixes the base rate."

There were murmurs of approval. The speaker added, "One

more thing, and it's the biggest thing. Most of you fellows don't belong to the union. I ain't blamin' you. Some learns fast, some learns slow. But this strike was started by union fellows. The union ain't the same one that sold out the boys last year. We threw Green out on his ear, in case you haven't heard. The union belongs to us now. The only way we can get anywhere is to have an industrial union, and everybody in it. We got application cards, lots of 'em right here. Nobody has to join, but I should think it would be a pretty dumb cluck who couldn't see now, in the middle of this strike, that the union means business. O.K., that's all."

It was enough. By three o'clock, the tirebuilders on the late shift belonged to the U.R.W.A. in a body. Downstairs the union delegate was sitting at the foreman's desk issuing brand-new union cards to a long line of laughing excited men. The foreman himself was gone and with him his two assistants. They were sitting in the factory superintendent's office, floors away, twisting their fingers and saying, "Yeah, it's easy to say we should 'a' stopped them, but, my God, it's like a revolution. What can you do? There's hundreds of them and a half a dozen of us."

The factory superintendent's office was a glum place. Every few minutes a new foreman came in, his eyes blazing, his mouth twitching with rage. "I don't know how they found out," the new ones would say. "My God, I had the fire door locked, but all of a sudden, one of them was up there pulling the switch and right away they open the door and this goddamned roving committee comes in and starts to appoint a police committee and pass out union cards, and get them to elect somebody to this here negotiation committee."

Firestone Plant One gradually shut down completely. The departments that didn't actually sitdown and strike were paralyzed by lack of work or materials. The delicate mechanism of mass production was dealt a brutal fatal blow. Engineers had worked for years to synchronize every labor process in the great factory. The most remote departments were dependent on the flow of materials from some other faraway corner of the great plant. But once the line was broken, factory operations came to an uneven jerking halt.

As dawn came, the day-shift workers lined up at the timehouse, punching in their cards. Still dazed with sleep, they stumbled off streetcars, not knowing what had happened inside the walls of the great yellow brick factory. Yet they found out instantly. Murphy could never understand this grapevine telegraph. How did tirebuilders standing patiently in line instantly learn that everything had gone blooey up there in the factory? But they did. And they straightened up, joking and laughing and strutting as they walked. Murphy didn't know whether to let them in or not, and being confused, he did nothing. So the new shift came on, and joined the old sitdowners, the veterans, and listened jealously to their bragging tales of how *they* started it, *they* turned off the current. By noon the men who had come to work at dawn were also veterans, able to lord it over the newcomers.

Murphy was at his wit's end. Once he thought of turning off the steam. But when the tirebuilders heard the hissing sound stop, and felt the pipes grow cold, they began to beat such an inferno of noisy rapping on the pipes that Murphy was afraid. Suppose they got sore and busted up the machinery? He turned the steam back on.

The elevators kept running too. Murphy burned up, but what could he do? The tirebuilders rode downstairs in lordly fashion to the factory cafeteria, and ate good breakfasts, and rode back upstairs picking their teeth and talking in loud pleased voices. Maybe he should starve them out? Murphy thought. But, my God, there were 1,200 tirebuilders actually on strike and, as a matter of fact, most of the workers in the other departments were really striking too, only their departments had just closed down for lack of material. But Murphy knew 'em—they, too, were really strikers at heart. Well, that's a lot of men roaming around inside a factory. Suppose he closed the cafeteria. Could he close it? Maybe they'd fight to keep it open. They probably would. Even if he could close it, could he really starve them out? Wouldn't that make them even sorer and wouldn't the guys outside who sympathized— and there were plenty of them—wouldn't they rush the factory with food?

My God, Murphy thought, what does a factory superinten- dent do on a spot like this? He simply didn't know, this sad pioneer, this superintendent faced with America's first indus- trial sitdown strike.

The strikers themselves were surprised and jubilant when they found so little resistance. They owned the factory. No- body dared say them nay. So they used power carefully. Clean-up squads kept the factory floors shining. The police committee looked darkly at a man who so much as swore. A tirebuilder, leaning on his machine to watch a tong game was warned by every other man on strike, "Watch out. Don't bust nothin'." Abashed sitdowners apologized to the union commit- tee for suggesting poker at a penny limit.

By a little after noon, the tire floors were so crowded a man could hardly find a place to sit down. Three shifts were on sit- down duty and men from the fourth shift illicitly sneaked past the gates and came up to get in on the excitement. Runners carried news between the sitdowners and the union hall. So- and-so's wife had called up to say more power to you, stick it out.

About one o'clock the next morning, the end of the first day, the strike committee decided that some of the sitdowners should leave to get a little sleep. Apparently the management would continue to let strikers in and out of the big plant. The committee divided the men into shifts: about half the sit- downers marched out the factory to go into South Akron and Kenmore and get a clean shirt, some sleep, and a chance to tell the world what was happening at Firestone.

Next day they returned, looking fresh, to relieve their comrades standing guard over their machines. All during the second day the strikers sat around at machines singing, playing cards, listening to speeches, and signing union cards. They ate in the factory cafeteria, and some of them caught cat-naps on newspapers stretched out on cement floors.

While they ate and slept and played cards, the news of the sitdown strike spread through Akron. The newspapers carried awestruck and rather incomplete accounts of the amazing strike, but few feature writers penetrated to the sitdown area, no pictures were printed of wives kissing their husbands through fences. The newspapers stuck to baffled and sketchy reports of an incident that they did not understand very well but feared very much.

East Akron, South Akron, Kenmore Hill, and Barberton did not depend on the newspaper stories of the great sitdown strike. The sitdowners themselves came home for shaves and clean underwear, and they spread the story with feverish excitement. Goodyear tirebuilders sat patiently downstairs in little frame houses for hours waiting for a Firestone sitdowner to wake up and tell them all about it. The Firestone local hall was jammed day and night, and men worked twenty hours of twenty-four signing up new members and explaining how the sitdown worked.

The valleys seethed with the story. Women ran, bundled up in old coats, across their front yards, to call on their neighbors and tell them what was going on at Firestone. Little boys boasted in school recess that their Pops were sitting down in the truck-tire department, and other small boys all but burst with envy and rushed home screaming, "Pa, why can't you sitdown?"

The management of the rubber shops were stunned by the news. Here was something they had never heard of before, something frightening and queer. How did you deal with it? How did you break it up? One thing they were sure of: Firestone must be very firm. Not by any chance should the sit-downers be allowed to think they had won their peculiar strike. That would be fatal. That would give the new idea just the proper halo of success to make it spread, and then heaven only knew what would happen next.

The Firestone management agreed at first. For twenty-four hours Murphy refused even to discuss settlement with the negotiation committee. He said the plant would have to be cleared before he would talk about the Dicks case or the base rate either. The second twenty-four hours Murphy began to change his mind. It was all very well for Goodrich and Good-year to beef about being firm and holding out and standing together. They were making tires, and he wasn't. Their fac-tories were running smoothly and his was a bedlam.

Still Murphy hesitated. But at the beginning of the third full day of the sitdown, after fifty-three hours, his foremen brought terrible news. All of Plant Two was ready to sitdown in sym-pathy unless there was an immediate settlement. The Plant Two pitworkers had already voted to stand by their curing boxes and cut off the steam. Murphy shuddered, and in his mind's eye, he could see the beginning of a real strike, a strike for union recognition or something of the kind. His spies told him there was plenty of talk about spreading the strike and increasing the demands. Now this terrible news about the men in Plant Two!

Murphy sent for the negotiating committee and consigned to hell the opinions of his fellow factory superintendents at Good-rich and Goodyear. It was all very well to talk about a solid employer front, but in the face of something like this, a man had to act quickly or the whole situation would simply blow up in his face.

The settlement allowed Dicks' immediate reinstatement and three hours' pay for every day lost. It promised immediate negotiation on the base rate. It offered three hours' pay per day to all workers who had lost time during the sitdown.

When the committee, breathless and excited, brought the news to the men up in the truck-tire department for a vote, they could hardly talk, they were so jubilant. And the strikers were quite beside themselves. They were getting paid, paid, mind you, for sittingdown! And Dicks was back, with pay. And the rate would be negotiated. Glory Hallelujah!

The sitdowners marched out singing, and the sound of their voices went everywhere in the valley. The Firestone sitdowners had won! They won! They won! This sitdown business worked.

27. The Cradle Will Rock

MARC BLITZSTEIN

With the production by the Mercury Theatre on the night of December 5, 1937 of The Cradle Will Rock, *its author became famous. Born in Philadelphia, Marc Blitzstein (1905–1964) was trained at the Curtis Institute, and studied with Nadia Boulanger and Arnold Schoenberg. In the thirties, under the influence of Bertolt Brecht and Kurt Weill (he dedicated* The Cradle Will Rock *to Brecht, and later it was his translation of* The Threepenny Opera *that played with dazzling success for so many years Off Broadway), Blitzstein determined to win a wider audience for his music. Thanks to the direction of Orson Welles and the production of John Houseman, he succeeded far beyond his expectations. "When the Federal Theatre production was banned with the first-night audience already on the sidewalk in front of the Maxine Elliott," Archi-*

bald MacLeish has written, "and when Welles and Houseman took over the play themselves, hired the Venice Theatre twenty blocks away, loaded an old piano into a truck and started off with their angry audience at their heels, they walked into the most exciting evening of theatre this generation has seen." Blitzstein's joyously revolutionary operetta took place "in Steeltown, U.S.A., on the night of a union drive" against Mr. Mister, their capitalist enemy. Using recitatives, arias, and chorales, he mixed pop music with traditional counterpoint, and mocked his solemn situations with blues and torch songs and parodies of serious forms, as the excerpts that follow (including the title song) demonstrate. The Cradle Will Rock *was revived in New York in 1947 and again in 1964, and in the years between, Blitzstein composed* No For An Answer, Symphony: The Airborne, *and* Regina, *but none was to be as memorable as this gay and jangling evocation of an era.*

[Liberty Committee, which comprises Reverend Salvation, Editor Daily, artists Yasha and Dauber, College President Prexy and Professors Mamie and Trixie, and Dr. Specialist, has been arrested by mistake and brought to Nightcourt. While its members await the arrival of their sponsor, Mr. Mister, who is to bail them out, Organizer Larry Foreman is brought into custody.—ED.]

SCENE SEVEN
NIGHTCOURT

... LARRY is the hero of the piece. He's not very good-looking—a humorous face, and an engaging manner. Confidence is there, too; not self-confidence; a kind of knowledge about the way things probably have to work out. It gives him a surprising modesty, and a young poise.

I just been grilled. Say, who made up that word, grilled?
I also been barbecued, frizzled, and
   Tries to sit.

pleated. Now I know what the dirty foreigners feel like. I guess I am a foreigner at that. Our property's been in the family for over sixty years. . . . But it's nine miles outa town, so that makes me a foreigner. Not that it's a good property. . . . If it was, we wouldn't have it no sixty minutes. Ever hear of Mr. Mister? There's an A-number-one homesnatcher; a lotta hard work and perseverance went into that reputation. . . .

> *He turns, sees the* Liberty Committee *all eyeing him balefully.*

Saaay, what's the whole Liberty Committee doin in a night-court? And on the wrong side of the bar? Wait till I tell my Aunt Jessie . . . She's got a comeback for everything. "Allus said they was the biggest cheats and whores in town." Excuse the language, Miss,

> *To* Moll.

My Aunt Jessie gets all them big words outa the Bible.

> *Looks at her more closely.*

You're new here. What's the matter, they catch you on the streets, kid?

Moll

Uh huh. Whatta they got you for?

Larry

Who, me?
Makin a speech and passin out leaflets!
The fawmal chahge is Incitin to Riot—
Ain't you ever seen my act?

> *He goes into it.*

Well, I'm creepin along in the dark;
My eyes is crafty, my pockets is bulging!
I'm loaded, armed to the teeth—with leaflets.
And am I quick on the draw!

I come up to you . . . very slow . . . very snaky;
And with one fell gesture—
I tuck a leaflet in your hand.
And then, one, two, three—
There's a riot. You're the riot.
I incited you . . . I'm terrific, I am!

MOLL

That don't sound like nothin to get arrested for;
Besides, you don't seem very worried.

LARRY

Listen, girlie, you don't want to talk that way, that's dangerous talk. First thing you know they'll have you deported as
well as fumigated. . . . But it's a good leaflet, we printed it
ourselves. We got a committee, too, farmers and city people,
doctors, lawyers, newspapermen, even a couple of poets—and
one preacher. We're middle class, we all got property—we also
got our eyes open. This crowd here?
    A chord.
Hidin up there in the cradle of the Liberty Committee?
    Another chord.
Upon the topmost bough of yonder tree now,
Like bees in their hives,
The lords and their lackeys and wives—
A swingin "Rockabye Baby" in a nice big cradle.
Then they remark the air is chilly up there;
The sky beetle-browed; can that be a cloud over there?
And then they put out their hands and feel stormy weather!
A birdie ups and cries . . . "Boys, this looks bad;
You haven't used your eyes; you'll wish you had."

That's thunder, that's lightning,
And it's going to surround you!

No wonder those stormbirds
Seem to circle around you!
Well, you can't climb down, and you can't sit still;
That's a storm that's going to last until
The final wind blows . . . and when the wind blows . . .
The cradle will rock!

That's thunder, that's lightning,
And it's going to surround you!
No wonder those stormbirds
Seem to circle around you!
Well, you can't climb down, and you can't say "No"!
You can't stop the weather, not with all your dough!
For when the wind blows . . . Oh, when the wind blows . . .
The cradle will rock!

The cradle will rock! Do you think we don't know what that
fight tonight's about? Why Murphy from the rolling mills and
Brown from the roughers, and Young from the boilermakers,
is sittin together in Union Headquarters? Why more people
than Steeltown ever saw at one time are crowdin around in the
square? Those boys don't know it, but they're fightin our fight,
too. They're makin onions grow all over the land where nothin
but cactus grew before . . . and they'll have the machinists
and the blasters with 'em before the week is out . . . try and
stop 'em!

YASHA

Did he say onions?

DAUBER

Yes, but he means unions!

YASHA

O.

LARRY

Did you see the people . . . the tons of 'em? And the order, the quiet? I lost my Aunt Jessie in a crowd of boilermakers, bunched together with their wives and kids on one side of the square . . . the kids all had bugles! I'll find her blowin a bugle, I guess! Unless they pull her in for carryin concealed deadly leaflets—two-gun Jessie herself! Over on the other side of the square, the roughers with their kids . . . and their kids had drums.

DRUGGIST

I saw them. In the middle of the square were the rolling mill workers—their kids out in front too, with fifes.

LARRY

Do you know what it takes to keep a kid from blowin his bugle or bangin his drum? They're all there now, not makin a sound—Just waitin, waitin—ready to strike up the band as soon as they hear the good news.

DRUGGIST

I asked one little boy why he wasn't playin his fife—and he said to me, "Mister, that's discipline."

LARRY

Tonight's the night! O boy, if they get together! O boy, O boy, O boy! Good-bye, open shop in Steeltown! Hello, closed shop!

MOLL

Comes over and sits by him.
What's the difference?

LARRY

The difference? Open shop is when a boilermaker can be kicked around, demoted, fired, like that—he's all alone, he's free—free to be wiped out. Closed shop—he's got fifty thousand other boilermakers behind him, ready to back him up, every one of them, to the last lunch pail. The difference? It's like the five fingers on your hand.
That's
Tapping one finger.
the boilermakers—just one finger—but this—
Pointing to finger for each.
rollers, roughers, machinists, blasters, boilermakers—that's closed shop!
Makes a fist of it.
that's a union!
Thumbing nose with that hand.
O boy! O boy! O boy!
The LIBERTY COMMITTEE *seem curiously the target for the gesture.*

CLERK

Order in the courtroom!
Next case. Name?

PREXY

I am President Prexy of College University, and these are Professors Mamie and Trixie of the same institution.

CLERK

Charge?

LARRY

Imitating his Aunt Jessie.
Maintaining a disorderly house!

SCENE EIGHT

FACULTYROOM

PREXY *dozes at his desk. Telephone bell rings.*

PREXY

Yes? Mr. Mister? Well, good heavens, man, show him in!
Enter MR. MISTER.
Mr. Mister!

MR. MISTER

President Prexy.

PREXY

Lovely morning!

MR. MISTER

It's raining.

PREXY

Oh, is it raining? I had no idea; well, of all things . . .

MR. MISTER

My wife's waiting for me. I'll come to the point at once.
    I need a speaker—one of your professors;
Someone who can put up a good front.

PREXY

We have lots of professors this year,
Who make lovely appearances. Just what kind of a man—?

MR. MISTER

Rally next Saturday night.
I'm extending your military tactics course.
Two years' compulsory training now.
Didn't they tell you?

PREXY

No, they didn't tell me. Heh, heh—heh—
    The last "heh" is rather sad.

MR. MISTER

Well, we're building up quite a nice little regiment.
You never know when you need 'em.
There was that Aliquippa strike in 1933.
The National Guard isn't any cheaper,
And I can handle college boys myself.

PREXY

Mmmmmm.

MR. MISTER

The country's going to the dogs,
What with the unions . . .

PREXY

    Anxious to corroborate.
Mmmmmmmmmm!

Mr. Mister

And sitdown strikes—
    Prexy *"Ts-Ts-Ts"-es.*
Well, I want a professor from the University,
To come and talk to the students, stir 'em up—
Someone who can talk.

Prexy

Let me see, who would be the kind of man
Most suited to your purpose?
    He thinks, then takes phone.
Send in Mamie, Scoot and Trixie.
    Hangs up.
Mamie's a new one, just up from the Argentine;
He may be the very article!
    Mr. Mister *grunts; takes out a newspaper. Enter*
    Mamie, Scoot *and* Trixie. Scoot, *whom we haven't*
    met yet, is the sort of eternally unwashed bookworm
    who sits bespectacled in the campus cafeteria utterly
    absorbed in his book, probably Sanskrit.

Prexy

Boys, this is Mr. Mister, our distinguished citizen—and
trustee. He—
    Whispers.
Pssssssst!

Scoot, Mamie and Trixie

Pssssst! Pssssst! Pssssst!
    They got into a football huddle.
Ta dee, ta doo, ta da da da!
Ta dee, ta doo, ta da da da!

SCOOT

Trying to rise.
But, President Prexy, I feel—

PREXY

Pulls him down.
Not now, Scoot, you first, Mamie!
Police whistle.

MAMIE

Steps forward modestly.
Applied science, Laboratory 54.
Thinks hard.
Military training? Mmmmmmm.
Has an idea.
Young gentlemen of the University—
I give you—the Triple-Flank-Maneuver!

SCOOT

President Prexy, I still feel—

PREXY

Shhhhhh!

MAMIE

*He goes right on, hoping to heaven something sensible
will come out.*
That maneuver is a sort of symbol, a connection if you will—
A connection so to speak with the times—
The times and the tides, the tides and the times as it were!
Cloistered life—sanctum of learning—

Home of the Higher Good—Haven of the—uh—Humanities,
the—
What shall I say?—The Humanities, in short!
   Very brightly.

Scoot

But—my dear sir!

Prexy

Scoot, your turn will come! Hush!

MAMIE

The University has a much broader *base* than many people
might give it credit for—having—a much—broader—base.
   Not so brightly, but still valiant.
May I, in conclusion, once again, as a sort of peroration, with-
out wishing to appear drastic, mind you, may I give you, but
also with no apologies, whatsoever, the Triple-Flank-
Maneuver?
   Mr. Mister *shakes his head emphatically.*

Prexy

   *Like the Madam whose first wench is discovered to be
   bowlegged.*
Thank you, thank you, thank you, thank you. Wait. We'll
let you know.
   Mamie *to the side, huffily.*

Mr. Mister

Too many long words. What's he think college boys are?
They won't know he's talking about military training.

PREXY

Hopefully to Number Two.
Now, Professor Scoot!

SCOOT

Very stern; his chance has come!
Ethics 42, Esthetics 6, Logic 1.

PREXY

How do you feel about our course in military tactics?

SCOOT

A fateful pause.
Do I have to say?

PREXY

What now?
Why, yes.

SCOOT

Poisonously.
Then I don't like military training,
Military training of any kind!
I'm a Tolstoyan!

MR. MISTER, PREXY, MAMIE, TRIXIE

A *what?*

SCOOT

A Little Brother.

MR. MISTER

Bellowing.
Where were you during the war?

SCOOT

Henry Ford's Peace Ship.

MR. MISTER, PREXY, MAMIE, TRIXIE

A mixture of rage, amazement and despair.
O! O! O! O!

PREXY

O, I'm sorry!
How did he get on our payroll?
Believe me, he's off it now.
Why, Trixie!

TRIXIE

*Has been removing his turtle-neck sweater, flings it on
the floor, and stands in robust and silly upper nakedness.*
Football Coach, also Elementary French . . .
He goes into his turn.
Listen, fellas!
Military course—two years?
Tree cheers! Listen, fellas!
Army training—Port in a storm!
There's nuttin like a uniform!
Soivice stripes—epaulettes—
Silver Shoit maybe—attababy!
Builds you up!—Alma Mater!
Sex Appeal!
Two years! Tree cheers!

Stick your chest out!
Be a man!

Mr. Mister

At last.
Wonderful! Wonderful!

Prexy

Beaming and helping Trixie *on with his sweater.*
Enchanting, enchanting, enchan*ting!*

Mr. Mister

You can both consider yourselves on my Liberty Committee.
Mamie *peeks forward.*
I guess we can use Mamie too, those long words may come
in handy there—but not that Peace Ship—!
Scoot *snorts.*
Now you can tell the boys we're buying them the best mili-
tary equipment—
The music gently goes lullaby.
Riot guns, tear gas, hand grenades, cartridges, everything—
they're going to find that three or even four years of such
training
Is not going to hurt—not going to hurt—

Not going to hurt—

SCENE NINE

dr. specialist's office

Mr. Mister *being examined by* Dr. Specialist.

MR. MISTER

Not going to hurt, is it, Doctor?
It's not going to hurt?

DR. SPECIALIST

Now, don't be alarmed, old man,
A purely routine examination. . . .
Just breathe naturally.

MR. MISTER

It hurts sometimes when I breathe, Doc, you know.

DR. SPECIALIST

Where—here?
    Tries various places.

MR. MISTER

No—not now, Doc. But it does hurt.

DR. SPECIALIST

Just breathe naturally.
    MR. MISTER *breathes heavily, with fear.*
Mmmm. Mostly nerves. There are some new injections,
rather rare in this country. We'll start them tomorrow; and
remember—a long cure at Vichy this summer. I think that's
all.

MR. MISTER

  All? You're certainly not forgetting to take my tempera-
ture and pulse, Doctor?

DR. SPECIALIST

Suppressing a smile.
Fair enough.
Does so.
Incidentally, old man, I want to thank you for being made chairman of the Liberty Committee. It means a great deal to me, as you probably knew. Among other things, I believe that's all I needed to get a research appointment I've been after for months.
Takes thermometer; looks at it.
Perfectly normal.

MR. MISTER

Really disappointed.
Normal?

DR. SPECIALIST

Completely. Pulse a bit jumpy. Just nerves, that's all.

ATTENDANT'S VOICE

Over desk-speaker.
Ella Hammer to see you, Doctor.

MR. MISTER

Ella Hammer?
That's the sister of the machinist who got hurt, isn't it?
What's she doing here?

DR. SPECIALIST

No idea. I treated him at the clinic.

MR. MISTER

He lights a cigar.
I think I know what she wants.
The man was drunk at the time, wasn't he?
Offers DR. SPECIALIST *a cigar.*

DR. SPECIALIST

Drunk? Why no.
He also refuses the cigar.

MR. MISTER

On the alert, but revealing it.
No? That's very interesting. I was sure I heard he slipped
Because he had been drinking.

DR. SPECIALIST

Well . . . Is it causing you any trouble?

MR. MISTER

Easily.
Oh, in a sort of way. He's been trying to put over
This new union stuff on the employees. . . .
The kind that's never satisfied.
His sister's beefing all over the place
How he got pushed into that ladle. . . .
Rather humorously.
You know I had a hard time deciding whether a doctor
Was the right type to head a Liberty Committee; I
   decided—
Well, for a number of reasons. . . .
I assumed, naturally, after you examined him—
Didn't *you* say he was drunk?

DR. SPECIALIST

I . . . ?

MR. MISTER

A bit sharply.

Yes, you! As a matter of fact, I phoned the newspapers only this morning to send someone over to get the story from you. . . .

Humorous again.

I'm wondering how easily you could explain your sudden resignation as chairman of the Liberty Committee to your extensive practice. . . . That is, if a change was found advisable. . . .

The cigar drops from his mouth; he is suddenly a sort of maniac.

Good God, I'm a sick man, Doctor! Doesn't anyone realize how sick I am? I have nightmares, I'm in the middle of an earthquake! Call it nerves, call it what you like! I don't understand the times . . . unions, unions . . .

He grinds the cigar under his heel.

We raised their wages, now they want a union! Things are slipping from my grasp; what's it coming to? My own doctor helps to make me sick!

He calms down.

There, you see.

Brokenly, and with great charm.

I guess you can handle her, eh?

There is a long pause. MR. MISTER, *completely recovered, leaves. On the way he meets* ELLA HAMMER *coming in. They stare at each other, then* MR. MISTER *looks once again at* DR. SPECIALIST, *and departs.*

ELLA

She wears a tam and windbreaker. She is no longer young; right now she is in dead earnest.

Hello, Doctor.
Doctor, you examined Joe—
Doctor, you're the one to know;
If he ever touched a drop of liquor,
He couldn't hold it. You know his stomach.
   They take enough out of his paycheck
For you to know his stomach by now!

DR. SPECIALIST

   He taps twice with his pencil.
Yes.

ELLA

Is the rumor true that they
Mean to say that he was drunk?

DR. SPECIALIST

   The pencil taps.
Yes.

ELLA

But, Doctor, you know those hoodlums framed him!
Pushed him into that ladle
Because he wasn't afraid to talk!
He's been expecting this for weeks!
He even told *you* that!

DR. SPECIALIST

   The pencil taps.
Yes.

ELLA

Workers who have been cheated and lied to and sold out—
They daren't trust anybody no more!

They mustn't lose their faith in Joe, now—
You see that, don't you?
> *Her voice rises. No tears, only fury.*

Dr. Specialist

> *The pencil taps.*

Yes.

Ella

> *His last "yes" disarms her. Somewhat more quietly.*

So—you will tell the workers it was all a frameup . . .
You'll say their confidence in him was not unfounded?
I hoped you would.

Attendant's Voice

Reporters from the newspapers, sir.

Dr. Specialist

> *The pencil taps.*

Yes.
> *Enter two* Reporters.

Reporter One

Good morning, Doctor.

Reporter Two

Mr. Mister phoned us to come here; we aren't quite sure
what for.
> *A pause.*

Dr. Specialist

> *Finally he speaks. He looks steadily down at something
> on his desk.*

Gentlemen, I'll be brief. My statement is this: I examined

the man Hammer shortly after his injury at the Steeltown mills
last Thursday. He was obviously intoxicated.
    ELLA *shoots a swift glance at him.*
That is all.

REPORTER ONE

But, Doctor, isn't there any more?

REPORTER TWO

That hardly makes a complete story.

ELLA

    Steps forward; so quietly you have to strain to hear her.
A story? Is that what your papers want, a story?

Listen, here's a story.
Not much fun, and not much glory;
Lowclass . . . lowdown. . . .
The thing you never care to see,
Until there is a showdown.
Here it is—I'll make it snappy:
Are you ready? Everybody happy?

Joe Worker gets gypped;
For no good reason, just gypped,
From the start until the finish comes . . .
They feed him out of garbage cans,
They breed him in the slums!
Joe Worker will go,
To shops where stuff is on show;
He'll look at the meat,
He'll look at the bread,
And too little to eat sort of goes to the head.

One big question inside me cries:
How many fakers, peace undertakers,
Paid strikebreakers,
How many toiling, ailing, dying, piledup bodies,
Brother, does it take to make you wise?

Joe Worker just drops,
Right at his workin he drops,
Weary, weary, tired to the core;
And then if he drops out of sight there's always plenty more!
Joe Worker must know
That somebody's got him in tow. . . .
Yet what is the good
For just one to be clear?
Oh, it takes a lot of Joes
To make a sound you can hear!
One big question inside me cries:
How many frameups, how many shakedowns,
Lockouts, sellouts,
How many times machine guns tell the same old story,
Brother, does it take to make you wise?

28. Puzzled America

SHERWOOD ANDERSON

Nothing could be more wrong than the impression that America's population during the depression years was composed

From *Puzzled America* (New York: Charles Scribner's Sons, 1935), pp. 54–65, 69–83. Copyright 1935 Charles Scribner's Sons; renewal copyright © 1963 Eleanor C. Anderson. Reprinted with the premission of Charles Scribner's Sons and Harold Ober Associates Inc.

*olely of apathetic unemployed and overworked or of disaf-
ected intellectuals yearning for a Soviet America. The New
Deal may not have succeeded in eradicating the depression,
but it engaged some of the best Americans as government
employees, "nonpolitical" technicians but idealists nonetheless,
working hard on the TVA and in the CCC camps to save men
who were going to waste and resources that were being frit-
tered away. No one was better able to understand and report
on these crucially important Americans than Sherwood Anderson, who found in them "something I have been hungry to find,
men working at work they love, not thinking of money or promotion, happy men, laughing men. They think they are saving something. They think they are making something."*

The TVA

There is the Tennessee River. It starts up in the Blue Ridge
country. Little rivers come racing down, the Clinch, the Hol-
ston, and others. The Tennessee is a hill-country river, working
its way down valleys, under big hills, little hills, now creeping
west, now south, now north—Virginia, West Virginia, Kentucky, Tennessee, down into northern Alabama. The hill country of north Georgia is in the TVA sphere of influence. That is
what this TVA thing is, "a sphere of influence."

It is something to dream and hope for, this land drained by
the Tennessee. There are a few rich valleys, growing blue
grass. There are mountain ranges. Once all these mountains
and hills were covered with magnificent forests. It was one of
the two Morgans who are in charge of this vast enterprise with
David Lilienthal, H. A. Morgan, the land man, the folk man
of the project, who talked to me of that. He was president of
the University of Tennessee before he got into this thing and he
is a land man.

He talked for an hour and I got a sharp sense of the land-
loving man. There was the story of how the hill lands had been

robbed. No use blaming any one. The big timber men came to denude the hills. Then the little ones with the "peckerwood" mills came to clean up.

The farmers were left on the hills. Traditions grew up about these people. John Fox wrote of them in *The Trail of the Lonesome Pine*. Not so good. Jeeter, of Erskine Caldwell's *Tobacco Road*, is nearer the real thing. They were of the feud country, a pretty romantic lot, in books and stories. In real life they were something else—in real life it was a pitiful rather than a romantic story.

It was the story of a people clinging, year after year, to little hillside farms. Every year they got poorer and poorer. Some of these men went out of their hills to the coal mines and later to the factory towns that had come into the hills, but many came back. There is the love of his own country in the hill man. He does not want to leave the hills.

The depression brought the hill men back faster. I went into little upland valleys where a farm of thirty or forty acres might once have sustained one family. (It would have been poor enough fare—hard enough living for the one family.)

But now, often, on such a farm I found three or four families. Sons had come back to their mountain fathers, bringing wives, bringing children. They had built little huts—often without windows.

"At least here, on my father's land, a little corn can be raised. There will be a cabin floor to sleep on at night. It is less terrible than walking among the out-of-works, in some industrial town."

There is a story of an Englishman coming into the hill country, going among the hill men. The Englishman was stunned.

"These hill men are English," he said. "I don't like it."

"You don't like what?"

"I don't like their failing; I don't like to think of Englishmen as failures in a new land."

It is a land of tall, straight men—the kind of stock out of which came Daniel Boone, Andrew Jackson, Andrew Johnson.

They have fine looking children, these men. The children fade young. The women fade young.

There is bad diet. No money. The soil gets thinner and thinner with every passing year. Most of this hill land should go back into forest. Every rain that washes down the hillsides takes more of the soil away.

Suppose you put the hills back into forest, what are you to do with these people? Are you to herd them down into industrial cities, where there are already too many men out of work, living on charity?

You have to think of the fact that what we call the modern world has pretty much gone on past these people, as it has gone completely past the tenant farmers, farther South. There are these mountaineers, millions of them scattered over a vast territory, touching several states. These are not the foreigners of whom we Americans can say so glibly—"If they do not like it here, let them go back where they came from." These men are from the oldest American stock we have. It is the kind of stock out of which came Abraham Lincoln. Robert Lincoln, his father, and Nancy Hanks, his mother, were poor whites of the hills.

And there is all this other stuff about us of which we Americans are so proud, our well-equipped houses, motor cars, bathrooms, warm clothes—what we call our American standard of living. All these things not touching these mountain people.

They are clinging to their hills in one of the most beautiful lands in the world.

"Can we take what they and their hills already have—adding nothing—find the riches in their hills—and give these men modern life? If this modern mechanical life is any good, it should be good for these people."

There is wealth in the land on which these people have tried to live. It is a new kind of wealth, the wealth of the modern man, of the modern world. It is wealth in the form of energy.

Power—the coinage of the modern world!

There is plenty of power—the private companies have only got a little of it so far—flowing silently away, along the Tennessee, along the rivers that come down out of the hills to make the Tennessee.

Long ago, I'm told, army engineers went through these hills. They drew up a kind of plan, having in mind the use of all this wasted power in case of war, power to be harnessed, to make munitions, to kill men.

There came the World War and the building of the Wilson Dam at Muscle Shoals. That is where the Tennessee, in its wanderings, dips down into northern Alabama, thrusts down into the land of cotton. It is something to be seen. All good Americans should go and see it. If the Russians had it there would be parades, special editions of illustrated magazines got out and distributed by the government.

There it is, however, completely magnificent. You go down, by elevator, some ten stories, under the earth, under the roaring river, and walk out into great light clean rooms. There is a song, the song of the great motors. You are stirred. Something in you—the mechanically-minded American in you, begins to sing. Everything is so huge, so suggestive of power and at the same time so delicate. You walk about muttering.

"No wonder the Russians wanted our engineers," you say to yourself.

The great motors sing on, each motor as large as a city room. There is a proud kind of rebirth of Americanism in you.

"Some of our boys did this," you say to yourself, throwing out your chest.

The Wilson Dam never was made to impound much water. The idea was to take the power directly out of the swirl of water rushing down over the shoals.

But sometimes it doesn't rush. Dry seasons come, far up-river and in the little rivers. The forest-denuded hills do not hold back the water after rains. Every time you build another dam upriver you get power out of the new dam and you increase the power at Muscles Shoals. They are building two dams now, each to make a great lake, the Joe Wheeler, some twenty-five miles above the Wilson, and the Norris, far up-river, a day's drive, near Knoxville. They will both make great lakes, the shore line of the Norris to be some nine hundred miles, it to be at places two hundred feet deep.

Power stored to make a steady stream of power—power from the Wilson being used to build the Joe Wheeler and the Norris —the river being made to harness itself. There is a new kind of poetry in that thought.

These, the first of perhaps a dozen dams to be built along one river—power aplenty for great stretches of country far outside the sphere of influence of the present TVA.

The power to be used, to give an opportunity to small industries, reduce the power costs in towns over a wide country, make electrical power available in homes where it cannot now be used—the money coming in to go back into the country out of which the power came——

Denuded hills to be reforested, soil washing stopped.

This soil washing, going on in every denuded hill country, filling your lakes with mud after you build your dams, utterly destroying, making a barren waste of wide stretches of country. It's hard to dramatize the slow, steady year-after-year eating away of soil richness. Whole lands have been destroyed by it, made into deserts. The government foresters, working with the CCC boys, are like wronged children in their eagerness to make their work understood. "Tell them about it. Please tell them," they keep saying. They follow you around eagerly. "You are a writer. Can't you tell them? Can't you make them understand that we are builders? These CCC camps. We are taking these city kids and making builders of them. The boys in the camps begin to understand. Please make every one understand."

Engineers and foresters going at night, after the day's work, to country towns in the district, to country school houses, lecturing, explaining. I found in these men working on the TVA something I have been hungry to find, men working at work they love, not thinking of money or promotion, happy men, laughing men. They think they are saving something. They think they are making something.

I went into the TVA accompanied by a friend, a business man who lives in Chicago. Formerly he was a college professor. Once he wrote a beautiful novel that got little or no attention. He was poor and went into business. He succeeded.

But like a good many American business men, he wasn't very happy in his success. When the New Deal was announced he went in for it, head over heels.

He was strong for the NRA, but recently he has been skeptical. I had written him, telling him that I was going to look at the TVA and he wanted to go along. We met in Knoxville and spent most of the first night in a hotel room, talking.

He was discouraged.

"It isn't going to work," he said. He was speaking of the NRA. "They are trying to fix prices now. The small man is doomed." He is himself not one of the small men. "You can't stop the chisellers. You can't. You can't."

We went to look at the TVA. We did look. We listened. We went down among the workers on the dams. We went into power houses, visited men in their offices. Sometimes we were accompanied by enthusiasts, engineers, foresters, and others, and often we were alone. We had our own car.

We kept talking. We kept looking. A change came over my friend.

"So this is the South," he said.

He had the Northern man's point of view. To the Southerner the South is the deep South. He began talking of the TVA as the South's opportunity. In spite of the fact that my friend was once a college professor he is an educated man. He knows his American history.

"Look what we Northerners did to the South," he kept saying as his enthusiasm grew. "And now this."

We took our look at the TVA, the immediate sphere of influence, and pushed on down into the deep South. We got into the back country, going by back roads.

Men were plowing in the Southern fields. There was the thing, always a new wonder to the city man, the patience of men with the earth, the way they cling to it. We were in a poor district. They are not hard to find in the back country of the deep South. There were these miles of back roads, deeply rutted, even dangerous, bridges fallen into decay.

"It is a kind of inferno," my friend kept saying. We had just left the land of new hope, men busy, the strikingly charming government-built town of Norris, at Norris Dam, going up, men laughing at their work——

Memory in us both of a lunch had with a dozen foresters in a town in the heart of the TVA—the town sitting on land that would presently be a lake bottom—the laughter in the room, the anxiety of the men that their story be told straight——

"Don't talk too big. Don't promise too much. We may be stopped."

That against the land of desolation, of no hope—the poor farmers, getting poorer every year. The cotton allotment in the South wasn't going to be of much help to the people along the road we had got into. It would go to the land owners and not one out of ten of the little farmers, white or black, along the road we travelled would own the land he was plowing——

Poor little unpainted cabins half fallen down. Pale women with tired eyes. Undernourished children playing in bare yards before the cabins.

"There are too many of these."

We had got into an argument. My friend had lived his boyhood on an Iowa farm.

"You have places as bad as this in your Chicago," I said, not wanting him to think all American misery was in the South.

"I know, but not on the land! In the end, everything comes back to the land."

"The people who cannot love the land on which they live are a lost people."

"It is right that all America should try this experiment in the South," he said. There were the one-mule farmers patiently plowing the land beside the road.

"It is wonderful the way man goes on. In spite of defeat he goes on," my friend said.

Two old men came out of a strip of pine woods. They were toothless, bent old men, Southerners, poor whites, going along the road in silence. We passed them.

My friend leaned out of the car. He was excited.

"Hey!" he called.

The two old men stopped and stared at us. I stopped the car. My friend hesitated.

"Drive on," he said. He turned to me and laughed. "I wanted to tell them something. I can't," he said. "It would sound too silly."

"What?" I said.

"Something new in American life is begun back there, and it mustn't be stopped," he said. I thought it was the feeling, alive in him, as it is still curiously alive in so many Americans, alive in spite of greed, chiseling, desire for fake money, bigness. The feeling of men for men—desire to some day work for others. The TVA may be a beginning.

Tough Babes in the Woods

They have made a little town under the hill—between two hills—in a narrow valley down which flows a mountain stream. This is one of a dozen such little towns I have been in during the last week, and they are all pretty much alike. There is an army man and a forester or two in each camp. The army men have charge of the camp. They differ. Some add little home-like touches, others do not. There may be twenty or thirty or fifty houses in such a camp town, and it may have one street or two or three. They are laying down sidewalks in the one I have just been in. This is the time of mud in the valleys and in the hills. Soon the spring rains will be coming here.

The boys in this camp town, at the edge of which I am sitting—I am sitting with my notebook on a flat stone under a rhododendron bush—the boys go up the hills and bring down flat stones. They are laying sidewalks along the street down which I look, making their town neat against the muddy time to come. A man goes about among them directing the work, a tall lean intelligent man of thirty. He is the forester of this camp—a soft-speaking Southerner—and this is Saturday, so the boys do not go to work in the woods. It is a clear quiet day and rather warm. Spring will be coming soon in this Southern Appalachian country. I hear a little animal moving back of me in the woods. A hawk floats in the clear blue sky above the valley.

When I drove over to this mountain camp this morning I saw a man plowing a hillside above the next valley to the South. He was a lean, ragged, hard-bitten mountain man, and he lived in a one-room cabin at the end of the field he was plowing. I have seen as many as nineteen children in one family in such a cabin. I have seen poverty that has made me halt. I have seen a thousand such cabins perched on hills in southwestern Virginia, Pennsylvania, West Virginia, Tennessee, north Georgia, Kentucky, and westward, across the Mississippi, in the Ozark mountains of the Missouri, and only two weeks ago, in the city of New York, I saw just such a cabin on the stage, in a play called *Tobacco Road*.

Tobacco Road, indeed! It is a road to ruin—this Poor White hillside farming going on year after year, over millions of acres of the American hill country. As for the Poor White Georgia Cracker man of the Georgia plains, tied to his cotton and tobacco farming on poor exhausted soil, his story is a different one. We are in the hills now. This is the story of the hill man. The story here also one of wasted fine material. I know the mountain men, and when I am at home I live among them. The story of the lives they live, how they got like that, the death of the children of this fine stock by undernourishment— this is another tragic American story. How I have hated the romanticists who have thrown the cloud of romance about such lives.

But I am trying to tell now the story of the camp towns, of the CCC coming to these hills. They are scattered out over the country, hundreds, even thousands of such little temporary towns—the government putting them up. The houses of the towns are long one-story affairs built of thick building paper. They stand up high and dry above the valley bottoms on stone foundations.

There is a commissary building, a mess hall, a post office, a library, a temporary hospital. They are all temporary houses.

Suppose they shouldn't be temporary. Suppose what is going on here is but a beginning. It is an interesting idea that this thing that has now begun in America—government having a thought of the land, men in Washington, in government, daring to say—"We'll begin trying it."

Trying what?

Suppose it should come down to this, that there is a plot on foot in America—men actually serious about it—a plot, let's say, to save America from the Americans.

Actually they are serious about the plot, some of them. I have been in Washington—talked to men there, men who struck me as first-rate, serious-minded men—not at all romantic. I do not mean bankers or industrialists. I mean men of another type—scientific men, government engineers, foresters, hard-working men, most of whom have been employed for years in the Interior and the Agricultural departments.

Much of what these men told me is, as they say in Washington now—"off the record." It is still, it seems, somewhat irregular even a little dangerous to have dreams of a greater America, an America really used. You can't call names.

"What, you dream of a physical America controlled, plowing of the land controlled—this or that section of America to be permanently in forest—river flow control, floods controlled at the flood source?"

"You say that one great flood—let us say of Mother Mississippi—may cost more than ten years' constructive work back in the hills, in denuded forests where floods begin?"

"This, off the record. Some one may think I am a Socialist or a Bolshevik."

Men's minds pushing, somewhat timidly, into a new social view of physical America. How are they to tell the story to that lean mountain man? Let us say that he owns his few poor hillside acres. Who is to tell him, "Thou shalt not"? The right to go on plowing, where plowing is sheer land destruction—the traditional right of the American individualist, big or little.

"It's mine."

"It's mine."

Who is to say to me, a free American, "Thou shalt not"?

Into this camp have come boys, the greater number of them from American cities. They are young boys, most of them about high school age. But for this depression, in the natural flow of an older American life—it seems suddenly old now—as things have been running in America for the last two, three or four generations these boys, being for the most part city and town boys, would have come out of school and would have become clerks or factory hands.

Or—and this would go for a lot of them—they would have become tough city guys—the kind that make bright young gangsters—the kind you see leaning against walls near gang hangouts in cities.

"How much to kill a man?"

"How much?"

But, you see, even the rackets have become a bit thin now, clerkships have fallen away, prohibition has gone, the factories are not exactly howling for men.

So these CCC camps have gathered them in, all kinds of men.

That forester down there, directing the boys as they lay sidewalks in their new woods town, was in Montana last year. He had under him out there some two or three hundred boys, mostly from the East Side of New York—tough birds—most of them, he says. He speaks of them with an affectionate grin. "Boy, what we had to do to them—what they did to us." They have been jerked up out of that environment, hauled in fast trains across two-thirds of the United States and thrown into a forest camp some seven thousand feet up in the magnificent hills. They had to build the camps, keep themselves clean, keep their bedding and their quarters clean, learn to swing an axe— "We had to watch them like babes that they did not kill each other with the axes." The boys learned to make beds, learned the necessary sanitary laws that must govern men living in camps, the give and take of man to man, so essential to life where men live, sleep, talk, dream in one great room—rows of cots all in the open—the door at the end of the room open—sight of the wooded hills when you go to sleep at night, when you wake in the morning——

These men, the greater majority of them out of the crowded factory towns.

"It's the beginning of some kind of revolution in life—for them at least."

"Sure."

Not every man can swing an axe. Some men born in the forests, never get the knack. There are Babe Ruths among axemen too.

It is a kind of revolution in many lives that goes both backward and forward. Forward, let's say, to a possible conception of an America that shall belong essentially to all Americans—as one thoughtful, serious-minded man, who felt he owed something to the ground under his feet, might feel toward one farm —such a man as might say to himself—"I want to leave this piece of ground, on which I have lived my life and made my living, a better piece of ground than it was when I came upon it." You get the idea—at least a dream of all American farmers saying "We'll live to build, not destroy."

Something of that sort.

Let's say, a new comprehensive forward look and then also, in this CCC thing something else—a kind of movement backward to an earlier American tone of life, when life did centre about the forests and the land, when men went out and fought it out with nature and got something men can get in no other way—a kind of man-making process that factory work and clerkships haven't as yet been able to bring into men's lives.

To use the land also to make men.

To use men also to make the land.

Who in America doesn't know what, over great stretches of country, we Americans have done to the land? Soil erosion going on that is costing us each year more than the entire cost of our military and naval establishments, and all of this due to the old belief that if I own a piece of land I have the right to do as I please with it. I can tear off the forest.

"It's mine, isn't it?"

The valley down which I look as I sit writing is one of a thousand such valleys in the range of mountains that stretch across our country from East to West, separating the North from the South. It is a stream-source country. This country with the great stretches of cut-over lands in northern Michigan, Wisconsin, and Minnesota is the stream source from which comes much of the water of the Mississippi. The valley down which I look is watered by one of the little rivers that come down from the hills. There might be fifty such streams in one county in this country. The natives tell me that all were formerly good trout and bass streams. They went softly along through the deep woods. They were icy cold even in summer. They were steady year-round streams, fed by mountain springs. The valley is broken by many little side valleys. It is like an old saw with many teeth broken out. In each little side valley may be found a few under-fed mountain families, persistently plowing hillside lands that will not and cannot make them a living.

These CCC camps are a beginning. If you look at the map you will see them scattered most thickly along the Pacific Coast, north at the headwaters of the Mississippi and in these border mountains between the North and South, and on the southern side of these hills where the streams go down to the Atlantic. There are camps now everywhere in these hills along the Southern Appalachian, the Cumberland, the Blue Ridge, and westward to the Mississippi and the Ozarks. They extend eastward to where, at Lynchburg, Virginia, the big hills end and the little ones step softly down to the Tidewater country.

It may well be that all of this land, except only the valley bottoms, should be wiped out as farming lands. Let the trees again have the hills. There should be better use for the life of these hill men, starving and destroying in these hills.

The hand of government is reaching out and out. The government is acquiring all the time more and more thousands of acres of these hill lands.

They are having classes in the camps. They are teaching geography and history. As the boys work in the forests, a forester goes with them. They are learning to tell the ash from the maple and the spruce from the oak. It is a tremendous educational experiment.

The greater number of the boys are city bred. They are from the families of the poor. They are young American born —Poles, Italians, Jews, Lithuanians, and Germans—the first generation away from the old country. They are short squat figures of American men in the making, with the twang of the city speech on their lips. Nearly all of the boys in this camp town are out of the back streets of Newark, Hoboken, Jersey City, and New York. "Where are you from, buddy?" I say to one of them.

"Oh, take a look. What do you t'ink?"

"I'm from Avenue A."

The mountain men who come into the camp, to work, or just to look, stand staring at the city boys. They laugh softly. Such awkward axe-swinging. Some of these mountain men have been axe-swingers since they were babes. Some of them, the older ones, worked in the lumber camps in these hills when the first forests, the great forests, were cut away. They tell you about it. First the great companies with the big band mills came, taking the best, and these were followed by the little peckerwood mills—often a model T Ford engine and a saw, cleaning up what the big ones left.

There was destruction and waste aplenty. Who cared? Individualism. The old America. "You should have seen it before they came," an old mountain man said. A kind of awe creeps into his voice. "The forest was like a great church. Oh, the great trees. You sank to your knees in the moss under foot."

I myself remember an old man who came to my father's house when I was a boy. He was an old, old man from an Ohio River town where my own father once lived and he talked to my father of the river. "I remember when I was a boy," he said. "I swam with other boys in the Ohio. It was a clear stream then. We used to swim way ,out and look down. The water was so clear we could see the bottom."

There is something still to be seen in this CCC movement. It isn't just an idea of giving a certain number of men work, helping them over the depression.

The leaves of the forest trees, even the young new trees, now growing, fall and lie on the ground. Next year more leaves fall. There is a soft porous bottom made. Moss begins to grow. It is a great blotter. Pinchot of Pennsylvania, when he was making his first fight against forest destruction, used to go before control committees with a wide board in his hand. He set the board on a table at an angle of forty-five degrees and poured a glass of water down it.

Then he took the same board and tacked blotting paper on it. Again he poured water down the board, but this time it did not rush off. That told the story. It is a thing the government can do and that the individual cannot do. There are these millions of acres of water-shed land, none of it any good for farming. It should go back into forests, making future wealth.

Rains come and wash the plowed lands away and every rain takes its toll of richness. You go through these hill lands in the spring and summer, seeing the hill men at the plow, often on lands so steep you wonder that the man and bony horse do not both roll to the bottom—men slowly and painfully plowing, planting, and hoeing—then the rains—there the fields go.

It would not have mattered so much if it were only one field, a few fields plowed and lost, great gashes in the hill-sides, water rushing down pell-mell, floods in the low lands, towns destroyed. There are still millions of such fields being plowed. The whole country pays.

Multiply it. Multiply it.

The forester comes up to me along the street of the camp. He sees me sitting and writing under the rhododendron bush and hesitates. "Hello," I say.

"I do not want to disturb you."

We grin at each other. "Come on," he says.

Putting my notebook into my pocket I go and get into his truck and we begin climbing up a mountain road. It's risky going. This is one of the new roads the city boys have made. It rained last night and the car slithers about. Up and up we go, far up into the hills and the car stops. We go on afoot. We go into the brush. Climbing over fallen logs, up and up. "I wanted to show you a tree they didn't get," he says, referring to the early lumber men. We stop before a great spruce far up in the hills. "They had to leave it," he says. "They couldn't get to it."

We are sitting now on a rocky promontory and looking way over the hills. From up here the smaller hills are like the waves of the sea in a storm. The man I am with is one of the believers. He talks and talks. He is sore at the lumberman who beat him into these forests.

"The government should never have let them do it," he keeps saying. "We should have had a chance. Our men should have been here." He declares that under the foresters the lumber companies might have taken as much lumber without denuding the hills. "They could have taken out all the good timber and left the half-grown trees that in another generation would have made a second great cutting."

Now it will take us fifty years to get back what was wantonly destroyed. He stands beside me on the mountain top swearing, but it is already an old story to me, this cry of the forester. Now they are in the woods again. They are directing the work of these boys in the CCC camps.

The depression has given them their chance. "Hurrah for the depression," one of them said to me. They are making a new kind of American man out of the city boy in the woods, and they are planning at least to begin to make a new land with the help of such boys.

PART SEVEN

Organizers, Capitalists, Fascists, Communists:

"GUYS LIKE ME AND YOU"

---

29. Devil's Dream

KENNETH FEARING

Born in a Chicago suburb, Oak Park, Illinois, the son of a lawyer, Kenneth Fearing (1902–1961) attracted considerable attention with his first volume of poems, Angel Arms *(1929), and with his second,* Poems *(1936), found the nervous staccato voice that seemed so characteristic of the decade. To Fearing's comrades, the depression radicals, it seemed characteristic of something else: "And as the poems in their chronological progression become more incisive and attain Marxist lucidity," wrote Edward Dahlberg in his introduction to the small paperback volume, "the ironic comments rise and expand into an affirmative Communist statement." Even though we in our time are interested in other literary matters than affirmative Communist statements, we may very possibly con-*

From *New and Selected Poems* by Kenneth Fearing (Bloomington: Indiana University Press, 1956). Reprinted with the permission of the Kenneth Fearing Estate, and the Indiana University Press.

cur in the judgment of Robert Cantwell at the time: "More than any other writer Fearing sums up the attitude of his generation; and in time the publication of his new poems may be recognized for what it is—a cultural event of the first importance." Fearing published Dead Reckoning *in 1938, still summing up the same attitude; by the time of the appearance of his* Collected Poems (1940) *he was already, like Robert Cantwell, in the employ of Henry Luce; and the attitude was changing. Fearing continued to publish poetry, as well as a number of extremely skillful psychological mystery thrillers, but he was no longer summing up his generation when death claimed him in 1961. The poem that follows originally appeared in* Dead Reckoning.

But it could never be
    how could it ever happen if it never did before and
        it's not so now

But suppose that the face behind those steel prison bars
    why do you dream about a face lying cold in the
        trenches streaked with rain and dirt and blood
    is it the very same face seen so often in the mirror
    just as though it could be true

But what if it is, what if it is, what if it is, what if the
        thing that cannot happen really happens just
        the same
    suppose the fever goes a hundred, then a hundred
        and one
    what if Holy Savings Trust goes from 98 to 88 to 78
        to 68, then drops down to 28 and 8 and out of
        sight
    and the fever shoots a hundred two, a hundred
        three, a hundred four, then a hundred five and
        out

But now there's only the wind and the sky and sunlight
    and the clouds,

with everyday people walking and talking as they
    always have before along the everyday street
doing ordinary things with ordinary faces and ordi-
    nary voices in the ordinary way
just as they always will

Then why does it feel like a bomb, why does it feel like
    a target
    like standing on the gallows with the trap about to
        drop
    why does it feel like a thunderbolt the second before
        it strikes, why does it feel like a tightrope walk
        high over hell

Because it is not, will not, never could be true
    that the whole wide, bright, green, warm, calm
        world goes
    CRASH.

30. U S A

JOHN DOS PASSOS

*When the unfledged young American writers of the Left at-
tempted to relate themselves to older writers who had been
successfully productive before the Crash, they turned not to
such models as Upton Sinclair, who had been writing socialist
propaganda novels for a generation, but to John Dos Passos*

(1896–   ). He was not only closer to their age, he was closer to their spirit, for he was no reformer but an active revolutionary in both art and politics. Respected as a brilliant young novelist, he had been arrested in 1927 on the picket line for Sacco and Vanzetti and jailed in the same cell with Michael Gold. In the thirties, he identified himself unhesitatingly with the extreme Left and seemed to draw from it the nourishment that he needed to produce his best work. Readers of the New Masses, *following with mounting excitement the episodes of his massive trilogy as they unfolded in the pages of the magazine like some extraordinary enlargement of their own lives, were often convinced that he was truly the embodiment of the idealized concept of the proletarian novelist. And* USA *has indeed lasted. What is more, there can be little doubt by now that with all its obvious failings, it will continue to last as one of the great fictional achievements of our age—even though in the midst of his task Dos Passos grew embittered toward the Communist party as a betrayer of American idealism and became suspicious of the Marxist philosophy that lay behind the very conception of his monumental work. With the passage of time, Dos Passos became an intellectually convinced conservative, but conservative philosophy (perhaps best seen at work in his trilogy,* District of Columbia, 1952*) never gave his subsequent fiction the strength and sweep of* USA. *These three excerpts, printed in the order in which they appear in the heart of the book, give an idea of the nervous excitement with which Dos Passos captured—by means of his own quasi-cinematic devices—the drama of the Crash and its impact upon the high and the low alike.*

NEWSREEL LXVIII

WALL STREET STUNNED

This is not Thirty-eight but it's old Ninety-seven
You must put her in Center on time

MARKET SURE TO RECOVER FROM SLUMP

Decline in Contracts

POLICE TURN MACHINE GUNS ON COLORADO MINE STRIKERS KILL 5 WOUND 40

sympathizers appeared on the scene just as thousands of office workers were pouring out of the buildings at the lunch hour. As they raised their placard high and started an indefinite march from one side to the other, they were jeered and hooted not only by the office workers but also by workmen on a building under construction

NEW METHODS OF SELLING SEEN

Rescue Crews Try to Upend Ill-fated Craft While Waiting For Pontoons

He looked 'round an' said to his black greasy fireman
Jus' shovel in a little more coal
And when we cross that White Oak Mountain
You can watch your Ninety-seven roll

I find your column interesting and need advice. I have saved four thousand dollars which I want to invest for a better income. Do you think I might buy stocks?

POLICE KILLER FLICKS CIGARETTE AS HE GOES TREMBLING TO DOOM

PLAY AGENCIES IN RING OF SLAVE GIRL MARTS

Maker of Love Disbarred as Lawyer

Oh the right wing clothesmakers
And the Socialist fakers
They make by the workers . . .
Double cross

They preach Social-ism
But practice Fasc-ism
To keep capitalism
By the boss

MOSCOW CONGRESS OUSTS OPPOSITION

It's a mighty rough road from Lynchburg to Danville
An' a line on a three mile grade
It was on that grade he lost his average
An' you see what a jump he made

MILL THUGS IN MURDER RAID

here is the most dangerous example of how at the decisive moment the bourgeois ideology liquidates class solidarity and turns a friend of the workingclass of yesterday into a most miserable propagandist for imperialism today

RED PICKETS FINED FOR PROTEST HERE

We leave our home in the morning
We kiss our children goodby

OFFICIALS STILL HOPE FOR RESCUE OF MEN

He was goin' downgrade makin' ninety miles an hour
When his whistle broke into a scream
He was found in the wreck with his hand on the throttle
An' was scalded to death with the steam

RADICALS FIGHT WITH CHAIRS AT UNITY MEETING

PATROLMEN PROTECT REDS

U. S. CHAMBER OF COMMERCE URGES CONFIDENCE

REAL VALUES UNHARMED

While we slave for the bosses
Our children scream an' cry
But when we draw our money
Our grocery bills to pay

PRESIDENT SEES PROSPERITY NEAR

Not a cent to spend for clothing
Not a cent to lay away

STEAMROLLER IN ACTION AGAINST MILITANTS

MINERS BATTLE SCABS

But we cannot buy for our children
Our wages are too low
Now listen to me you workers
Both you women and men
Let us win for them the victory
I'm sure it ain't no sin

CARILLON PEALS IN SINGING TOWER

the President declared it was impossible to view the increased advantages for the many without smiling at those who a short time ago expressed so much fear lest our country might come under the control of a few individuals of great wealth

HAPPY CROWDS THRONG CEREMONY

on a tiny island nestling like a green jewel in the lake that mirrors the singing tower, the President today participated in the dedication of a bird sanctuary and its pealing carillon, fulfilling the dream of an immigrant boy

THE CAMERA EYE (51)

at the head of the valley in the dark of the hills on the broken floor of a lurchedover cabin a man halfsits halflies propped up by an old woman two wrinkled girls that might be young   chunks of coal flare in the hearth flicker in his face white and sagging as dough   blacken the cavedin mouth the taut throat the belly swelled enormous with the wound he got working on the minetipple   the barefoot girl brings him a tincup of water   the woman wipes sweat off his streaming face with a dirty denim sleeve   the firelight flares in his eyes stretched big with fever in the women's scared eyes and in the blanched faces of the foreigners

without help in the valley hemmed by dark strike-silent hills the man will die (my father died we know what it is like to see a man die) the women will lay him out on the rickety cot the miners will bury him

in the jail it's light too hot the steamheat hisses we talk through the greenpainted iron bars to a tall white mustachioed old man some smiling miners in shirtsleeves a boy   faces white from mining have already the tallowy look of jailfaces
       foreigners what can we say to the dead?   foreigners what can we say to the jailed?   the representative of the political party talks fast through the bars join up with us and no other union we'll send you tobacco candy solidarity our lawyers will write briefs speakers will shout your names at meetings they'll carry your names on cardboard on picket-lines   the men in jail shrug their shoulders smile thinly our eyes look in their eyes through the bars   what can I say?
       (in another continent I have seen the faces looking out through the barred basement windows behind the ragged sentry's boots I have seen before day the straggling footsore prisoners herded through the streets limping between bayonets   heard the volley
       I have seen the dead lying out in those distant deeper valleys)   what can we say to the jailed?

in the law's office we stand against the wall the law is a big man with eyes angry in a big pumpkinface who sits and stares at us meddling foreigners through the door the deputies crane with their guns   they stand guard at the mines
       they blockade the miners' soupkitchens   they've cut off the road up the valley   the hiredmen with guns stand ready to shoot (they have made us foreigners in the land where we were born they are the conquering army that has filtered into the country unnoticed they have taken the hilltops by stealth they levy toll they stand at the minehead   they stand at the polls   they stand by when the bailiffs carry the furniture of the family evicted from the city tenement out on the sidewalk

they are there when the bankers foreclose on a farm they are ambushed and ready to shoot down the strikers marching behind the flag up the switchback road to the mine   those that the guns spare they jail)

the law stares across the desk out of angry eyes his face reddens in splotches like a gobbler's neck with the strut of the power of submachineguns sawedoffshotguns teargas and vomitinggas the power that can feed you or leave you to starve

sits easy at his desk his back is covered he feels strong behind him he feels the prosecutingattorney the judge an owner himself the political boss the minesuperintendent the board of directors   the president of the utility the manipulator of the holdingcompany

he lifts his hand towards the telephone
the deputies crowd in the door
we have only words against

POWER SUPERPOWER

In eighteen eighty when Thomas Edison's agent was hooking up the first telephone in London, he put an ad in the paper for a secretary and stenographer. The eager young cockney with sprouting muttonchop whiskers who answered it

had recently lost his job as officeboy. In his spare time he had been learning shorthand and bookkeeping and taking dictation from the editor of the English *Vanity Fair* at night and jotting down the speeches in Parliament for the papers. He came of temperance smallshopkeeper stock; already he was butting his bullethead against the harsh structure of caste that doomed boys of his class to a life of alpaca jackets, penmanship, subordination. To get a job with an American firm was to put a foot on the rung of a ladder that led up into the blue.

He did his best to make himself indispensable; they let him operate the switchboard for the first halfhour when the telephone service was opened. Edison noticed his weekly reports on the electrical situation in England

and sent for him to be his personal secretary.

Samuel Insull landed in America on a raw March day in eighty-one. Immediately he was taken out to Menlo Park, shown about the little group of laboratories, saw the strings of electriclightbulbs shining at intervals across the snowy lots, all lit from the world's first central electric station. Edison put him right to work and he wasn't through till midnight. Next morning at six he was on the job; Edison had no use for any nonsense about hours or vacations. Insull worked from that time on until he was seventy without a break; no nonsense about hours or vacations. Electric power turned the ladder into an elevator.

Young Insull made himself indispensable to Edison and took more and more charge of Edison's business deals. He was tireless, ruthless, reliable as the tides, Edison used to say, and fiercely determined to rise.

In ninetytwo he induced Edison to send him to Chicago and put him in as president of the Chicago Edison Company. Now he was on his own. *My engineering,* he said once in a speech, when he was sufficiently czar of Chicago to allow himself the luxury of plain speaking, *has been largely concerned with engineering all I could out of the dollar.*

He was a stiffly arrogant redfaced man with a closecropped mustache; he lived on Lake Shore Drive and was at the office at 7:10 every morning. It took him fifteen years to merge the five electrical companies into the Commonwealth Edison Company. *Very early I discovered that the first essential, as in other public utility business, was that it should be operated as a monopoly.*

When his power was firm in electricity he captured gas, spread out into the surrounding townships in northern Illinois. When politicians got in his way, he bought them, when laborleaders got in his way, he bought them. Incredibly his power grew. He was scornful of bankers, lawyers were his hired men.

He put his own lawyer in as corporation counsel and through him ran Chicago. When he found to his amazement that there were men (even a couple of young lawyers, Richberg and Ickes) in Chicago that he couldn't buy, he decided he'd better put on a show for the public;

Big Bill Thompson, the Builder:
punch King George in the nose,
the hunt for the treeclimbing fish,
the Chicago Opera.

It was too easy; the public had money, there was one of them born every minute, with the founding of Middlewest Utilities in nineteen twelve Insull began to use the public's money to spread his empire. His companies began to have open stockholders' meetings, to ballyhoo service, the small investor could sit there all day hearing the bigwigs talk. It's fun to be fooled. Companyunions hypnotized his employees; everybody had to buy stock in his companies, employees had to go out and sell stock, officeboys, linemen, trolley-conductors. Even Owen D. Young was afraid of him. *My experience is that the greatest aid in the efficiency of labor is a long line of men waiting at the gate.*

War shut up the progressives (no more nonsense about trustbusting, controlling monopoly, the public good) and raised Samuel Insull to the peak.

He was head of the Illinois State Council of Defense. *Now,* he said delightedly, *I can do anything I like.* With it came the perpetual spotlight, the purple taste of empire. If anybody didn't like what Samuel Insull did he was a traitor. Chicago damn well kept its mouth shut.

The Insull companies spread and merged put competitors out of business until Samuel Insull and his stooge brother Martin controlled through the leverage of holdingcompanies and directorates and blocks of minority stock

light and power, coalmines and tractioncompanies
in Illinois, Michigan, the Dakotas, Nebraska, Arkansas,

Oklahoma, Missouri, Maine, Kansas, Wisconsin, Virginia, Ohio, North Carolina, Indiana, New York, New Jersey, Texas, in Canada, in Louisiana, in Georgia, in Florida and Alabama.

(It has been figured out that one dollar in Middle West Utilities controlled seventeen hundred and fifty dollars invested by the public in the subsidiary companies that actually did the work of producing electricity. With the delicate lever of a voting trust controlling the stock of the two top holdingcompanies he controlled a twelfth of the power output of America.)

Samuel Insull began to think he owned all that the way a man owns the roll of bills in his back pocket.

Always he'd been scornful of bankers. He owned quite a few in Chicago. But the New York bankers were laying for him; they felt he was a bounder, whispered that this financial structure was unsound. Fingers itched to grasp the lever that so delicately moved this enormous power over lives,

superpower, Insull liked to call it.

A certain Cyrus S. Eaton of Cleveland, an exBaptistminister, was the David that brought down this Goliath. Whether it was so or not he made Insull believe that Wall Street was behind him.

He started buying stock in the three Chicago utilities. Insull in a panic for fear he'd lose his control went into the market to buy against him. Finally the Reverend Eaton let himself be bought out, shaking down the old man for a profit of twenty million dollars.

The stockmarket crash.

Paper values were slipping. Insull's companies were intertwined in a tangle that no bookkeeper has ever been able to unravel.

The gas hissed out of the torn balloon. Insull threw away his imperial pride and went on his knees to the bankers.

The bankers had him where they wanted him. To save the face of the tottering czar he was made a receiver of his own concerns. But the old man couldn't get out of his head the illusion that the money was all his. When it was discovered that he was using the stockholders' funds to pay off his brother's brokerage accounts it was too thick even for a federal judge. Insull was forced to resign.

He held directorates in eightyfive companies, he was chairman of sixtyfive, president of eleven: it took him three hours to sign his resignations.

As a reward for his services to monopoly his companies chipped in on a pension of eighteen thousand a year. But the public was shouting for criminal prosecution. When the handouts stopped newspapers and politicians turned on him. Revolt against the money-manipulators was in the air. Samuel Insull got the wind up and ran off to Canada with his wife.

Extradition proceedings. He fled to Paris. When the authorities began to close in on him there he slipped away to Italy, took a plane to Tirana, another to Saloniki and then the train to Athens. There the old fox went to earth. Money talked as sweetly in Athens as it had in Chicago in the old days.

The American ambassador tried to extradite him. Insull hired a chorus of Hellenic lawyers and politicos and sat drinking coffee in the lobby of the Grande Bretagne, while they proceeded to tie up the ambassador in a snarl of chicanery as complicated as the bookkeeping of his holdingcompanies. The successors of Demosthenes were delighted. The ancestral itch in many a Hellenic palm was temporarily assuaged. Samuel Insull settled down cozily in Athens, was stirred by the sight of the Parthenon, watched the goats feeding on the Pentelic slopes, visited the Areopagus, admired marble fragments ascribed to Phidias, talked with the local bankers about reorganizing the public utilities of Greece, was said to be promoting Macedonian lignite. He was the toast of the Athenians; Mme. Kouryoumdjouglou the vivacious wife of a Bagdad datemerchant devoted herself to his comfort. When the first effort at extradition failed, the old gentleman declared in the courtroom, as he struggled out from the embraces of his four lawyers: *Greece is a small but great country.*

The idyll was interrupted when the Roosevelt Administration began to put the heat on the Greek foreign office. Government lawyers in Chicago were accumulating truckloads of evidence and chalking up more and more drastic indictments.

Finally after many a postponement (he had hired physicians as well as lawyers, they cried to high heaven that it would kill him to leave the genial climate of the Attic plain),

he was ordered to leave Greece as an undesirable alien to the great indignation of Balkan society and of Mme. Kouryoumdjouglou.

He hired the *Maiotis* a small and grubby Greek freighter and panicked the foreignnews services by slipping off for an unknown destination.

It was rumored that the new Odysseus was bound for Aden, for the islands of the South Seas, that he'd been invited to Persia. After a few days he turned up rather seasick in the Bosporus on his way, it was said, to Rumania where Madame Kouryoumdjouglou had advised him to put himself under the protection of her friend la Lupescu.

At the request of the American ambassador the Turks were delighted to drag him off the Greek freighter and place him in a not at all comfortable jail. Again money had been mysteriously wafted from England, the healing balm began to flow, lawyers were hired, interpreters expostulated, doctors made diagnoses;

but Angora was boss

and Insull was shipped off to Smyrna to be turned over to the assistant federal districtattorney who had come all that way to arrest him.

The Turks wouldn't even let Mme. Kouryoumdjouglou, on her way back from making arrangements in Bucharest, go ashore to speak to him. In a scuffle with the officials on the steamboat the poor lady was pushed overboard

and with difficulty fished out of the Bosporus.

Once he was cornered the old man let himself tamely be taken home on the *Exilona,* started writing his memoirs, made

himself agreeable to his fellow passengers, was taken off at
Sandy Hook and rushed to Chicago to be arraigned.

In Chicago the government spitefully kept him a couple
of nights in jail; men he'd never known, so the newspapers said,
stepped forward to go on his twohundredandfiftythousanddol-
lar bail. He was moved to a hospital that he himself had
endowed. Solidarity. The leading businessmen in Chicago were
photographed visiting him there. Henry Ford paid a call.

The trial was very beautiful. The prosecution got bogged
in finance technicalities. The judge was not unfriendly. The
Insulls stole the show.

They were folks, they smiled at reporters, they posed for
photographers, they went down to the courtroom by bus. Investors might have been ruined but so, they allowed it to be
known, were the Insulls; the captain had gone down with the
ship.

Old Samuel Insull rambled amiably on the stand, told his
lifestory: from officeboy to powermagnate, his struggle to make
good, his love for his home and the kiddies. He didn't deny
he'd made mistakes; who hadn't, but they were honest errors.
Samuel Insull wept. Brother Martin wept. The lawyers wept.
With voices choked with emotion headliners of Chicago business told from the witnessstand how much Insull had done for
business in Chicago. There wasn't a dry eye in the jury.

Finally driven to the wall by the prosecutingattorney Samuel Insull blurted out that yes, he had made an error of some
ten million dollars in accounting but that it had been an honest
error.

Verdict: Not Guilty.

Smiling through their tears the happy Insulls went to their
towncar amid the cheers of the crowd. Thousands of ruined
investors, at least so the newspapers said, who had lost their
life savings sat crying over the home editions at the thought of
how Mr. Insull had suffered. The bankers were happy, the
bankers had moved in on the properties.

In an odor of sanctity the deposed monarch of superpower, the officeboy who made good, enjoys his declining years spending the pension of twenty-one thousand a year that the directors of his old companies dutifully restored to him. *After fifty years of work,* he said, *my job is gone.*

31. A Cool Million

NATHANAEL WEST

Nathanael West (1902–1940) may seem an improbable writer to turn up in a book about the Great Depression, even though everything that he wrote was published in the thirties: The Dream Life of Balso Snell *(1931),* Miss Lonelyhearts *(1933), which was unquestionably his finest work,* A Cool Million *(1934), which mixes the picaresque and the surrealist in its wild story of the adventures of a depression Pangloss, and* The Day of the Locust *(1939). To those of his contemporaries who bothered to read his books (he had worked for five inconspicuous years as a Hollywood screenwriter) he was a man who told private jokes, not as funny as those of his brother-in-law, S. J. Perelman. (Yet Perelman himself was writing for the* New Masses *even while he did scripts for the Marx Brothers movies.) But West, born Nathan Wallerstein Weinstein, was more acutely aware of the tragicomedy of an America in which the traditions had been broken, in which the Weinsteins had gone West and the Jews were outfitting the Fascists ("everything for the American Fascist at rock-bottom prices"), than*

From *Collected Works* (New York: Farrar, Straus & Cudahy, 1957), Chaps. XII–XXII, pp. 184–219 of *A Cool Million.* Reprinted with the permission of the Estate of Nathanael West.

such official leftist humorists as Robert Forsythe (born Kyle Crichton), busy throughout the decade pouring scorn not only on the approved butts of humor, but on any who dared question the wisdom of Earl Browder or the morality of Josef Stalin. One of the few who could see what West was up to was his fellow screenwriter, Scott Fitzgerald, to whom West wrote in humble gratitude for the praise Fitzgerald had bestowed upon him in the preface to the Modern Library edition of The Great Gatsby. *Both men died within days of each other, in December 1940—Fitzgerald of a heart attack, West in an auto accident with his wife (Ruth McKenney's sister Eileen) —and with their passing two lights were extinguished in a new and dark decade, although it was to be years before Americans realized how much darker the scene was without them.*

One wintry morning, several weeks after the incident in the park, Lem was dismissed from the hospital minus his right eye. It had been so severely damaged that the physicians had thought best to remove it.

He had no money, for, as we have recounted, Snodgrasse's henchmen had robbed him. Even the teeth that Warden Purdy had given him were gone. They had been taken from him by the hospital authorities, who claimed that they did not fit properly and were therefore a menace to his health.

The poor lad was standing on a windy corner, not knowing which way to turn, when he saw a man in a coonskin hat. This remarkable headgear made Lem stare, and the more he looked the more the man seemed to resemble Shagpoke Whipple.

It was Mr. Whipple. Lem hastened to call out to him, and the ex-President stopped to shake hands with his young friend.

"About those inventions," Shagpoke said immediately after they had finished greeting each other. "It was too bad that you left the penitentiary before I could hand them over to you. Not knowing your whereabouts, I perfected them myself.

"But let us repair to a coffee place," he added, changing the subject, "where we can talk over your prospects together. I am still very much interested in your career. In fact, my young friend, America has never had a greater need for her youth than in these parlous times."

After our hero had thanked him for his interest and good wishes, Mr. Whipple continued to talk. "Speaking of coffee," he said, "did you know that the fate of our country was decided in the coffee shops of Boston during the hectic days preceding the late rebellion?"

As they paused at the door of a restaurant, Mr. Whipple asked Lem still another question. "By the way," he said, "I am temporarily without funds. Are you able to meet the obligation we will incur in this place?"

"No," replied Lem, sadly, "I am penniless."

"That's different," said Mr. Whipple with a profound sigh. "In that case we will go where I have credit."

Lem was conducted by his fellow townsman to an extremely poor section of the city. After standing on line for several hours, they each received a doughnut and a cup of coffee from the Salvation Army lassie in charge. They then sat down on the curb to eat their little snack.

"You are perhaps wondering," Shagpoke began, "how it is that I stand on line with these homeless vagrants to obtain bad coffee and soggy doughnuts. Be assured that I do it of my own free will and for the good of the state."

Here he paused long enough to skillfully "shoot a snipe" that was still burning. He puffed contentedly on his catch.

"When I left jail, it was my intention to run for office again. But I discovered to my great amazement and utter horror that my party, the Democratic Party, carried not a single plank in its platform that I could honestly endorse. Rank socialism was and is rampant. How could I, Shagpoke Whipple, ever bring myself to accept a program which promised to take from American citizens their inalienable birthright; the right to sell their labor and their children's labor without restrictions as to either price or hours?

"The time for a new party with the old American principles was, I realized, overripe. I decided to form it; and so the National Revolutionary Party, popularly known as the 'Leather Shirts,' was born. The uniform of our 'Storm Troops' is a coonskin cap like the one I am wearing, a deerskin shirt and a pair of moccasins. Our weapon is the squirrel rifle."

He pointed to the long queue of unemployed who stood waiting before the Salvation Army canteen. "These men," he said, "are the material from which I must fill the ranks of my party."

With all the formality of a priest, Shagpoke turned to our hero and laid his hand on his shoulder.

"My boy," he said, and his voice broke under the load of emotion it was forced to bear, "my boy, will you join me?"

"Certainly, sir," said Lem, a little unsurely.

"Excellent!" exclaimed Mr. Whipple. "Excellent! I herewith appoint you a commander attached to my general staff."

He drew himself up and saluted Lem, who was startled by the gesture.

"Commander Pitkin," he ordered briskly, "I desire to address these people. Please obtain a soapbox."

Our hero went on the errand required of him, and soon returned with a large box, which Mr. Whipple immediately mounted. He then set about attracting the attention of the vagrants collected about the Salvation Army canteen by shouting:

"Remember the River Raisin!

"Remember the Alamo!

"Remember the Maine!"

and many other famous slogans.

When a large group had gathered, Shagpoke began his harangue.

"I'm a simple man," he said with great simplicity, "and I want to talk to you about simple things. You'll get no highfalutin talk from me.

"First of all, you people want jobs. Isn't that so?"

An ominous rumble of assent came from the throats of the poorly dressed gathering.

"Well, that's the only and prime purpose of the National Revolutionary Party—to get jobs for everyone. There was enough work to go around in 1927, why isn't there enough now? I'll tell you; because of the Jewish international bankers and the Bolshevik labor unions, that's why. It was those two agents that did the most to hinder American business and to destroy its glorious expansion. The former because of their hatred of America and love for Europe and the latter because of their greed for higher and still higher wages.

"What is the role of the labor union today? It is a privileged club which controls all the best jobs for its members. When one of you applies for a job, even if the man who owns the plant wants to hire you, do you get it? Not if you haven't got a union card. Can any tyranny be greater? Has Liberty ever been more brazenly despised?"

These statements were received with cheers by his audience.

"Citizens, Americans," Mr. Whipple continued, when the noise had subsided, "we of the middle class are being crushed between two gigantic millstones. Capital is the upper stone and Labor the lower, and between them we suffer and die, ground out of existence.

"Capital is international; its home is in London and in Amsterdam. Labor is international; its home is in Moscow. We alone are American; and when we die, America dies.

"When I say that, I make no idle boast, for history bears me out. Who but the middle class left aristocratic Europe to settle on these shores? Who but the middle class, the small farmers and storekeepers, the clerks and petty officials, fought for freedom and died that America might escape from British tyranny?

"This is our country and we must fight to keep it so. If America is ever again to be great, it can only be through the triumph of the revolutionary middle class.

"We must drive the Jewish international bankers out of Wall Street! We must destroy the Bolshevik labor unions! We must purge our country of all the alien elements and ideas that now infest her!

"America for Americans! Back to the principles of Andy Jackson and Abe Lincoln!"

Here Shagpoke paused to let the cheers die down, then called for volunteers to join his "Storm Battalions."

A number of men came forward. In their lead was a very dark individual, who had extra-long black hair of an extremely coarse quality, and on whose head was a derby hat many sizes too small for him.

"Me American mans," he announced proudly. "Me got heap coon hat, two maybe six. By, by catchum plenty more coon maybe." With this he grinned from ear to ear.

But Shagpoke was a little suspicious of his complexion, and looked at him with disfavor. In the South, where he expected to get considerable support for his movement, they would not stand for Negroes.

The good-natured stranger seemed to sense what was wrong, for he said, "Me Injun, mister, me chief along my people. Gotum gold mine, oil well. Name of Jake Raven. Ugh!"

Shagpoke grew cordial at once. "Chief Jake Raven," he said, holding out his hand, "I am happy to welcome you into our organization. We 'Leather Shirts' can learn much from your people, fortitude, courage and relentless purpose among other things."

After taking down his name, Shagpoke gave the Indian a card which read as follows:

EZRA SILVERBLATT
Official Tailor
to the
NATIONAL REVOLUTIONARY PARTY

> Coonskin hats with extra long tails,
> deerskin shirts with or without fringes,
> blue jeans, moccasins, squirrel rifles,
> everything for the American Fascist at
> rock bottom prices. 30% off for Cash.

But let us leave Mr. Whipple and Lem busy with their re-cruiting to observe the actions of a certain member of the crowd.

The individual in question would have been remarkable in any gathering, and among the starved, ragged men that sur-rounded Shagpoke, he stuck out like the proverbial sore thumb. For one thing he was fat, enormously fat. There were other fat men present to be sure, but they were yellow, un-healthy, while this man's fat was pink and shone with health.

On his head was a magnificent bowler hat. It was a beautiful jet in color, and must have cost more than twelve dollars. He was snugly encased in a tight-fitting Chesterfield overcoat with a black velvet collar. His stiff-bosomed shirt had light gray bars, and his tie was of some rich but sober material in black and white pin-checks. Spats, rattan stick and yellow gloves completed his outfit.

This elaborate fat man tiptoed out of the crowd and made his way to a telephone booth in a nearby drug store, where he called two numbers.

His conversation with the person answering his first call, a Wall Street exchange, went something like this:

"Operative 6384XM, working out of the Bourse, Paris, France. Middle-class organizers functioning on unemployed front, corner of Houston and Bleecker Streets."

"Thank you, 6384XM, what is your estimate?"

"Twenty men and a fire hose."

"At once, 6384XM, at once."

His second call was to an office near Union Square.

"Comrade R, please. . . . Comrade R?"

"Yes."

"Comrade R, this is Comrade Z speaking. Gay Pay Oo, Moscow, Russia. Middle-class organizers recruiting on the corner of Houston and Bleecker Streets."

"Your estimate, comrade, for liquidation of said activities?"

"Ten men with lead pipes and brass knuckles to cooperate with Wall Street office of the I.J.B."

"No bombs required?"

"No, comrade."

"Der Tag!"

"Der Tag!"

Mr. Whipple had just enrolled his twenty-seventh recruit, when the forces of both the international Jewish bankers and the Communists converged on his meeting. They arrived in high-powered black limousines and deployed through the streets with a skill which showed long and careful training in that type of work. In fact their officers were all West Point graduates.

Mr. Whipple saw them coming, but like a good general his first thoughts were for his men.

"The National Revolutionary Party will now go underground!" he shouted.

Lem, made wary by his past experiences with the police, immediately took to his heels, followed by Chief Raven. Shagpoke, however, was late in getting started. He still had one foot on the soapbox when he was hit a terrific blow on the head with a piece of lead pipe.

"My man, if you can wear this glass eye, I have a job for you."

The speaker was an exceedingly dapper gentleman in a light gray fedora hat and a pince-nez with a black silk ribbon that fell to his coat opening in a graceful loop.

As he spoke, he held out at arm's length a beautiful glass eye.

But the object of his words did not reply; it did not even

move. To anyone but a trained observer, he would have appeared to be addressing a bundle of old rags that someone had propped up on a park bench.

Turning the eye from side to side, so that it sparkled like a jewel in the winter sun, the man waited patiently for the bundle to reply. From time to time, he stirred it sharply with the Malacca walking stick he carried.

Suddenly a groan came from the rags and they shook slightly. The cane had evidently reached a sensitive spot. Encouraged, the man repeated his original proposition.

"Can you wear this eye? If so, I'll hire you."

At this, the bundle gave a few spasmodic quivers and a faint whimper. From somewhere below its peak a face appeared, then a greenish hand moved out and took the glittering eye, raising it to an empty socket in the upper part of the face.

"Here, let me help you," said the owner of the eye kindly. With a few deft motions he soon had it fixed in its proper receptacle.

"Perfect!" exclaimed the man, standing back and admiring his handiwork. "Perfect! You're hired!"

He then reached into his overcoat and brought forth a wallet from which he extracted a five-dollar bill and a calling card. He laid both of these on the bench beside the one-eyed man, who by now had again become a quiescent bundle of greasy rags.

"Get yourself a haircut, a bath and a big meal, then go to my tailors, Ephraim Pierce and Sons, and they will fit you out with clothes. When you are presentable, call on me at the Ritz Hotel."

With these words, the man in the gray fedora turned sharply on his heel and left the park.

If you have not already guessed the truth, dear reader, let me acquaint you with the fact that the bundle of rags contained our hero, Lemuel Pitkin. Alas, to such a sorry pass had he come.

After the unfortunate termination of Shagpoke's attempt to recruit men for his "Leather Shirts," he had rapidly gone from bad to worse. Having no money and no way in which to obtain any, he had wandered from employment agency to employment agency without success. Reduced to eating from garbage pails and sleeping in empty lots, he had become progressively shabbier and weaker, until he had reached the condition we discovered him in at the beginning of this chapter.

But now things were looking up again, and just in time I must admit, for our hero had begun to doubt whether he would ever make his fortune.

Lem pocketed the five dollars that the stranger had left and examined the card.

ELMER HAINEY, ESQUIRE
RITZ HOTEL

This was all the bit of engraved pasteboard said. It gave no evidence of either the gentleman's business or profession. But this did not in any way bother Lem, for at last it looked as though he were going to have a job; and in the year of our Lord nineteen thirty-four that was indeed something.

Lem struggled to his feet and set out to follow Mr. Hainey's instructions. In fact he ate two large meals and took two baths. It was only his New England training that prevented him from getting two haircuts.

Having done as much as he could to rehabilitate his body, he next went to the shop of Ephraim Pierce and Sons, where he was fitted out with a splendid wardrobe complete in every detail. Several hours later, he walked up Park Avenue to wait on his new employer, looking every inch a prosperous young businessman of the finest type.

When Lem asked for Mr. Hainey, the manager of the Ritz bowed him into the elevator, which stopped to let him off at the fortieth floor. He rang the doorbell of Mr. Hainey's suite and in a few minutes was ushered into that gentleman's presence by an English personal servant.

Mr. Hainey greeted the lad with great cordiality. "Excellent! Excellent!" he repeated three or four times in rapid succession as he inspected the transformed appearance of our hero.

Lem expressed his gratitude by a deep bow.

"If there is anything about your outfit that you dislike," he went on to say, "please tell me now before I give you your instructions."

Emboldened by his kind manner, Lem ventured an objection. "Pardon me, sir," he said, "but the eye, the glass eye you gave me is the wrong color. My good eye is blue-gray, while the one you provided me with is light green."

"Exactly," was Mr. Hainey's surprising answer. "The effect is, as I calculated, striking. When anyone sees you I want to make sure that they notice that one of your eyes is glass."

Lem was forced to agree to this strange idea and he did so with all the grace he could manage.

Mr. Hainey then got down to business. His whole manner changed, becoming as cold as a steep trap and twice as formal.

"My secretary," he said, "has typed a set of instructions which I will give you tonight. I want you to take them home and study them carefully, for you will be expected to do exactly as they order without the slightest deviation. One slip, please remember, and you will be immediately discharged."

"Thank you, sir," replied Lem. "I understand."

"Your salary," said Mr. Hainey, softening a bit, "will be thirty dollars a week and found. I have arranged room and board for you at the Warford House. Please go there tonight."

Mr. Hainey then took out his wallet and gave Lem three ten-dollar bills.

"You are very generous," said Lem, taking them. "I shall do my utmost to satisfy you."

"That's nice, but please don't show too much zeal, simply follow instructions."

Mr. Hainey next went to his desk and took from it several typewritten sheets of paper. He gave these to Lem.

"One more thing," he said, shaking hands at the door, "you may be a little mystified when you read your instructions, but that cannot be helped, for I am unable to give you a complete explanation at this time. However, I want you to know that I own a glass eye factory, and that your duties are part of a sales-promotion campaign."

Lem restrained his curiosity. He waited until he was safely ensconced in his new quarters in the Warford House before opening the instructions Mr. Hainey had given him.

Here is what he read:

"Go to the jewelry store of Hazelton Frères and ask to see their diamond stickpins. After looking at one tray, demand to see another. While the clerk has his back turned, remove the glass eye from your head and put it in your pocket. As soon as the clerk turns around again, appear to be searching frantically on the floor for something.

"The following dialogue will then take place:

"*Clerk:* 'Have you lost something, sir?'

"*You:* 'Yes, my eye.' (Here indicate the opening in your head with your index finger.)

"*Clerk:* 'That's unfortunate, sir. I'll help you look, sir.'

"*You:* 'Please do. (With much agitation.) I must find it.'

"A thorough search of the premises is then made, but of course the missing eye cannot be found because it is safe in your pocket.

"*You:* 'Please may I see one of the owners of this store; one of the Hazelton Brothers?' (Note: Frères means brothers and is not to be mistaken for the storekeeper's last name.)

"In a few minutes the clerk will bring Mr. Hazelton from his office in the rear of the store.

"*You:* 'Mr. Hazelton, sir, I have had the misfortune to lose my eye here in your shop.'

"*Mr. Hazelton:* 'Perhaps you left it at home.'

"*You:* 'Impossible! I would have felt the draft for I walked here from Mr. Hamilton Schuyler's house on Fifth Avenue. No, I'm afraid that it was in its proper position when I entered your place.'

"*Mr. Hazelton:* 'You can be certain, sir, that we will make a thorough search.'

"*You:* 'Please do. I am, however, unable to wait the outcome of your efforts. I have to be in the Spanish embassy to see the ambassador, Count Raymon de Guzman y Alfrache (the y is pronounced like the e in eat) within the hour.'

"Mr. Hazelton will bow profoundly on hearing with whom your appointment is.

"*You* (continuing): 'The eye I have lost is irreplaceable. It was made for me by a certain German expert, and cost a very large sum. I cannot get another because its maker was killed in the late war and the secret of its manufacture was buried with him. (Pause for a brief moment, bowing your head as though in sorrow for the departed expert.) However (you continue), please tell your clerks that I will pay one thousand dollars as a reward to anyone who recovers my eye.'

"*Mr. Hazelton:* 'That will be entirely unnecessary, sir. Rest assured that we will do everything in our power to discover it for you.'

"*You:* 'Very good. I am going to visit friends on Long Island tonight, but I will be in your shop tomorrow. If you have the eye, I will insist on paying the reward.'

"Mr. Hazelton will then bow you out of the shop.

"Until you receive further instructions from Mr. Hainey, you are to stay away from the near vicinity of Hazelton Frères.

"On the day following your visit to the shop call the Ritz

Hotel and ask for Mr. Hainey's secretary. Tell him whether or not everything went off in accordance with these instructions. The slightest deviation on the part of Mr. Hazelton from the prescribed formula must be reported."

Lem's job was a sinecure. He had merely to enact the same scene over one morning a week, each time in a different store. He soon had his part by heart, and once he had lost his embarrassment over having to say that he knew the Spanish Ambassador, he quite enjoyed his work. It reminded him of the amateur theatricals he had participated in at the Ottsville High School.

Then, too, his position permitted him a great deal of leisure. He used this spare time to good advantage by visiting the many interesting spots for which New York City is justly famous.

He also made an unsuccessful attempt to find Mr. Whipple. At the Salvation Army post they told him that they had observed Mr. Whipple lying quietly in the gutter after the meeting of the "Leather Shirts," but that when they looked the next day to see if he were still there they found only a large blood stain. Lem looked himself but failed even to find this stain, there being many cats in the neighborhood.

He was a sociable youth and quickly made friends with several of the other guests of the Warford House. None of them were his age, however, so that he was pleased when a young man named Samuel Perkins spoke to him.

Sam worked in a furnishing goods store on lower Broadway. He was very fond of dress and indulged in a variety of showy neckties, being able to get them at reduced rates.

"What line are you in?" he asked our hero in the lobby one evening while they were waiting for the supper bell to ring.

"I'm in the glass business," Lem answered cautiously, for he had been warned not to explain his duties to anyone.

"How much do you get?" was the forward youth's next question.

"Thirty dollars a week and found," said Lem, honestly.

"I get thirty-five without keep, but it's too little for me. A man can't live on that kind of money, what with the opera once a week and decent clothes. Why, my carfare alone comes to over a dollar, not counting taxicabs."

"Yes, it must be rather a tight squeeze for you," said Lem with a smile as he thought of all the large families who lived on smaller incomes than Mr. Perkins'.

"Of course," Sam went on, "the folks at home allow me another ten dollars a week. You see the old gent has money. But I tell you it sure melts away in this town."

"No doubt," said Lem. "There are a good many ways to spend money here."

"Suppose we go to the theater tonight?"

"No," Lem replied, "I'm not as fortunate as you are. I have no wealthy father to fall back on and must save the little I earn."

"Well, then," said Sam, for that youth could not live without excitement of some sort, "what do you say we visit Chinatown? It'll only cost us carfare."

To this proposition Lem readily agreed. "I'd like very much to go," he said. "Perhaps Mr. Warren would like to join us."

Mr. Warren was another guest whose acquaintance Lem had made.

"What, that crank!" exclaimed Sam, who was by way of being somewhat of a snob. "He's soft in his upper story. Pretends that he's literary and writes for the magazines."

"He does, doesn't he?"

"Very likely, but did you ever see such shabby neckties as he wears?"

"He hasn't your advantages for getting them," said Lem with a smile, for he knew where the young man worked.

"How do you like the tie I have on? It's a stunner, isn't it?" asked Sam complacently.

"It's very striking," said Lem, whose tastes were much more sober.

"I get a new necktie every week. You see, I get them at half price. The girls always notice a fellow's necktie."

The supper bell sounded, and the two youths parted to go to their own tables. After eating, they met again in the lobby and proceeded to Chinatown.

Lem and his new friend wandered through Mott Street and its environs, observing with considerable interest the curious customs and outlandish manners of that neighborhood's large oriental population.

Early in the evening, however, an incident occurred which made our hero feel sorry that he had ventured out with Sam Perkins. When they came upon an ancient celestial, who was quietly reading a newspaper under an arc lamp, Sam accosted him before Lem could interfere.

"Hey, John," said the youth mockingly, "no tickee, no washee." And he laughed foolishly in the manner of his kind.

The almond-eyed old man looked up from his newspaper and stared coldly at him for a full minute, then said with great dignity, "By the blessed beard of my grandfather, you're the lousiest pimple-faced ape I ever did see."

At this Sam made as though to strike the aged oriental. But that surprising individual was not in the least frightened. He took a small hatchet out of his pocket and proceeded to shave the hair from the back of his hand with its razor-sharp edge.

Sam turned quite pale and began to bluster until Lem thought it best to intervene.

But even his lesson in manners had no effect on the brash youth. He so persisted in his unmannerly conduct that our hero was tempted to part company with him.

Sam stopped in front of what was evidently an unlicensed liquor parlor.

"Come on in," he said, "and have a whisky."

"Thank you," said our hero, "but I don't care for whisky."

"Perhaps you prefer beer?"

"I don't care to drink anything, thank you."

"You don't mean to say you're a temperance crank?"

"Yes, I think I am."

"Oh, go to the devil, you prude," said Sam, ringing a signal button that was secreted in the door of the "blind pig."

To Lem's great relief, he at last found himself alone. It was still early, so he decided to continue his stroll.

He turned a corner not far from Pell Street, when, suddenly, a bottle smashed at his feet, missing his skull by inches.

Was it intentional or accidental?

Lem looked around carefully. The street was deserted and all the houses that faced on it had their blinds drawn. He noticed that the only store front on the block carried a sign reading, "Wu Fong, Wet Wash Laundry," but that meant nothing to him.

When he looked closer at the bottle, he was surprised to see a sheet of notepaper between the bits of shattered glass and stooped to pick it up.

At this the door of the laundry opened noiselessly to emit one of Wu Fong's followers, an enormous Chinaman. His felt slippers were silent on the pavement, and as he crept up on our hero, something glittered in his hand.

It was a knife.

Many chapters earlier in this book, we left our heroine, Betty Prail, in the bad house of Wu Fong, awaiting the visit of a pockmarked Armenian from Malta.

Since then numbers of orientals, Slavs, Latins, Celts and Semites had visited her, sometimes as many as three in one night. However, so large a number was rare because Wu Fong held her at a price much above that of the other female inmates.

Naturally enough, Betty was not quite as happy in her situation as was Wu Fong. At first she struggled against the series of "husbands" that were forced on her, but when all her efforts proved futile she adapted herself as best she could to her onerous duties. Nevertheless, she was continuously seeking a method of escape.

It was Betty, of course, who had authored the note in the bottle. She had been standing at her window, thinking with horror of the impending visit of a heavyweight wrestler called Selim Hammid Bey, who claimed to be in love with her, when she suddenly saw Lem Pitkin turn the corner and pass in front of the laundry. She had hastily written a note describing her predicament, and putting it into a bottle had tossed it into the street.

But, unfortunately, her action had not gone unobserved. One of Wu Fong's many servants had been carefully watching her through the keyhole, and had immediately carried the intelligence to his master, who had sent the enormous Chinaman after Lem with a knife.

Before I take up where I left off in my last chapter, there are several changes in Wu Fong's establishment which I would like to report. These changes seem significant to me, and while their bearing on this story may not be obvious, still I believe it does exist.

The depression hit Wu Fong as hard as it did more respectable merchants, and like them he decided that he was over-stocked. In order to cut down, he would have to specialize and could no longer run a "House of All Nations."

Wu Fong was a very shrewd man and a student of fashions. He saw that the trend was in the direction of home industry and home talent, and when the Hearst papers began their "Buy American" campaign he decided to get rid of all the foreigners in his employ and turn his establishment into an hundred per centum American place.

Although in 1928 it would have been exceedingly difficult

for him to have obtained the necessary girls, by 1934 things were different. Many respectable families of genuine native stock had been reduced to extreme poverty and had thrown their female children on the open market.

He engaged Mr. Asa Goldstein to redecorate the house and that worthy designed a Pennsylvania Dutch, Old South, Log Cabin Pioneer, Victorian New York, Western Cattle Days, California Monterey, Indian, and Modern Girl series of interiors. In general the results were as follows:

Lena Haubengrauber from Perkiomen Creek, Bucks County, Pennsylvania. Her rooms were filled with painted pine furniture and decorated with slip ware, spatter ware, chalk ware and "Gaudy Dutch." Her simple farm dress was fashioned of bright gingham.

Alice Sweethorne from Paducah, Kentucky. Besides many fine pieces of old Sheraton from Savannah, in her suite there was a wonderful iron grille from Charleston whose beauty of workmanship made every visitor gasp with pleasure. She wore a ball gown of the Civil War period.

Mary Judkins from Jugtown Hill, Arkansas. Her walls were lined with oak puncheons chinked with mud. Her mattress was stuffed with field corn and covered by a buffalo robe. There was real dirt on her floors. She was dressed in homespun, butternut stained, and wore a pair of men's boots.

Patricia Van Riis from Gramercy Park, Manhattan, New York City. Her suite was done in the style known as Biedermeier. The windows were draped with thirty yards of white velvet apiece and the chandelier in her sitting room had over eight hundred crystal pendants attached to it. She was dressed like an early "Gibson Girl."

Powder River Rose from Carson's Store, Wyoming. Her apartment was the replica of a ranch bunkhouse. Strewn around it in well-calculated confusion were such miscellaneous articles as spurs, saddle blankets, straw, guitars, quirts, pearl-handled revolvers, hayforks and playing cards. She wore goatskin chaps, a silk blouse and a five-gallon hat with a rattlesnake band.

Dolores O'Riely from Alta Vista, California. In order to save money, Wu Fong had moved her into the suite that had been occupied by Conchita, the Spanish girl. He merely substituted a Mission chair for the horsehide one with the steer-horn arms and called it "Monterey." Asa Goldstein was very angry when he found out, but Wu Fong refused to do anything more about it, because he felt that she was bound to be a losing proposition. The style, he said was not obviously enough American even in its most authentic forms.

Princess Roan Fawn from Two Forks, Oklahoma Indian Reservation, Oklahoma. Her walls were papered with birch bark to make it look like a wigwam and she did business on the floor. Except for a necklace of wolf's teeth, she was naked under her bull's-eye blanket.

Miss Cobina Wiggs from Woodstock, Connecticut. She lived in one large room that was a combination of a locker in an athletic club and the office of a mechanical draughtsman. Strewn around were parts of an aeroplane, T-squares, callipers, golf clubs, books, gin bottles, hunting horns and paintings by modern masters. She had broad shoulders, no hips and very long legs. Her costume was an aviator's jumper complete with helmet attached. It was made of silver cloth and fitted very tightly.

Betty Prail from Ottsville, Vermont. Her furnishings and costume have already been described, and it should suffice to say here that they remained untouched.

These were not the only vital changes Wu Fong made in his establishment. He was as painstaking as a great artist, and in order to be as consistent as one he did away with the French cuisine and wines traditional to his business. Instead, he substituted an American kitchen and cellar.

When a client visited Lena Haubengrauber, it was possible for him to eat roast groundhog and drink Sam Thompson rye.

While with Alice Sweethorne, he was served sow belly with grits and bourbon. In Mary Judkins' rooms he received, if he so desired, fried squirrel and corn liquor. In the suite occupied by Patricia Van Riis, lobster and champagne wine were the rule. The patrons of Powder River Rose usually ordered mountain oysters and washed them down with forty-rod. And so on down the list: while with Dolores O'Riely, tortillas and prune brandy from the Imperial Valley; while with Princess Roan Fawn, baked dog and firewater; while with Betty Prail, fish chowder and Jamaica rum. Finally, those who sought the favors of the "Modern Girl," Miss Cobina Wiggs, were regaled with tomato and lettuce sandwiches and gin.

The enormous Chinaman with the uplifted knife did not bring it down, because he had been struck by a sudden thought. While he debated the pros and cons of his idea over in his mind, the unsuspecting youth picked up the note Betty had thrown at him.

> *"Dear Mr. Pitkin—"* he read.
> *"I am held captive. Please save me.*
> *Your grateful friend,*
> *Elizabeth Prail."*

When our hero had thoroughly digested the contents of the little missive, he turned to look for a policeman. It was this that made the Chinaman decide on a course of action. He dropped the knife, and with a skillful oriental trick that took our hero entirely by surprise pinned Lem's arms in such a way as to render him helpless.

He then whistled through his nose in coolie fashion. In obedience to this signal several more of Wu Fong's followers came running to his assistance. Although Lem struggled valiantly, he was overpowered and forced to enter the laundry.

Lem's captors dragged him into the presence of the sinister

Wu Fong, who rubbed his hands gleefully as he inspected the poor lad.

"You have done well, Chin Lao Tse," he said, praising the man who had captured Lem.

"I demand to be set free!" expostulated our hero. "You have no right to keep me here."

But the crafty oriental ignored his protests and smiled inscrutably. He could well use a nice-looking American boy. That very night, he expected a visit from the Maharajah of Kanurani, whose tastes were notorious. Wu Fong congratulated himself; the gods were indeed good.

"Prepare him," said he in Chinese.

The poor lad was taken to a room that had been fitted out like a ship's cabin. The walls were paneled in teak, and there were sextants, compasses and other such gear in profusion. His captors then forced him to don a tight-fitting sailor suit. After warning him in no uncertain terms not to try to escape, they left him to his own devices.

Lem sat on the edge of a bunk that was built into one corner of the room with his head buried in his hands. He wondered what new ordeal fate had in store for him, but being unable to guess he thought of other things.

Would he lose his job if he failed to report to Mr. Hainey? Probably, yes. Where was his dear mother? Probably in the poorhouse, or begging from door to door, if she were not dead. Where was Mr. Whipple? Dead and buried in Potter's Field more than likely. And how could he get a message to Miss Prail?

Lem was still trying to solve this last problem when Chin Lao Tse, the man who had captured him, entered the room, carrying a savage-looking automatic in his hand.

"Listen, boy," he said menacingly, "see this gat? Well, if you don't behave I'll drill you clean."

Chin then proceeded to secrete himself in a closet. Before closing the door, he showed Lem that he intended to watch his every move through the keyhole.

The poor lad racked his brains, but could not imagine what was wanted of him. He was soon to find out, however.

There was a knock on the door and Wu Fong entered followed by a little dark man whose hands were covered with jewels. It was the Maharajah of Kanurani.

"My, wath a pithy thailer boy," lisped the Indian prince with unfeigned delight.

"I'm extremely happy that he finds favor in your august eyes, excellency," said Wu Fong with a servile bow, after which he backed out of the room.

The Maharajah minced up to our hero, who was conscious only of the man in the closet, and put his arm around the lad's waist.

"Thom on, pithy boy, giff me a kith," he said with a leer that transfigured his otherwise unremarkable visage into a thing of evil.

A wave of disgust made Lem's hair stand on end. "Does he think me a girl?" the poor lad wondered. "No, he called me a boy at least twice."

Lem looked towards the closet for instructions. The man in that receptacle opened his door and poked his head out. Puckering up his lips, he rolled his eyes amorously, at the same time pointing at the Indian Prince.

When our hero realized what was expected of him, he turned pale with horror. He looked again at the Maharajah and what he saw of lust in that man's eyes made him almost swoon.

Fortunately for Lem, however, instead of swooning, he opened his mouth to scream. This was the only thing that could have saved him, for he spread his jaws too wide and his store teeth fell clattering to the carpet.

The Maharajah jumped away in disgust.

Then another lucky accident occurred. When Lem bent awkwardly to pick up his teeth, the glass eye that Mr. Hainey had given him popped from his head and smashed to smithereens on the floor.

This last was too much for the Maharajah of Kanurani. He became enraged. Wu Fong had cheated him! What kind of a pretty boy was this that came apart so horribly?

Livid with anger, the Indian prince ran out of the room to demand his money back. After he had gotten it, he left the house, vowing never to return.

Wu Fong blamed the loss of the Maharajah's trade on Lem and was extremely vexed with the poor lad. He ordered his men to beat him roundly, strip him of his sailor suit, then throw him into the street with his clothes after him.

Lem gathered together his clothing and crawled into the areaway of a deserted house, where he donned his things. His first thought was to find a policeman.

As is usual in such circumstances, a guardian of the law was not immediately forthcoming and he had to go several miles before he found a "peeler."

"Officer," said our hero as best he could minus his oral equipment, "I want to lodge a complaint."

"Yes," said Patrolman Riley shortly, for the poor lad's appearance was far from prepossessing. The Chinaman had torn his clothing and his eye was gone as well as his teeth.

"I want you to summon reinforcements, then immediately arrest Wu Fong who is running a disorderly house under the guise of a laundry."

"Wu Fong is it that you want me to arrest? Why, you drunken fool, he's the biggest man in the district. Take my advice and get yourself a cup of black coffee, then go home and sleep it off."

"But I have positive proof that he's keeping a girl in his house against her will, and he did me physical violence."

"One more word out of you about my great good friend," said the officer, "and off you go to jail."

"But . . ." began Lem indignantly.

Officer Riley was a man of his word. He did not let the poor lad finish, but struck him a smart blow on the head with his truncheon, then took him by the collar and dragged him to the station house.

When Lem regained consciousness several hours later, he found himself in a cell. He quickly remembered what had happened to him and tried to think of a way in which to extricate himself from his difficulties. The first thing was to tell his story to some superior police officer or magistrate. But no matter how loudly he called, he was unable to attract the attention of anyone.

Not until the next day was he fed, and then a small man of the Jewish persuasion entered his cell.

"Have you any money?" said this member of the chosen people.

"Who are you?" countered Lem with another question.

"Me? I'm your lawyer, Seth Abromovitz, Esquire. Please answer my first question or I won't be able to handle your case properly."

"My case?" queried Lem in astonishment. "I've done nothing."

"Ignorance of the law is no defense," said Lawyer Abromovitz pompously.

"Of what am I accused?" asked the poor lad in confusion.

"Of several things. Disorderly conduct and assaulting a police officer, for one; of conspiring to overthrow the Government, for two; and last but not least, of using the glim racket to mulct storekeepers."

"But I didn't do any of these things," protested Lem.

'Listen, bud," said the lawyer, dropping all formality. "I'm not the judge, you don't have to lie to me. You're One-eyed Pitkin, the glim dropper, and you know it."

"It's true that I have but one eye, but . . ."

"But me no buts. This is a tough case. That is, unless you can grow an eye overnight in that hole in your mug."

"I am innocent," repeated Lem sadly.

"If that's the line you intend to take, I wouldn't be surprised if you got life. But tell me, didn't you go to the store of Hazelton Frères and make believe you lost your eye?"

"Yes," said Lem, "but I didn't take anything or do anything."

"Didn't you offer a reward of one thousand dollars for the return of your eye?"

"Yes, but . . ."

"Again, but. Please don't but me no buts. Your accomplice went around the next day and made believe he had found a glass eye on the floor of the store. Mr. Hazelton said that he knew who it belonged to and asked him for the eye. He refused to give it up, saying that it looked like a very valuable eye to him and that if Mr. Hazelton would give him the address of the man who owned it, he would return the eye himself. Mr. Hazelton thought that he was going to lose all chances of collecting the thousand-dollar reward, so he offered the man a hundred dollars for the eye. After some bargaining your accomplice went out with two hundred and fifty dollars, and Mr. Hazelton is still waiting for you to come and claim your eye."

"I didn't know about all that or I wouldn't have taken the job even if I was starving," said Lem. "I was told that it was a promotion idea for a glass eye company."

"O.K., son, but I'll have to think up a little better story. Before I begin thinking, how much money have you?"

"I worked three weeks and was paid thirty dollars a week. I have ninety dollars in a savings bank."

"That's not much. This conference is going to cost you one hundred dollars with ten per cent off for cash or ninety dollars. Hand it over."

"I don't want you as my lawyer," said Lem.

"That's all right with me; but come through with the dough for this conference."

"I don't owe you anything. I didn't hire you."

"Oh, yeh, you one-eyed rat," said the lawyer, showing his true colors. "The courts appointed me and the courts will decide how much you owe me. Give me the ninety and we'll call it square. Otherwise I'll sue you."

"I'll give you nothing!" exclaimed Lem.

"Getting tough, eh? We'll soon see how tough you are. I'll tell my friend the district attorney and you'll get life."

With this last as a parting shot, Lawyer Abromovitz left our hero alone again in his cell.

Several days later the prosecuting attorney paid the poor lad a visit. Elisha Barnes was that official's name, and he appeared to be a rather good-natured, indolent gentleman.

"Well, son," he said, "so you're about to discover that crime doesn't pay. But, tell me, have you any money?"

"Ninety dollars," said Lem truthfully.

"That's very little, so I guess you'd better plead guilty."

"But I'm innocent," protested Lem. "Wu Fong . . ."

"Stop," interrupted Mr. Barnes, hurriedly. He had turned pale on hearing the Chinaman's name. "Take my advice and don't mention him around here."

"I'm innocent!" repeated Lem, a little desperately.

"So was Christ," said Mr. Barnes with a sigh, "and they nailed Him. However, I like you; I can see you're from New England and I'm a New Hampshire man myself. I want to help you. You've been indicted on three counts; suppose you plead guilty to one of the three and we forget the other two."

"But I'm innocent," repeated Lem again.

"Maybe, but you haven't got enough money to prove it, and besides you've got some very powerful enemies. Be sensible, plead guilty to the charge of disorderly conduct and take thirty days in the workhouse. I'll see that you don't get more. Well, what do you say?"

Our hero was silent.

"I'm giving you a fine break," Mr. Barnes went on. "If I

wasn't too busy to prepare the state's case against you, I probably could get you sent away for at least fifteen years. But you see, elections are coming and I have to take part in the campaign. Besides I'm a busy man, what with this and what with that. . . . Do me a favor and maybe I can help you some time. If you make me prepare a case against you I'll get sore. I won't like you."

Lem finally agreed to do as the prosecuting attorney asked. Three days later he was sent to the workhouse for thirty days. The judge wanted to give him ninety, but Mr. Barnes lived up to his part of the bargain. He whispered something to the judge, who changed the term to the thirty days agreed upon.

A month later, when Lem was set free, he went directly to the savings bank for his ninety dollars. It was his intention to draw out the entire amount, so that he could get himself another set of false teeth and a glass eye. Without those things, he could not hope to get a job.

He presented his passbook at the paying teller's window. After a little wait, he was told that they could not give him his money because it had been attached by Seth Abromovitz. This was too much. It took all the manliness of our hero to suppress the tear that started to his good eye. With the faltering step of an old man, he stumbled out of the bank building.

Lem stood on the steps of the imposing edifice, and looked blankly at the swirling crowds that eddied past the great savings institution. Suddenly he felt a touch on his arm and a voice in his ear.

"Why so blue, duckie? How about a little fun?"

He turned mechanically and to his amazement saw that it was Betty Prail who had solicited him.

"You!" exclaimed both of the hometown friends together.

Anyone who had ever seen these two youngsters on their way home from church in Ottsville would have been struck by the great change that only a few years in the great world had made.

Miss Prail was rouged most obviously. She smelled of cheap

perfume, and her dress revealed much too much of her figure. She was a woman of the streets, and an unsuccessful one at that.

As for our hero, Lemuel, minus an eye and all his teeth, he had acquired nothing but a pronounced stoop.

"How did you escape Wu Fong?" asked Lem.

"You helped me without knowing it," replied Betty. "He and his henchmen were so busy throwing you into the street that I was able to walk out of the house without anyone seeing me."

"I'm glad," said Lem.

The two young people were silent, and stood looking at each other. They both wanted to ask the same question, but they were embarrassed. Finally, they spoke at the same time.

"Have you . . ."

That was as far as they got. They both stopped to let the other finish. There was a long silence, for neither wanted to complete the question. Finally, however, they spoke again.

". . . any money?"

"No," said Lem and Betty answering the question together as they had asked it.

"I'm hungry," said Betty sadly. "I just wondered."

"I'm hungry, too," said Lem.

A policeman now approached. He had been watching them since they met.

"Get along, you rats," he said gruffly.

"I resent your talking that way to a lady," said Lem indignantly.

"What's that?" asked the officer lifting his club.

"We are both citizens of this country and you have no right to treat us in this manner," went on Lem fearlessly.

The patrolman was just about to bring his truncheon down on the lad's skull, when Betty interfered and dragged him away.

The two youngsters walked along without talking. They felt a little better together because misery loves company. Soon they found themselves in Central Park, where they sat down on a bench.

Lem sighed.

"What's the matter?" asked Betty sympathetically.

"I'm a failure," answered Lem with still another sigh.

"Why, Lemuel Pitkin, how you talk!" exclaimed Betty indignantly. "You're only seventeen going on eighteen and . . ."

"Well," interrupted Lem, a little ashamed of having admitted that he was discouraged. "I left Ottsville to make my fortune and so far I've been to jail twice and lost all my teeth and one eye."

"To make an omelette you have to break eggs," said Betty. "When you've lost both your eyes, you can talk. I read only the other day about a man who lost both of his eyes yet accumulated a fortune. I forget how, but he did. Then, too, think of Henry Ford. He was dead broke at forty and borrowed a thousand dollars from James Couzens; when he paid him back it had become thirty-eight million dollars. You're only seventeen and say you're a failure. Lem Pitkin, I'm surprised at you."

Betty continued to comfort and encourage Lem until it grew dark. With the departure of the sun, it also grew extremely cold.

From behind some shrubs that did not quite conceal him, a policeman began to eye the two young people suspiciously.

"I have nowhere to sleep," said Betty, shivering with cold.

"Nor have I," said Lem with a profound sigh.

"Let's go to the Grand Central Station," suggested Betty. "It's warm there, and I like to watch the people hurrying through. If we make believe we are waiting for a train, they won't chase us."

"It all seems like a dream to me, Mr. Whipple. This morning when I was set free from jail I thought I would probably starve, and here I am on my way to California to dig gold."

Yes, it was Lem, our hero, talking. He was sitting in the dining room of the "Fifth Avenue Special" *en route* to Chicago, where he and the party he was traveling with were to change to "The Chief," crack train of the Atchison, Topeka and Santa Fe, and continue on to the high Sierras.

With him in the dining room were Betty, Mr. Whipple and Jake Raven, and the four friends were in a cheerful mood as they ate the excellent food provided by the Pullman Company.

The explanation of how this had come about is quite simple. While Lem and Betty were warming themselves in the waiting room of the Grand Central Station, they had spied Mr. Whipple on line at one of the ticket booths. Lem had approached the ex-banker and had been greeted effusively by him, for he was indeed glad to see the boy. He was also glad to see Betty, whose father he had known before Mr. Prail's death in the fire.

After listening to Lem's account of the difficulties the two of them were in, he invited them to accompany him on his trip to California. It seemed that Mr. Whipple was going there with Jake Raven to dig gold from a mine that the redskin owned. With this money, he intended to finance the further activities of the National Revolutionary Party.

Lem was to help Mr. Whipple in the digging operations, while Betty was to keep house for the miners. The two young people jumped at this opportunity, as we can well imagine, and overwhelmed Mr. Whipple with their gratitude.

"In Chicago," said Shagpoke, when the dining car waiter had brought coffee, "we will have three hours and a half before 'The Chief' leaves for the Golden West. During that time, Lem, of course, will have to get himself a new set of store teeth and an eye, but I believe that the rest of us will still have time to pay a short visit to the World's Fair."

Mr. Whipple went on to describe the purpose of the fair, until, on a courteous signal from the head waiter, the little party was forced to leave their table and retire to their berths.

In the morning, when the train pulled into the depot, they disembarked. Lem was given some money to purchase the things he needed, while the others started immediately for the fair. He was to look for them on the grounds, if he got through in time.

Lem hurried as much as he could and managed quickly to select an eye and a set of teeth in a store devoted to that type of equipment. He then set out for the fair grounds.

As he was walking down Eleventh Street towards the North Entrance, he was accosted by a short, stout man, who wore a soft, black felt hat, the brim of which was slouched over his eyes. A full, brown beard concealed the lower part of his face.

"Excuse me," he said in a repressed tone of voice, "but I think you are the young man I am looking for."

"How is that?" asked Lem, instantly on his guard, for he did not intend to be snared by a sharper.

"Your name is Lemuel Pitkin, is it not?"

"It is, sir."

"I thought you answered the description given me."

"Given you by whom?" queried our hero.

"By Mr. Whipple, of course," was the surprising answer the stranger made.

"Why should he have given you a description of me?"

"So I could find you at the fair."

"But why, when I am to meet him at the depot in two hours from now?"

"An unfortunate accident has made it impossible for him to be there."

"An accident?"

"Exactly."

"What kind of an accident?"

"A very serious one, I am afraid. He was struck by a sight-seeing bus and . . ."

"Killed!" cried Lem in dismay. "Tell me the truth, was he killed?"

"No, not exactly, but he was seriously injured, perhaps fatally. He was taken unconscious to a hospital. When he regained his senses, he asked for you and I was sent to fetch you to him. Miss Prail and Chief Raven are at his bedside."

Lem was so stunned by the dire news that it required some five minutes for him to recover sufficiently to gasp, "This is terrible!"

He asked the bearded stranger to take him to Mr. Whipple at once.

This was just what the man had counted on. "I have a car with me," he said with a bow. "Please enter it."

He then led our hero to a powerful limousine that was drawn up at the curb. Lem got in, and the chauffeur, who was wearing green goggles and a long linen duster, drove off at top speed.

All this seemed natural to the lad because of his agitated state of mind, and the rate at which the car traveled pleased him rather than otherwise, for he was anxious to get to Mr. Whipple's bedside.

The limousine passed rapidly under one elevated structure and then another. There were fruit vendors on the street corners and merchants peddling neckties. People moved to and fro on the sidewalks; cabs, trucks and private vehicles flitted past. The roar of the great city rose on every side, but Lem saw and heard nothing.

"Where was Mr. Whipple taken?" he asked presently.

"To the Lake Shore Hospital."

"And is this the quickest way there?"

"Most certainly."

With this the stranger lapsed into moody silence again.

Lem looked from the window of the limousine and saw that the cars and trucks were growing less in number. Soon they disappeared from the streets altogether. The people also became fewer till no more than an occasional pedestrian was to be observed and then only of the lowest type.

As the car approached an extremely disreputable neighborhood, the bearded stranger drew the shade of one of its two windows.

"Why did you do that?" demanded Lem.

"Because the sun hurts my eyes," he said as he deliberately drew the other shade, throwing the interior into complete darkness.

These acts made Lem think that all was not quite as it should be.

"I must have one or both of these shades up," he said, reaching for the nearest one to raise it.

"And I say that they must both remain down," returned the man in a low harsh voice.

"What do you mean, sir?"

A strong hand suddenly fastened in a grip of iron on Lem's throat, and these words reached his ears:

"I mean, Lemuel Pitkin, that you are in the power of the Third International."

32. A Letter on the Use of Machine Guns at Weddings

KENNETH PATCHEN

After a year at the Meiklejohn Experimental College at the University of Wisconsin, Kenneth Patchen (1911–   ) went to work in a steel mill at the age of seventeen (his father had been a mill man all his life in Ohio). For several years there-

---

From *Before the Brave* (New York: Random House, 1936), p. 61. Reprinted with the premission of the author.

after he was a migratory worker, and by the time he was ready to publish his first volume of verse, Before the Brave *(1936), he was a revolutionary redhot. Despite the apocalyptic manner, however, and the invocations of all the approved Communist heroes, symbols, pennants, and paraphernalia, there was a genuine vitality (as one can see in the poem which follows) that precluded the possibility of Patchen's being silenced by shifts in political allegiance. And in fact, while he has gone since those days from communism to surrealism to formalism and is now as much concerned with painting as with poetry, he has been a steadily productive and always provocative writer of verse and fiction, despite severe incapacitating illnesses and other reverses:* Journal of Albion Moonlight *(1941),* Memoirs of a Shy Pornographer *(1946) and* Selected Poems *(1947) are among his most highly regarded works.*

Like the soldier, like the sailor, like the bib and tuck and bailer,
like the corner where we loiter, like the congressman and lawyer,
like the cop on the hill, like the lead in weary Will,
like the kittens in the water, like the names on Hearst's blotter,
like the guys and dames who laugh and chatter,
like the boys and girls who don't matter,
like the preacher and the Pope, like the punks who dish the dope,
like the hungry singing Home on the Range,
like Father Coughlin acting like Red Grange,
like the grumble of the tuba, like the sugar war in Cuba,
like the bill-collectors, like the Law-respecters,
like the pimps and prostitutes, like Mickey Mouse and Puss-in-
      Boots,
like the churches and the jails, like Astor's hounds and quails,
she's like you like her, now don't you try to spike her,
she's the nuts, she's a mile of Camel butts,
she's a honey in the money, she's my pearl,
what am I offered for being alive and willing to marry the girl?

though her insides rumble and her joints are out of whack,
let's give her a whirl, why grumble or try to draw back?
though her hair is false and her teeth are yellow,
let's get chummy, let's all get a break. For what's a fellow
got at stake, for what's a guy to do
who hasn't the guts to deal with sluts, guys like me and you.

PART EIGHT

America:

---

33. Speech to Those Who Say Comrade

ARCHIBALD MACLEISH

Archibald MacLeish (1892–   ), Yale (B.A., 1915), Harvard (LL.B., 1919), has been many things, to himself and to others, in the course of a long and varied life. With the coming of the thirties, MacLeish shifted away from an aristocratic-expatriate stance and identified himself with the social mood (see the poem which follows) and with the popular arts (verse plays for radio). In 1937, speaking as chairman of the National Congress of American Writers, he declared, "We, writers who contend for freedom, are ourselves, and whether we so wish or not, engaged [in the war against Fascism]." When international war did come, MacLeish, along with Bernard DeVoto and other patriots, attacked many of America's distinguished writers as "Irresponsibles" who by their criticisms of American

---

society had rendered their country ideologically unprepared and thus weakened the will to fight. "It is hopeless," remarked the late Morton Dauwen Zabel in Partisan Review *in 1941, "to try to cope with MacLeish's statements when those of one year are set against those of another; it is often impossible to clarify his contributions or ambiguities within a single essay." And, since by then MacLeish was serving as Librarian of Congress and one of President Roosevelt's cronies, Zabel characterized him bitterly: "Poet, scholar, gentleman, and librarian, he has become a major American prophet and Voice of Destiny." As if in fulfillment of Zabel's definition, MacLeish went on to become Assistant Secretary of State, and thereafter Boylston Professor at Harvard. His* Collected Poems *(1952) earned him his second Pulitzer Prize, the Bollingen Prize, and the National Book Award.*

The brotherhood is not by the blood certainly,
But neither are men brothers by speech—by saying so:
Men are brothers by life lived and are hurt for it.

Hunger and hurt are the great begetters of brotherhood:
Humiliation has gotten much love:
Danger I say is the nobler father and mother.

Those are as brothers whose bodies have shared fear
Or shared harm or shared hurt or indignity.
Why are the old soldiers brothers and nearest?

For this: with their minds they go over the sea a little
And find themselves in their youth again as they were in
Soissons and Meaux and at Ypres and those cities:

A French loaf and the girls with their eyelids painted
Bring back to aging and lonely men
Their twentieth year and the metal odor of danger.

It is this in life which of all things is tenderest—
To remember together with unknown men the days
Common also to them and perils ended:

It is this which makes of many a generation—
A wave of men who having the same years
Have in common the same dead and the changes.

The solitary and unshared experience
Dies of itself like the violations of love
Or lives on as the dead live eerily:

The unshared and single man must cover his
Loneliness as a girl her shame for the way of
Life is neither by one man nor by suffering.

Who are the born brothers in truth? The puddlers
Scorched by the same flame in the same foundries,
Those who have spit on the same boards with the blood in it,

Ridden the same rivers with green logs,
Fought the police in the parks of the same cities,
Gained for the same blows, the same flogging,

Veterans out of the same ships, factories,
Expeditions for fame: the founders of continents:
Those that hid in Geneva a time back,

Those that have hidden and hunted and all such—
Fought together, labored together: they carry the
Common look like a card and they pass touching.

Brotherhood! No word said can make you brothers!
Brotherhood only the brave earn and by danger or
Harm or by bearing hurt and by no other.

Brotherhood here in the strange world is the rich and
Rarest giving of life and the most valued,
Not to be had for a word or a week's wishing.

34. Let America Be America Again

LANGSTON HUGHES

*Vachel Lindsay, the wandering bard whose chanted poetry
was a fascinating feature of many middle-class public gather-
ings during the twenties, "was giving, in 1925, one of his unforgettable recitals at the Wardman Park Hotel in Washington to
an audience of the governmental elite," Michael Gold has written in his introduction to* A New Song. *"Negroes could not
enter such a gathering in Washington. But on his program,
Lindsay recited three poems by a young unknown Negro
named Langston Hughes. . . . While the recital went on, in
the ornate dining room of that same hotel, the young poet so
distinguished was carrying off the dirtied glasses and greasy
dishes of the guests. The poet was a busboy in that white man's
hotel." At that time Hughes (1902–   ) had already gone from
his native Joplin to Cleveland, to Mexico, to Columbia University, to sea, to Paris. And he had written* Weary Blues
*(1925). But it was not until the end of the decade, and the
thirties, that he was to gain wide recognition as a poet and an
all-around man of letters (he is currently a columnist for the*
New York Post*). Even during his Communist period, in the
heart of the depression, his verse, his stories and novels, his
plays and filmscripts were to be marked by charm and robust
good humor as much as by revolutionary militancy. "Let Amer-*

From *A New Song* (New York: International Workers Order, 1938),
pp. 9–11. Copyright 1938, © 1965 by Langston Hughes. Reprinted by
permission of Harold Ober Associates Inc.

ica Be America Again" is charged not only with these qualities but with that fervently affirmative radicalism so characteristic of the later years of the depression.

Let America be America again.
Let it be the dream it used to be.
Let it be the pioneer on the plain
Seeking a home where he himself is free.

(America never was America to me.)

Let America be the dream the dreamers dreamed—
Let it be that great strong land of love
Where never kings connive nor tyrants scheme
That any man be crushed by one above.

(It never was America to me.)

O, let my land be a land where Liberty
Is crowned with no false patriotic wreath,
But opportunity is real, and life is free,
Equality is in the air we breathe.

(There's never been equality for me,
Nor freedom in this "homeland of the free.")

Say who are you that mumbles in the dark?
And who are you that draws your veil across the stars?

I am the poor white, fooled and pushed apart,
I am the Negro bearing slavery's scars.
I am the red man driven from the land,
I am the immigrant clutching the hope I seek—
And finding only the same old stupid plan.
Of dog eat dog, of mighty crush the weak.

I am the young man, full of strength and hope,
Tangled in that ancient endless chain
Of profit, power, gain, of grab the land!
Of grab the gold! Of grab the ways of satisfying need!
Of work the men! Of take the pay!
Of owning everything for one's own greed!

I am the farmer, bondsman to the soil.
I am the worker sold to the machine.
I am the Negro, servant to you all.
I am the people, humble, hungry, mean—
Hungry yet today despite the dream.
Beaten yet today—O, Pioneers!
I am the man who never got ahead,
The poorest worker bartered through the years.

Yet I'm the one who dreamt our basic dream
In that Old World while still a serf of kings,
Who dreamt a dream so strong, so brave, so true,
That even yet its mighty daring sings
In every brick and stone, in every furrow turned
That's made America the land it has become.
O, I'm the man who sailed those early seas
In search of what I meant to be my home—
For I'm the one who left dark Ireland's shore,
And Poland's plain, and England's grassy lea,
And torn from Black Africa's strand I came
To build a "homeland of the free."

The free?

Who said the free? Not me?
Surely not me? The millions on relief today?
The millions shot down when we strike?

The millions who have nothing for our pay?
For all the dreams we've dreamed
And all the songs we've sung
And all the hopes we've held
And all the flags we've hung,
The millions who have nothing for our pay—
Except the dream that's almost dead today.

O, let America be America again—
The land that never has been yet—
And yet must be—the land where *every* man is free.
The land that's mine—the poor man's, Indian's, Negro's, ME—
Who made America,
Whose sweat and blood, whose faith and pain,
Whose hand at the foundry, whose plow in the rain,
Must bring back our mighty dream again.

Sure, call me any ugly name you choose—
The steel of freedom does not stain.
From those who live like leeches on the people's lives,
We must take back our land again,
America!

O, yes,
I say it plain,
America never was America to me,
And yet I swear this oath—
America will be!

Out of the rack and ruin of our gangster death,
The rape and rot of graft, and stealth, and lies,
We, the people, must redeem
The land, the mines, the plants, the rivers,
The mountains and the endless plain—
All, all the stretch of these great green states—
And make America again!

35. You Can't Go Home Again

THOMAS WOLFE

The Asheville, North Carolina, giant who astonished the liter-
ary world with his remarkable autobiographical first novel,
Look Homeward, Angel *(1929), had exhausted himself in the*
years that followed with Of Time and the River *(1935), From*
Death to Morning *(1935), and* The Web and the Rock *(1939).*
By 1938, Thomas Wolfe (1900–1938) was gone, burned out like
a rocket; but he had left behind a mass of manuscript, part of
which was pieced together and published as the posthumous
You Can't Go Home Again. *(It is partly the paste-up nature of*
the novel which has emboldened the editor of this volume to
cull out several disconnected episodes from it.) Thomas Wolfe
is usually thought of as the unparalleled chronicler of adoles-
cence, the young person's novelist, the romantic celebrating
his personal agonies and triumphs, and only marginally aware
of the world as a social organism. But Wolfe was maturing as
he moved on into his thirties; his firsthand experience with
German fascism sobered him; his brief sketches of the effects of
the Great Depression in both the small town and the big
city are among the finest renderings of the period; and he con-
cluded the work as he concluded his life, with a haunting ex-
pression of faith in the future of an America that had lost itself,
but could yet find itself. These last lines of the decade, and
of Thomas Wolfe's life as well, can readily stand as a summa-

From *You Can't Go Home Again* (New York: Scribner's, 1939), pp.
366–372, 395–396, 412–414, 741–742. Copyright 1934, 1937, 1938, 1939,
1940 by Maxwell Perkins as Executor. Reprinted by permission of Harper
& Row, Publishers, and of William Heinemann Ltd., Publishers.

tion of everything that his fellow artists of the depression era hoped and believed about their desperately confused native land.

Then it happened.

March 12, 1930 was a day that will be long remembered in the annals of Libya Hill. The double tragedy set the stage as nothing else could have done for the macabre weeks to follow.

If all the fire bells in town had suddenly begun to ring out their alarm at nine o'clock that morning, the news could not have spread more rapidly that the Citizens Trust Company was closed. Word of it leapt from mouth to mouth. And almost instantly, from every direction, white-faced men and women came running toward the Square. There were housewives with their aprons on, their hands still dripping dishwater; workmen and mechanics with their warm tools in their hands; hatless business men and clerks; young mothers carrying babies in their arms. Everyone in town, it seemed, had dropped whatever he was doing and rushed out in the streets the moment the news had reached him.

The Square itself was soon a seething mass of frenzied people. Frantically, over and over, they asked each other the same questions: Was it really true? How had it happened? How bad was it?

In front of the bank itself the crowd was quieter, more stunned. To this spot, sooner or later, they all came, drawn by a common desperate hope that they would yet be able to see with their own eyes that it was not so. Like a sluggish current within that seething mass the queue moved slowly past, and as the people saw those locked and darkened doors they knew that all hope was gone. Some just stared with stricken faces, some of the women moaned and wailed, from the eyes of strong men silent tears coursed down, and from the mouths of others came the rumble of angry mutterings.

For their ruin had caught up with them. Many of the people

in that throng had lost their life savings. But it was not only the bank's depositors who were ruined. Everyone now knew that their boom was over. They knew that the closing of the bank had frozen all their speculations just as they were, beyond the possibility of extricating themselves. Yesterday they could count their paper riches by ten thousands and by millions; to-day they owned nothing, their wealth had vanished, and they were left saddled with debts that they could never pay.

And they did not yet know that their city government was bankrupt, too—that six million dollars of public money had been lost behind those closed and silent doors.

It was a little before noon on that ill-omened day that Mayor Kennedy was found dead. And, just to put the final touch of gruesome irony upon the whole event, a blind man found him.

Judge Rumford Bland testified at the inquest that he left his front office, upstairs in the ramshackle building that he owned there on the Square, and went out in the hall, heading in the direction of the toilet, where he proposed to perform an essential function of nature. It was dark out there, he said with his ghostly smile, and the floors creaked, but this didn't matter to him—he knew the way. He said he couldn't have lost his way even if he had wanted to. At the end of the hall he could hear a punctual drip of water, dropping with its slow, incessant monotone; and besides, there was the pervasive smell of the tin urinal—all he had to do was to follow his nose.

He arrived in darkness and pushed open the door, and suddenly his foot touched something. He leaned over, his white, thin fingers groped down, and all at once they were plunged—wet, warm, sticky, reeking—into the foundering mass of what just five minutes before had been the face and brains of a living man.

—No, he hadn't heard the shot—there was all that infernal commotion out in the Square.

—No, he had no idea how *he* had got there—walked it, he supposed—the City Hall was only twenty yards away.

—No, he couldn't say why His Honor should have picked that spot to blow his brains out—there was no accounting for tastes—but if a man wanted to do it, that was probably as good a place as any.

So it was that weak, easy-going, procrastinating, good-natured Baxter Kennedy, Mayor of Libya Hill, was found—all that was left of him—in darkness, by an evil old blind man.

In the days and weeks that followed the closing of the bank, Libya Hill presented a tragic spectacle the like of which had probably never before been seen in America. But it was a spectacle that was to be repeated over and over again, with local variations, in many another town and city within the next few years.

The ruin of Libya Hill was much more than the ruin of the bank and the breakdown of the economic and financial order. True, when the bank failed, all that vast and complicated scheme of things which had been built upon it, the ramifications of which extended into every element of the community's life, toppled and crashed. But the closing of the bank was only like the action of a rip cord which, once jerked, brought the whole thing down, and in doing so laid bare the deeper and more corrosive ruin within. And this deeper ruin—the essence of the catastrophe—was the ruin of the human conscience.

Here was a town of fifty thousand people who had so abdicated every principle of personal and communal rectitude, to say nothing of common sense and decency, that when the blow fell they had no inner resources with which to meet it. The town almost literally blew its brains out. Forty people shot themselves within ten days, and others did so later. And, as so often happens, many of those who destroyed themselves were among the least guilty of the lot. The rest—and this was the most shocking part of it—suddenly realizing their devastating guilt to such a degree that they could not face the results of it, now turned like a pack of howling dogs to rend each other.

Cries of vengeance rose up from all their throats, and they howled for the blood of Jarvis Riggs. But these cries proceeded not so much from a conviction of wounded justice and deceived innocence as from their opposites. It was the sublime, ironic, and irrevocable justice of what had happened to them, and their knowledge that they alone had been responsible for it, that maddened them. From this arose their sense of outrage and their cries of vengeance.

What happened in Libya Hill and elsewhere has been described in the learned tomes of the overnight economists as a breakdown of "the system, the capitalist system." Yes, it was that. But it was also much more than that. In Libya Hill it was the total disintegration of what, in so many different ways, the lives of all these people had come to be. It went much deeper than the mere obliteration of bank accounts, the extinction of paper profits, and the loss of property. It was the ruin of men who found out, as soon as these symbols of their outward success had been destroyed, that they had nothing left—no inner equivalent from which they might now draw new strength. It was the ruin of men who, discovering not only that their values were false but that they had never had any substance whatsoever, now saw at last the emptiness and hollowness of their lives. Therefore they killed themselves; and those who did not die by their own hands died by the knowledge that they were already dead.

How can one account for such a complete drying up of all the spiritual sources in the life of a people? When one observes a youth of eighteen on a city street and sees the calloused scar that has become his life, and remembers the same youth as he was ten years before when he was a child of eight, one knows what has happened though the cause be hidden. One knows that there came a time when life stopped growing for that youth and the scar began; and one feels that if he could only find the reason and the cure, he would know what revolutions are.

In Libya Hill there must have been a time when life stopped growing and the scar began. But the learned economists of "the system" do not bother about this. For them, it belongs to the realm of the metaphysical—they are impatient of it, they will not trouble with it, they want to confine the truth within their little picket fence of facts. But they cannot. It is not enough to talk about the subtle complications of the credit structure, the intrigues of politics and business, the floating of bond issues, the dangers of inflation, speculation, and unsound prices, or the rise and decline of banks. When all these facts are added up, they still don't give the answer. For there is something more to say.

So with Libya Hill:

One does not know at just what moment it began, but one suspects that it began at some time long past in the lone, still watches of the night, when all the people lay waiting in their beds in darkness. Waiting for what? They did not know. They only hoped that it would happen—some thrilling and impossible fulfillment, some glorious enrichment and release of their pent lives, some ultimate escape from their own tedium.

But it did not come.

Meanwhile, the stiff boughs creaked in the cold bleakness of the corner lights, and the whole town waited, imprisoned in its tedium.

And sometimes, in furtive hallways, doors opened and closed, there was a padding of swift, naked feet, the stealthy rattling of brass casters, and behind old battered shades, upon the edge of Niggertown, the dull and fetid quickenings of lust.

Sometimes, in grimy stews of night's asylumage, an oath, a blow, a fight.

Sometimes, through the still air, a shot, the letting of nocturnal blood.

And always, through broken winds, the sounds of shifting engines in the station yards, far off, along the river's edge—and suddenly the thunder of great wheels, the tolling of the bell,

the loneliness of the whistle cry wailed back, receding toward
the North, and toward the hope, the promise, and the memory
of the world unfound.

Meanwhile, the boughs creaked bleakly in stiff light, ten
thousand men were waiting in the darkness, far off a dog
howled, and the Court House bell struck three.

No answer? Impossible? . . . Then let those—if such there
be—who have not waited in the darkness, find answers of their
own.

But if speech could frame what spirit utters, if tongue could
tell what the lone heart knows, there would be answers somewhat other than those which are shaped by the lean pickets of
rusty facts. There would be answers of men waiting, who have
not spoken yet.

Below the starred immensity of mountain night old Rumford
Bland, he that is called "The Judge," strokes his sunken jaws
reflectively as he stands at the darkened window of his front
office and looks out with sightless eyes upon the ruined town.
It is cool and sweet tonight, the myriad promises of life are
lyric in the air. Gem-strewn in viewless linkage on the hills the
lights make a bracelet for the town. The blind man knows that
they are there, although he cannot see them. He strokes his
sunken jaws reflectively and smiles his ghostly smile.

It is so cool and sweet tonight, and spring has come. There
never was a year like this, they say, for dogwood in the hills.
There are so many thrilling, secret things upon the air tonight
—a burst of laughter, and young voices, faint, half-broken, and
the music of a dance—how could one know that when the
blind man smiles and strokes his sunken jaws reflectively, he is
looking out upon a ruined town?

The new Court House and City Hall are very splendid in the
dark tonight. But he has never seen them—they were built
since he went blind. Their fronts are bathed, so people say, in
steady, secret light just like the nation's dome at Washington.

The blind man strokes his sunken jaws reflectively. Well, they *should* be splendid—they cost enough.

Beneath the starred immensity of mountain night there is something stirring in the air, a rustling of young leaves. And around the grass roots there is something stirring in the earth tonight. And below the grass roots and the sod, below the dew-wet pollen of young flowers, there is something alive and stirring. The blind man strokes his sunken jaws reflectively. Aye, there below, where the eternal worm keeps vigil, there is something stirring in the earth. Down, down below, where the worm incessant through the ruined house makes stir.

What lies there stir-less in the earth tonight, down where the worm keeps vigil?

The blind man smiles his ghostly smile. In his eternal vigil the worm stirs, but many men are rotting in their graves tonight, and sixty-four have bullet fractures in their skulls. Ten thousand more are lying in their beds tonight, living as shells live. They, too, are dead, though yet unburied. They have been dead so long they can't remember how it was to live. And many weary nights must pass before they can join the buried dead, down where the worm keeps vigil.

Meanwhile, the everlasting worm keeps vigil, and the blind man strokes his sunken jaws, and slowly now he shifts his sightless gaze and turns his back upon the ruined town. . . .

The next few years were terrible ones for all America, and especially terrible for Randy Shepperton.

He didn't get another job. He tried everything, but nothing worked. There just weren't any jobs. Men were being let off by the thousands everywhere, and nowhere were new ones being taken on.

After eighteen months his savings were gone, and he was desperate. He had to sell the old family house, and what he got for it was a mere pittance. He and Margaret rented a small apartment, and for another year or so, by careful management, they lived on what the house had brought them. Then that, too, was gone. Randy was on his uppers now. He fell ill, and it was an illness of the spirit more than of the flesh. At last, when there was nothing else to do, he and Margaret moved away from Libya Hill and went to live with the older sister who was married, and stayed there with her husband's family —dependents on the bounty of these kindly strangers.

And at the end of all of this, Randy—he of the clear eyes and the quick intelligence—he who was nobody's fool—he who thought he loved the truth and had always been able to see straight to the heart of most things—Randy went on relief.

And by that time George thought he understood it. Behind Randy's tragedy George thought he could see a personal devil in the form of a very bright and plausible young man, oozing confidence and crying, "Faith!" when there was no faith, and dressed like a traveling salesman. Yes, salesmanship had done its job too well. Salesmanship—that commercial brand of special pleading—that devoted servant of self-interest—that sworn enemy of truth. George remembered how Randy had been able to look at *his* alien problem and see it in the abstract, whole and clear, because there was no self-interest to cast its shadow on his vision. He could save others—himself he could not save, because he could no longer see the truth about himself.

And it seemed to George that Randy's tragedy was the essential tragedy of America. America—the magnificent, unrivaled, unequaled, unbeatable, unshrinkable, supercolossal, 99-and-44-one-hundredths-per-cent-pure, schoolgirl-complexion, covers-the-earth, I'd-walk-a-mile-for-it, four-out-of-five-have-it, his-master's-voice, ask-the-man-who-owns-one, blueplate-special home of advertising, salesmanship, and special pleading in all its many catchy and beguiling forms.

Had not the real rulers of America—the business men—been wrong about the depression from the start? Had they not pooh-poohed it and tried to wipe it out with words, refusing

to see it for what it was? Had they not kept saying that prosperity was just around the corner—long after "prosperity," so
called, had vanished, and the very corner it was supposed to
be around had flattened out and bent into a precipitate downward curve of hunger, want, and desperation?

Well, Randy had been right about the wounded faun. For
George knew now that his own self-pity was just his precious
egotism coming between him and the truth he strove for as a
writer. What Randy didn't know was that business also had its
wounded fauns. And they, it seemed, were a species that you
could not kill so lightly. For business was the most precious
form of egotism—self-interest at its dollar value. Kill that with
truth, and what would be left?

A better way of life, perhaps, but it would not be built on
business as we know it. . . .

. . . On his nocturnal ramblings about New York, he would observe the homeless men who prowled in the vicinity of restaurants, lifting the lids of garbage cans and searching around
inside for morsels of rotten food. He saw them everywhere, and
noticed how their numbers increased during the hard and
desperate days of 1932. He knew what kind of men they were,
for he talked to many of them; he knew what they had been,
where they had come from, and even what kind of scraps they
could expect to dig out of the garbage cans. He found out the
various places all over the city where such men slept at night.
A favorite rendezvous was a corridor of the subway station at
Thirty-third Street and Park Avenue in Manhattan. There one
night he counted thirty-four huddled together on the cold
concrete, wrapped up in sheathings of old newspaper.

It was his custom almost every night, at one o'clock or later,
to walk across the Brooklyn Bridge, and night after night, with
a horrible fascination, he used to go to the public latrine or
"comfort station" which was directly in front of the New York

City Hall. One descended to this place down a steep flight of stairs from the street, and on bitter nights he would find the place crowded with homeless men who had sought refuge there. Some were those shambling hulks that one sees everywhere, in Paris as well as New York, in good times as well as bad—old men, all rags and bags and long white hair and bushy beards stained dirty yellow, wearing tattered overcoats in the cavernous pockets of which they carefully stored away all the little rubbish they lived on and spent their days collecting in the streets—crusts of bread, old bones with rancid shreds of meat still clinging to them, and dozens of cigarette butts. Some were the "stumble bums" from the Bowery, criminal, fumed with drink or drugs, or half insane with "smoke." But most of them were just flotsam of the general ruin of the time—honest, decent, middle-aged men with faces seamed by toil and want, and young men, many of them mere boys in their teens, with thick, unkempt hair. These were the wanderers from town to town, the riders of freight trains, the thumbers of rides on highways, the uprooted, unwanted male population of America. They drifted across the land and gathered in the big cities when winter came, hungry, defeated, empty, hopeless, restless, driven by they knew not what, always on the move, looking everywhere for work, for the bare crumbs to support their miserable lives, and finding neither work nor crumbs. Here in New York, to this obscene meeting place, these derelicts came, drawn into a common stew of rest and warmth and a little surcease from their desperation.

George had never before witnessed anything to equal the indignity and sheer animal horror of the scene. There was even a kind of devil's comedy in the sight of all these filthy men squatting upon those open, doorless stools. Arguments and savage disputes and fights would sometimes break out among them over the possession of these stools, which all of them wanted more for rest than for necessity. The sight was revolting, disgusting, enough to render a man forever speechless with very pity.

He would talk to the men and find out all he could about them, and when he could stand it no more he would come out of this hole of filth and suffering, and there, twenty feet above it, he would see the giant hackles of Manhattan shining coldly in the cruel brightness of the winter night. The Woolworth Building was not fifty yards away, and a little farther down were the silvery spires and needles of Wall Street, great fortresses of stone and steel that housed enormous banks. The blind injustice of this contrast seemed the most brutal part of the whole experience, for there, all around him in the cold moonlight, only a few blocks away from this abyss of human wretchedness and misery, blazed the pinnacles of power where a large portion of the entire world's wealth was locked in mighty vaults. . . .

I believe that we are lost here in America, but I believe we shall be found. And this belief, which mounts now to the catharsis of knowledge and conviction, is for me—and I think for all of us—not only our own hope, but America's everlasting, living dream. I think the life which we have fashioned in America, and which has fashioned us—the forms we made, the cells that grew, the honeycomb that was created—was self-destructive in its nature, and must be destroyed. I think these forms are dying, and must die, just as I know that America and the people in it are deathless, undiscovered, and immortal, and must live.

I think the true discovery of America is before us. I think the true fulfillment of our spirit, of our people, of our mighty and immortal land, is yet to come. I think the true discovery of our own democracy is still before us. And I think that all these things are certain as the morning, as inevitable as noon. I think

I speak for most men living when I say that our America is Here, is Now, and beckons on before us, and that this glorious assurance is not only our living hope, but our dream to be accomplished.

I think the enemy is here before us, too. But I think we know the forms and faces of the enemy, and in the knowledge that we know him, and shall meet him, and eventually must conquer him is also our living hope. I think the enemy is here before us with a thousand faces, but I think we know that all his faces wear one mask. I think the enemy is single selfishness and compulsive greed. I think the enemy is blind, but has the brutal power of his blind grab. I do not think the enemy was born yesterday, or that he grew to manhood forty years ago, or that he suffered sickness and collapse in 1929, or that we began without the enemy, and that our vision faltered, that we lost the way, and suddenly were in his camp. I think the enemy is old as Time, and evil as Hell, and that he has been here with us from the beginning. I think he stole our earth from us, destroyed our wealth, and ravaged and despoiled our land. I think he took our people and enslaved them, that he polluted the fountains of our life, took unto himself the rarest treasures of our own possession, took our bread and left us with a crust, and, not content, for the nature of the enemy is insatiate— tried finally to take from us the crust.

I think the enemy comes to us with the face of innocence and says to us:

"I am your friend."

I think the enemy deceives us with false words and lying phrases, saying:

"See, I am one of you—I am one of your children, your son, your brother, and your friend. Behold how sleek and fat I have become—and all because I am just one of you, and your friend. Behold how rich and powerful I am—and all because I am one of you—shaped in your way of life, of thinking, of accomplishment. What I am, I am because I am one of you, your humble brother and your friend. Behold," cries Enemy, "the man I am, the man I have become, the thing I have accomplished—and reflect. Will you destroy this thing? I assure you that it is the most precious thing you have. It is yourselves, the projection of each of you, the triumph of your individual lives, the thing that is rooted in your blood, and native to your stock, and inherent in the traditions of America. It is the thing that all of you may hope to be," says Enemy, "for—" humbly—"am I not just one of you? Am I not just your brother and your son? Am I not the living image of what each of you may hope to be, would wish to be, would desire for his own son? Would you destroy this glorious incarnation of your own heroic self? If you do, then," says Enemy, "you destroy yourselves—you kill the thing that is most gloriously American, and in so killing, kill yourselves."

He lies! And now we know he lies! He is not gloriously, or in any other way, ourselves. He is not our friend, our son, our brother. And he is not American! For, although he has a thousand familiar and convenient faces, his own true face is old as Hell.

Look about you and see what he has done.

Index

THE AMERICAN HERITAGE SERIES

THE MIDDLE PERIOD

THE LATE NINETEENTH CENTURY

THE TWENTIETH CENTURY

TOPICAL VOLUMES

The Library of Literature

CRANE, STEPHEN, *The Red Badge of Courage*, ed. Frederick C. Crews, 6

DICKENS, CHARLES, *Great Expectations*, ed. Louis Crompton, 2

HAWTHORNE, NATHANIEL, *The Scarlet Letter*, ed. Larzer Ziff, 1

MELVILLE, HERMAN, *Moby Dick*, ed. Charles Feidelson, 5

One Hundred Middle English Lyrics, ed. Robert D. Stevick, 7

SWIFT, JONATHAN, *Gulliver's Travels*, ed. Martin Price, 3

TWAIN, MARK, *The Adventures of Huckleberry Finn*, ed. Leo Marx, 4